易說館09

豬頭也要會的
3500
初/中級英檢必考
單字

CONTENTS

目錄

作者序

多年前，聽到廣播電台英語快速記憶法的廣告：earthquake地震，就叫「二十塊」，地震震破了二十塊玻璃，所以地震叫二十塊。我瞠目結舌的開著車，心想曾幾何時台灣的英語已經淪落到此地步，任何學語言的人都知道這並非學習語言的「正道」。

我們常說學語言就像蓋房子一樣，一塊塊的磚就像單字一樣、骨架就像文法，到最後的粉刷牆壁貼瓷磚就像修辭一樣，一步步的建立起正確的學習方法，就像蓋房子一樣，才能屹立不搖。

這本書以教育部公布的38類單字編排方式為依據，收錄了3500個單字，依字母序排列，比教育部的初級英檢2000單字多了1500個字，大約是高中一年級單字的能力。如果想查「烏龜、陸龜」tortoise除了可在T字部查到，也可在書後索引分類的animal主題裡查到。因此大家可以在同主題裡可以學到相關的主題單字。其他無法歸類的字像是transportation、clothes、personalities、country、money、tableware......就以名詞、動詞、形容詞、副詞來歸類。

希望各位英語學習者能利用最正確的方式，從多聽單字、學習自然發音，累積英語實力。

相信我「二十塊」不會讓你的英語突飛猛進。

朱立安

使用說明

38分類編號

依教育部公布的38類主題分類。分類字表附在書後索引部分。

MP3序號

請依MP3序號選播美籍播音員發音示範。

MP3 1701-1709

absolute [ˋæbsə,lut] (a.) 根本的
What you said was absolute nonsense.
你說的根本是胡說八道。

absorb [əbˋsɔrb] (v.) 吸收
The color black can absorb heat.
黑色會吸熱。

abstract [ˋæbstrækt] (a.) 抽象的
The painting is abstract and difficult to understand.
這幅畫既抽象又難懂。

academic [,ækəˋdɛmɪk] (a.) 學術的，學業的
The academic research has been cancelled because of lacking budget.
因為缺乏經費，這個學術研究被取消了。

accent [ˋæksɛnt] (n.) 口音
He speaks English with the French accent.
他說的英語帶有法國口音。

accept [əkˋsɛpt] (v.) 接受
This is an expensive gift that I can't accept.
這份昂貴的禮物我不能收。

acceptable [əkˋsɛptəbl] (a.) 可接受的
The offer is acceptable.
這個提議可以接受。

accident [ˋæksədənt] (n.) 事故
Careless drivers often cause car accidents.
粗心的駕駛人時常導致交通事故。

accompany [əˋkʌmpənɪ] (v.) 陪伴
I have to accompany my grandparents to the market every weekend.
我每個週末都必須陪伴祖父母去市場。

17

A B C D E F G H I J K L M N O P Q R S T U V W X Y Z

書標

全書依A~Z字母順序為書標，便於讀者檢索、翻閱。

單字例句

搭配英文例句，加強了解單字用法。

3500初／中級單字

收錄2000字初級程度單字，及1500字中級程度單字。

詞類

名詞 nouns

· 是人、事、物、地方以及抽象概念的名稱。

· 可分為可數名詞，例如(a boy)、不可數名詞(water)、專有名詞(English)（第一個字母要大寫）。

· 可數名詞，有單複數之分，例如a boy、two boys。

代名詞pronouns

· 代名詞是代替名詞的字。

· 代名詞包括人稱代名詞he, his, him, himself...，所有代名詞mine, yours, his, hers...，不定代名詞anyone, both, all...，指示代名詞this, that, those, these...，疑問代名詞who, which..., what，關係代名詞who, which, that...。

形容詞adjectives

· 修飾名詞或代名詞的字詞。

· 分為形狀形容詞big, long, heavy, tall...，數量形容詞one, ten, some, many...，指示形容詞that, this, these, such...。

冠詞 articles

· 用來限定名詞的字詞。

· 不定冠詞有a和an，用於單數可數名詞前，a用於子音前面，an用於母音前面。

· 定冠詞the用於特定描述的名詞前。

動詞verbs

· 動詞是表示動作或狀態的字。

· 分為be動詞am, is, are, was, were...，一般動詞eat, take, walk...。

· 一般動詞因時態或語態又可變化為動名詞looking, watching...，現在分詞 interesting, taking...、過去分詞interested, taken...，不定詞 to read, to take...。

助動詞 auxiliry verbs

· 幫助動詞形成否定或疑問的字詞如do, does, did, can, will, should…。

介系詞 prepositions

· 用來表示名詞和其他詞之間關係的字。

· 介系詞分為時間介系詞at, in, before, after...，地方介系詞in, on, under, over...。

副詞 adverbs

· 副詞主要修飾動詞，形容詞或其他副詞或修飾片語和子句。

· 副詞可分為情狀副詞sadly, happily, well...，程度副詞very, a lot...，地方副詞here, there...，時間副詞yesterday, today, tomorrow...，頻率副詞always, often, never...，疑問副詞when, where, how, why...。

連接詞 conjunctions

- 連接詞是連接單字，片語或子句的字或字群，不能單獨視為一個句子。
- 連接詞分為對等連接詞and, but, or，從屬連接詞when, after, so。

感歎詞 exclamations

- 表示強烈的喜怒哀樂情緒或感情 hi, hello, oh, wow。

五大基本句型

1. 主詞 (S) + 動詞 (V)

Time flies.

時間飛逝。

2. 主詞 (S)+動詞 (V) +主詞補語 (SC)

Time is money.

時間就是金錢。

3. 主詞 (S)+動詞 (V) +受詞 (O)

Plants need water and sunshine.

植物需要陽光和水。

4. 主詞(S)+動詞 (V)+間接受詞 (IO)+直接受詞 (DO)

My mom bought me a watch.

我媽媽買給我一只手錶。

5. 主詞 (S)+動詞 (V) +受詞 (O) + 受詞補語 (OC)

Students find it difficult to master English.

學生們覺得要精通英文很難。

基本句式

敘述句

· 敘述句用以敘述事實或表示說話人的看法。

· 分為肯定句和否定句。

I am a student. 我是個學生。

I cannot swim. 我不會游泳。

疑問句

· 疑問句包括一般疑問句(Yes/No回答的問句)，Wh-疑問句，選擇疑問句（有or的問句）和附加問句等四種

· 一般疑問句 Are you a student? Yes, I am.

· Wh-疑問句 Who is the girl? She is my teacher.

· 選擇疑問句 Which one do you like, tea or coffee?

· 附加問句 You are a teacher, aren't you?

祈使句

· 祈使句用來表示命令、請求、禁止特殊語意，用原形動詞開始。

· 表示命令 Close the window, Get out.

· 表示請求 Give me a hand, please.

· 表示禁止 Don't go out.

感歎句

· 感歎句用來表示強烈的情緒或感覺。

· What a + N! What a beautiful day!

· How + adj + N! How stupid I am!

KK音標

有聲子音

[b] [d] [g] [v] [z] [ð] [dʒ] [ʒ] [m] [n] [ŋ] [l] [r] [j] [w]

無聲子音

[p] [t] [k] [f] [s] [θ] [ʃ] [tʃ] [h]

母音

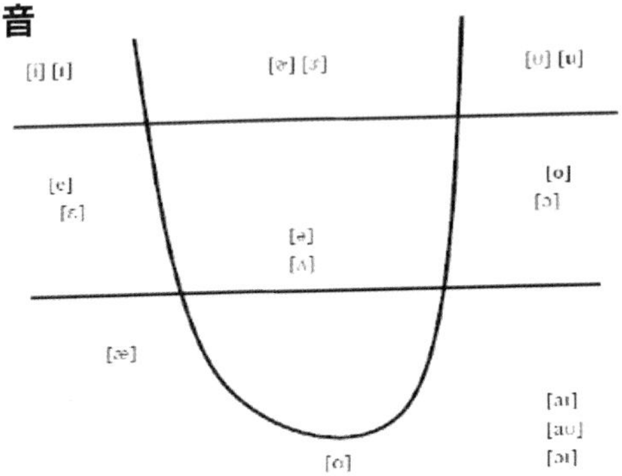

自然發音表

Aa	Bb	Cc	Dd	Ee	Ff	Gg	Hh	Ii	Jj	Kk	Ll
[æ]	[b]	[k]	[d]	[ɛ]	[f]	[g]	[h]	[ɪ]	[dʒ]	[k]	[l]
Mm	Nn	Oo	Pp	Qq							
[m]	[n]	[ɑ]	[p]	[kw]							
Rr	Ss	Tt	Uu	Vv	Ww	Xx	Yy	Zz			
[r]	[s]	[t]	[ʌ]	[v]	[w]	[ks]	[j]	[z]			

標點符號

句點 (.) period

· 句點用於當一句話完全結束時。句點也可以用於英文單詞的縮寫，如 Mr., Dr., U.S.A. 等。

逗點 (,) comma

· 逗點用於分隔一系列的簡單內容，如I like sports, such as baseball, tennis, and football.

· 逗點用於連接兩個較長的獨立子句，如 When I was taking a shower, the phone rang.

問號 (?) question mark

· 在直接問句後面須接問號。如 Where were you last night?

· 在疑問口氣的句型下也可用問號，如 And you? , Really?

感歎號 (!) exclamation

· 感嘆號用於感歎和驚歎的陳述中，如What a day! , How stupid I am!

分號 (;) semicolon

· 分號用於分隔兩相關的獨立子句，視為一個句子，分號後之句子開頭不得大寫。

He tried to drive fast home; however, the rain was getting stronger and stronger.

冒號 (:) colon

· 冒號用於句子後面內容的介紹、解釋或補充，如 He comes up with some ideas: quitting the job, taking a trip, or going back to his hometown.

· 冒號可用於一段引言之前。

引號 (“ ”) quotation mark

· 引號用在引言上，句號和逗號必須置於引號(雙引號和單引號) 之內。 “Well,” I said, “you don’t know anything, do you?”

連字號 (—) hyphen

· 連字號大小主要用於某些字首(如: self-,ex-和all-) ，和一些複合字後構成複合詞。如:ex-husband。

· 用於數字裡，forty-seven, seventy-nine。

刪節號 (...) ellipsis

· 刪節號表示直接引語中的省略或表示說話中的猶豫或遲疑，The man wrote down, “... no matter how the condition is... .”

所有格號（省略號）(’) apostrophe

· 構成名詞所有格John’s mom。

· 縮寫符號，it’s, that’s, I’d...

教育部公布初級英檢字彙範圍38分類

1	People	人
2	Personal characteristics	人格特質
3	Parts of body	人體部位
4	Health	健康
5	Forms of address	表達方式
6	Family	家庭
7	Numbers	數字
8	Time	時間
9	Money	金錢
10	Food & drink	飲食
11	Tableware	餐具
12	Clothing & accessories	衣服配件
13	Colors	顏色
14	Sports, interests & hobbies	運動、興趣及嗜好
15	Houses & apartments	房屋住宅
16	School	學校
17	Places & locations	地點及位置
18	Transportation	運輸
19	Sizes & measurements	度量衡

A

3 **abdomen** [ˋæbdəmən] (n.) 腹部
I felt a sharp pain in my abdomen.
我感到腹部一陣刺痛。

35 **ability** [əˋbɪlətɪ] (n.) 能力
He doesn't have the ability to finish the work.
他沒有能力完成這個工作。

37 **able** [ˋebl̩] (a.) 能夠
She won't be able to come on Sunday.
她星期天沒辦法來。

38 **aboard** [əˋbord] (adv.) 上船，登機
Welcome aboard!
歡迎搭機！

38 **about** [əˋbaʊt] (adv.) 大約
He's about 20 years old now.
他現在大約二十歲。

38 **above** [əˋbʌv] (adv.) 在上面
The bird is flying above the tree.
那隻小鳥在樹頂上飛。

38 **abroad** [əˋbrɔd] (adv.) 在國外
I plan to study abroad next year.
我打算明年到國外念書。

37 **absent** [ˋæbsn̩t] (a.) 缺席的
She was absent yesterday.
她昨天缺席。

37 **absolute** [ˋæbsə,lut] (a.) 根本的
What you said was absolute nonsense.
你說的根本是胡說八道。

10 **absorb** [əbˋsɔrb] (v.) 吸收
The color black can absorb heat.
黑色會吸熱。

37 **abstract** [ˋæbstrækt] (a.) 抽象的
The painting is abstract and difficult to understand.
這幅畫既抽象又難懂。

16 **academic** [,ækəˋdɛmɪk] (a.) 學術的，學業的
The academic research has been cancelled because of lacking budget.
因為缺乏經費，這個學術研究被取消了。

21 **accent** [ˋæksɛnt] (n.) 口音
He speaks English with the French accent.
他說的英語帶有法國口音。

36 **accept** [əkˋsɛpt] (v.) 接受
This is an expensive gift that I can't accept.
這份昂貴的禮物我不能收。

37 **acceptable** [əkˋsɛptəbḷ] (a.) 可接受的
The offer is acceptable.
這個提議可以接受。

35 **accident** [ˋæksədənt] (n.) 事故
Careless drivers often cause car accidents.
粗心的駕駛人時常導致交通事故。

36 **accompany** [əˋkʌmpənɪ] (v.) 陪伴
I have to accompany my grandparents to the market every weekend.
我每個週末都必須陪伴祖父母去市場。

36 **accomplish** [əˋkʌmplɪʃ] (v.) 完成
The soldier hasn't accomplished the mission.
那個士兵還沒有完成任務。

19 **account** [əˋkaʊnt] (n.) 理由，根據，說明
You must take his age into account.
你必須考慮到他的年齡。

37 **accurate** [ˋækjərɪt] (a.) 正確的
The figures of the income are not accurate.
這個收入數字並不正確。

4 **ache** [ek] (v.) 痛
My back has been aching all day.
我的背已經痛了一整天。

36 **achieve** [əˋtʃiv] (v.) 達成
He can't achieve his parents' expectations.
他無法達到父母的期望。

37 **acid** [ˋæsɪd] (a.) 酸
The acid rain damages the soil.
酸雨破壞土壤。

38 **across** [əˋkrɔs] (adv.) 越過
No one can swim across the river.
沒有人可以游過這條河。

36 **act** [ækt] (v.) 表現
Please grow up and act like an adult.
拜託成熟一點，表現得像個大人。

35 **action** [ˋækʃən] (n.) 行動
We need to take action right away to solve this problem.
我們需要立刻採取行動解決問題。

37 **active** [`æktɪv] (a.) 活躍的
Alice is so active in her school.
愛莉絲在學校相當活躍。

35 **activity** [æk`tɪvətɪ] (n.) 活動
Stamp collecting is my favorite activity.
集郵是我最喜愛的活動。

24 **actor** [`æktɚ] (n.) 男演員
He won an Oscar for best actor in 2004.
他於二〇〇四年贏得奧斯卡最佳男主角獎。

24 **actress** [`æktrɪs] (n.) 女演員
She's dreaming to be an actress in Hollywood.
她夢想成為好萊塢女演員。

37 **actual** [`æktʃʊəl] (a.) 真實的，實際的
The movie is based on the actual event.
這電影是由真實事件改編。

38 **actually** [`æktʃʊəlɪ] (adv.) 實際上，竟然
It was actually eleven when I came home last night.
我昨晚回家時竟然十一點了。

36 **adapt** [ə`dæpt] (v.) 使適應
My teacher told me to adapt myself to the new class as soon as possible.
老師要我盡快適應新的班級。

36 **add** [æd] (v.) 添加
Please add some cheese to my sandwich.
請幫我的三明治加些起司。

35 **addition** [ə`dɪʃən] (n.) 附加
In addition to having a crew cut, you have to wear the uniform.
除了理平頭，你還必須穿制服。

37 **additional** [ə`dɪʃənl̩] (a.) 附加的
How much additional tax do we owe?
我們還要繳多少額外的稅？

15 **address** [ə`drɛs] (n.) 地址
What's your email address?
你的電子郵件信箱是？

16 **adjective** [`ædʒɪktɪv] (n.) 形容詞
"Late" can be both an adjective and an adverb.
late這個字可以當形容詞，也可以當副詞。

35 **admiration** [,ædmə`reʃən] (n.) 欽佩
I was filled with admiratin for her courage.
我對她的勇氣深感敬佩。

36 **admire** [əd`maɪr] (v.) 欣賞
She admires his art work very much.
她很欣賞他的藝術作品。

36 **admit** [əd`mɪt] (v.) 承認
The politician finally admitted his error.
這個政治人物終於承認他的錯誤。

35 **admission** [əd`mɪʃən] (n.) 許可
The school sent an admission letter to the student.
那間學校寄了一封入學許可給那個學生。

36 **adopt** [ə`dɑpt] (v.) 收養，採納
The scientists adopted a new way to treat AIDS patients.
科學家們採用一種新方法治療愛滋病患。

1 **adult** [ə`dʌlt] (n.) 成年人
Adults are more mature than teenagers.
成年人比青少年成熟。

35 **advance** [əd`væns] (n.) 發展
Technological advances are growing rapidly.
科技方面的發展不斷迅速成長。

37 **advanced** [əd`vænst] (a.) 高級的，進階的
He is not qualified to enter the advanced class.
他還不夠資格進入高級班。

35 **advantage** [əd`væntɪdʒ] (n.) 優點
There are many advantages to having computers.
擁有電腦的好處很多。

35 **adventure** [əd`vɛntʃɚ] (n.) 冒險
The trip to the waterfall is indeed an adventure.
這次的瀑布之行真是一場冒險。

36 **advertise** [`ædvɚ,taɪz] (v.) 廣告
We need to advertise our product more in media.
我們需要加強產品的媒體宣傳。

35 **advertisement** [,ædvɚ`taɪzmənt] (n.) 廣告
Did you see the advertisement on TV yesterday?
你昨天有看見電視上的廣告嗎？

35 **advice** [əd`vaɪs] (n.) 忠告
The teacher gave me a piece of advice.
老師給我一個忠告。

36 **advise** [əd`vaɪz] (v.) 勸告
My lawyer advised me to sign a contract first.
我的律師建議我先簽一份合約。

24 **adviser** [əd`vaɪzɚ] (n.) 顧問
The school adviser asked me to hand in my career plan.
學校顧問要我交一份自己的生涯規劃。

35 **affair** [ə`fɛr] (n.) 事件

What he did was his own affair.

他做什麼是他自己的事。

36 **affect** [ə`fɛkt] (v.) 影響

Global warming affects lots of creatures on the planet.

溫室效應影響了很多地球上的生物。

36 **afford** [ə`ford] (v.) 買得起

I can't afford the house.

我買不起這房子。

37 **afraid** [ə`fred] (a.) 害怕的

Jenny is afraid of dogs.

珍妮害怕狗。

32 **after** [`æftɚ] (prep.) 在…之後

We usually play soccer after school.

放學後，我們經常踢足球。

8 **afternoon** [ˌæftɚ`nun] (n.) 下午

We have a math class in the afternoon.

我們下午有一堂數學課。

38 **afterward** [`æftɚwɚd] (adv.) 之後

First we went to the movies and afterwards we ate some ice cream.

我們先去看了電影，之後去吃冰淇淋。

38 **again** [ə`gɛn] (adv.) 再一次

I feel like having the ice cream again.

我想要再吃一次冰淇淋。

32 **against** [ə`gɛnst] (prep.) 倚靠

Put the ladder against the wall.

把梯子靠在牆上。

35 **age** [edʒ] (n.) 年齡
Dad went to work at the age of eighteen.
爸爸十八歲開始工作。

24 **agency** [ˋedʒənsɪ] (n.) 經銷商，代理，仲介
If there are any problems, please contact our local agency.
如果有任何問題，請聯絡我們當地經銷商。

24 **agent** [ˋedʒənt] (n.) 代理商，仲介人
The insurance agent called me every day for a week.
那個保險經紀人整個星期每天都打電話給我。

37 **aggressive** [əˋgrɛsɪv] (a.) 積極進取的，侵略性的
Football players need to be aggressive to succeed.
足球選手需要積極求勝。

8 **ago** [əˋgo] (adv.) 在…以前
Tim left two hours ago.
提姆離開兩個鐘頭了。

36 **agree** [əˋgri] (v.) 贊成
I agree with what he says.
我同意他的說法。

37 **agreeable** [əˋgriəbḷ] (a.) 宜人的
We'll go picnicking if the weather is agreeable tomorrow.
如果明天天氣不錯，我們會去野餐。

35 **agriculture** [ˋægrɪ͵kʌltʃɚ] (n.) 農業
I want to study agriculture and have my own farm.
我想攻讀農業，並擁有自己的農場。

38 **ahead** [əˋhɛd] (adv.) 在前面
His scores are always ahead of mine.
他的成績一直都比我好。

35 **aid** [ed] (n.) 幫助
I know how to give first aid in an emergency.
我懂得如何進行緊急醫療急救。

35 **aid** [ed] (v.) 幫助
We should aid those who are less fortunate than us.
我們應該幫助那些比我們不幸的人。

4 **AIDS** [edz] (n.) 愛滋病
Lots of children are suffering from AIDS.
很多小孩為愛滋病所苦。

35 **aim** [em] (n.) 目標
My aim is to get a great job.
我的目標是找一份好工作。

25 **air** [ɛr] (n.) 空氣
I need fresh air after driving for three hours.
開了三小時車，我需要呼吸新鮮空氣。

15 **air conditioner** [ɛr kən`dɪʃənɚ] (n.) 空調
Would you mind turning on the air conditioner?
你介意將空調打開嗎？

18 **aircraft** [`ɛr,kræft] (n.) 飛行器
This aircraft carries up to 160 passengers.
這架飛機可搭載一百六十位乘客。

18 **airline** [`ɛr,laɪn] (n.) 航班
There are no airlines flying directly to Russia.
這裡沒有直飛俄羅斯的航班。

18 **airplane** [`ɛr,plen] (n.) 飛機
We took an airplane to Japan.
我們搭飛機去日本。

18 **airport** [ˋɛr,pɔrt] (n.) 機場
I always try to arrive at the airport two hours before my flight.
我總是比班機時間提早兩小時到機場。

8 **alarm** [əˋlɑrm] (n.) 鬧鐘
Please turn off her alarm clock.
請關掉她的鬧鐘。

35 **album** [ˋælbəm] (n.) 相簿
I put all my vacation pictures in a photo album.
我把度假所有的照片都放進相簿裡。

10 **alcohol** [ˋælkə,hɔl] 酒類，含酒精飲料
I don't drink alcohol.
我不喝酒。

37 **alike** [əˋlaɪk] (a.) 相似的
The twins look much alike.
這對雙胞胎看起來好像。

37 **alive** [əˋlaɪv] (a.) 活著的
They are still alive after the war.
戰爭過後，他們仍然還活著。

7 **all** [ɔl] (a.) 所有的
All of the boys are very naughty.
所有的男孩都很調皮。

35 **alley** [ˋælɪ] (n.) 小巷
It's not safe to walk in alleys at midnight.
午夜裡走小巷子並不安全。

36 **allow** [əˋlaʊ] (v.) 允許
My mother won't allow me to eat snacks between meals.
我媽媽不准我在正餐之間吃零食。

35 **allowance** [ə`laʊəns] (n.) 零用錢
My parents give me allowances every week.
我爸媽每星期給我零用錢。

38 **almost** [`ɔl,most] (adv.) 幾乎
My homework is almost done now.
我的功課快要做完了。

38 **alone** [ə`lon] (adv.) 獨自地
She is home alone.
她一個人在家。

32 **along** [ə`lɔŋ] (prep.) 沿著
Walk along this street, and you will find the restaurant.
沿著這條路走，就可以找到那家餐廳。

38 **aloud** [ə`laʊd] (adv.) 大聲地
Can everyone read out aloud?
各位可以大聲唸嗎？

16 **alphabet** [`ælfə,bɛt] (n.) 字母
The kids are learning alphabets now.
那些小孩正在學習字母。

8 **already** [ɔl`rɛdɪ] (adv.) 已經
She has finished her homework already.
她已經做完功課了。

38 **also** [`ɔlso] (adv.) 也
I like rice, but I also like noodles.
我喜歡米飯，但也喜歡麵條。

33 **although** [ɔl`ðo] (conj.) 儘管
Although she is old, she swims well.
她雖然老，但是游泳游得很好。

38 **altogether** [,ɔltə`gɛðɚ] (adv.) 全然，一起
I am not altogether satisfied with the result.
我並不全然滿意這個結果。

38 **always** [`ɔlwez] (adv.) 總是
Mom always cooks for us.
媽媽總是為我們做飯。

36 **amaze** [ə`mez] (v.) 使驚奇
Jack amazed his friends with his magic tricks?
傑克的魔術戲法把大家嚇了一跳。

36 **amazement** [ə`mezmənt] (n.) 驚愕
To my amazement, he passed the exam.
真是嚇了我一跳，他通過考試了。

35 **ambassador** [æm`bæsədɚ] (n.) 大使
The ambassador has great power.
這位大使擁有很大的權力。

35 **ambition** [æm`bɪʃən] (n.) 抱負
My ambition is to be a great movie star.
我的抱負是成為一個棒的電影明星。

18 **ambulance** [`æmbjələns] (n.) 救護車
Many ambulances parked outside by the hospital.
很多救護車停在醫院外面。

20 **America** [ə`mɛrɪkə] (n.) 美國
She took a trip to America.
她去了一趟美國。

21 **American** [ə`mɛrɪkən] (a.) 美國的，美式的
Children like American food very much.
小孩子非常喜歡美式食物。

21 **American** [ə`mɛrɪkən] (n.) 美國人
Americans love fast food.
美國人喜愛速食。

32 **among** [ə`mʌŋ] (prep.) 在…之中
Among all the students, John is the tallest.
在所有學生當中，約翰長得最高。

35 **amount** [ə`maʊnt] (n.) 數量
I spent a great amount of money on this house.
我為這棟房子花了一大筆錢。

35 **ancestor** [`ænsɛstɚ] (n.) 祖先
The ancestor of Australians came from Britain.
澳洲人的祖先來自英國。

37 **ancient** [`enʃənt] (a.) 古老的
On top of the mountain is an ancient church.
在山頂上有座古老的教堂。

33 **and** [ænd] (conj.) 和
You and I are good friends.
你和我是好朋友。

35 **angel** [`endʒl̩] (n.) 天使
She has the heart of an angel.
她有天使般的好心腸。

35 **anger** [`æŋgɚ] (n.) 憤怒
Mother shouted in anger.
媽媽氣得大叫。

35 **angle** [`æŋgl̩] (n.) 角度
You have to see the problem from a different angle.
你必須由不同的角度來看這個問題。

2 **angry** [ˋæŋgrɪ] (a.) 生氣的
Kevin is too angry to speak.
凱文氣得說不出話來。

27 **animal** [ˋænəml̩] (n.) 動物
Keep away from wild animals.
遠離野生動物。

3 **ankle** [ˋæŋkl̩] (n.) 足踝
Betty twisted her ankle.
貝蒂扭傷了腳踝。

23 **anniversary** [ˌænəˋvɜsərɪ] (n.) 週年紀念日
Today is our wedding anniversary.
今天是我們結婚週年紀念日。

36 **announce** [əˋnaʊns] (v.) 宣布
The president announced that he will leave office.
總統宣布他將辭去職位。

35 **announcement** [əˋnaʊnsmənt] (n.) 宣布
We couldn't hear the announcement in the noisy hall.
在吵雜的大廳裡我們聽不見宣布的事項。

37 **another** [əˋnʌðɚ] (a.) 另一
The pants are too short. Can you give me another pair?
這褲子太短了。可以給我另外一件嗎？

36 **answer** [ˋænsɚ] (v.) 回答
No one can answer the teacher's question.
沒人能回答老師的問題。

27 **ant** [ænt] (n.) 螞蟻
Ants love sweets and sugar.
螞蟻喜歡糖。

37 **any** [ˋɛnɪ] (a.) 任一
Do you have any erasers?
你有橡皮擦嗎？

29 **anybody** [ˋɛnɪ͵bɑdɪ] (n.) 任何人
Is anybody hungry?
有人餓了嗎？

29 **anyone** [ˋɛnɪ͵wʌn] (pron.) 任何一個人
Don't tell anyone about the news.
別把這消息告訴任何人。

29 **anything** [ˋɛnɪ͵θɪŋ] (pron.) 任何事物
Anything else to drink?
還想喝點什麼嗎？

38 **anyway** [ˋɛnɪ͵we] (adv.) 無論如何
It wasn't her fault, anyway.
無論如何，那不是她的錯。

35 **anywhere** [ˋɛnɪ͵hwɛr] (n.) 任何地方
Just take me to anywhere you want.
帶我到任何你想去的地方。

38 **anywhere** [ˋɛnɪ͵hwɛr] (adv.) 在任何地方
Dad said he would take us anywhere we'd like for our summer vacation!
爸爸說我們想去任何地方度暑假，他都會帶我們去！

38 **apart** [əˋpɑrt] (adv.) 分離
The boy lived apart from his parents for a long time.
這個小男孩和父母分開住了很長一段時間。

15 **apartment** [əˋpɑrtmənt] (n.) 公寓
We have to rent an apartment near the office.
我們必須在辦公室附近租一間公寓。

36 **apologize** [ə`pɑlə,dʒaɪz] (v.) 道歉
My girlfriend apologized for what she said.
我女朋友為她所說的話道歉。

37 **apparent** [ə`pærənt] (a.) 明顯的
It's apparent that the old man is under the weather.
很明顯的，這個老人身體不太舒服。

36 **appeal** [ə`pil] (v.) 有吸引力
This idea didn't appeal to me.
這主意並不吸引我。

36 **appear** [ə`pɪr] (v.) 出現
Sam's date didn't appear at the restaurant.
山姆的約會對象並沒有在餐廳出現。

3 **appearance** [ə`pɪrəns] (n.) 外觀
Don't ever judge people by their appearance.
切勿以貌取人。

10 **apple** [`æpl̩] (n.) 蘋果
My grandmother made the best apple pie with the apples from her own tree.
我祖母用她自家樹上摘的蘋果做出最棒的蘋果派。

36 **apply** [ə`plaɪ] (v.) 申請
Have you applied to the university?
你已經申請大學了嗎？

36 **appreciate** [ə`priʃɪ,et] (v.) 欣賞，感激
I really appreciate what you have done for me.
我真的很感激你為我所做的一切。

36 **approach** [ə`protʃ] (v.) 接近
The magican approached the children.
魔術師走向小朋友們。

36 **approve** [ə`pruv] (v.) 贊同
The boss didn't approve the project.
這老闆並不贊同這案子。

8 **April** [`eprəl] (n.) 四月
We always take a trip to the mountains in April because the weather is so nice.
我們總是趁四月天氣晴朗時去山區旅行。

35 **aquarium** [ə`kwɛrɪəm] (n.) 水族館，水族箱
People like to go to the aquarium on weekends.
人們喜歡在週末時到水族館。

31 **are** [ɑr] (v.) 是
They are at the airport.
他們在機場。

20 **area** [`ɛrɪə] (n.) 地區
The area he lives in isn't very safe.
他住的地區不是很安全。

36 **argue** [`ɑrgju] (v.) 爭論
Don't argue with your parents.
不要跟爸媽爭吵。

35 **arithmetic** [ə`rɪθmətɪk] (n.) 算術技巧，計算
The boy is poor at arithmetic.
這男孩的算數很差。

3 **arm** [ɑrm] (n.) 手臂
Her arms got a lot stronger because of playing tennis.
她的手臂因為練網球而越來越壯。

15 **armchair** [`ɑrm,tʃɛr] (n.) 扶手椅
My father is sitting on the armchair by the lamp.
我爸正坐在燈旁邊的扶手椅上。

35 **army** [`ɑrmɪ] (n.) 軍隊
His brother is in the army.
他的哥哥在軍中服務。

38 **around** [ə`raʊnd] (prep.) 圍繞
The students sit around the table.
學生圍著桌子坐著。

32 **around** [ə`raʊnd] (adv.) 附近，到處
We had fun running around the yard, chasing the dog.
我們在院子裡追著狗跑來跑去，玩得很樂。

36 **arrange** [ə`rendʒ] (v.) 安排
I am very busy arranging my wedding.
我正忙著籌備我的婚禮。

36 **arrest** [ə`rɛst] (v.) 逮捕
The criminal was arrested yesterday.
那罪犯昨天被逮捕了。

18 **arrival** [ə`raɪvl̩] (n.) 到來
We celebrated the baby's arrival at the restaurant.
我們在餐廳為慶祝這名新生兒的誕生。

18 **arrive** [ə`raɪv] (v.) 到達
We arrived in Tokyo safely.
我們平安抵達東京。

16 **art** [ɑrt] (n.) 藝術，美術
She's an art teacher in the school.
她是學校裡的美術老師。

35 **article** [`ɑrtɪkl̩] (n.) 物品，文章
Antique shops have expensive articles.
古董店中有昂貴的物品。

A B C D E F G H I J K L M N O P Q R S T U V W X Y Z

24 **artist** [ˋɑrtɪst] (n.) 藝術家
Scott is a very talented artist.
史考特是一位才華出眾的藝術家。

38 **as** [æz] (adv.) 同樣地
He is as tall as his father.
他跟他爸爸一樣高。

33 **as** [æz] (prep.) 當…，以…的身份
He works as an agent for my father's company.
他在我爸的公司裡當仲介。

35 **ash** [æʃ] (n.) 灰燼
The house was burnt to ashes.
這棟房子被燒成灰燼。

20 **Asia** [ˋeʃə] (n.) 亞洲
Taiwan and Japan are both in Asia.
台灣和日本均位於亞洲。

21 **Asian** [ˋeʃən] (n.) 亞洲人
Asians are very proud of their long history and fascinating culture.
亞洲人很自傲於悠久的歷史和迷人的文化。

38 **aside** [əˋsaɪd] (adv.) 在一旁
Could you put the comics aside and pay attention?
請將漫畫書擱到一邊，注意聽好嗎？

36 **ask** [æsk] (v.) 問
May I ask you a personal question?
我可以問你一個私人問題嗎？

37 **asleep** [əˋslip] (a.) 睡著的
He often falls asleep in class.
他常常在課堂上睡著。

36 **assist** [ə`sɪst] (v.) 幫助
They assisted in building the dam.
他們有協助建造水壩。

24 **assistant** [ə`sɪstənt] (a.) 助理的
He is an assistant professor in the university.
他是大學裡的助理教授。

36 **assume** [ə`sjum] (v.) 假設
I assume that you didn't bring your math book today?
我看你今天應該是沒帶數學課本吧？

32 **at** [æt] (prep.) 在
Please arrive at 5 o'clock sharp.
請於五點整準時到達。

28 **athlete** [`æθlɪt] (n.) 運動員
Athletes should have sportsmanship.
運動員應有運動員家精神。

36 **attack** [ə`tæk] (v.) 攻擊，襲擊
Gina was attacked this morning.
吉娜今天早上遭到攻擊。

36 **attempt** [ə`tɛmpt] (v.) 企圖，嘗試
We made two attempts to deliver the package, but the person wasn't home.
我們嘗試投遞包裹兩次，但那個人不在家。

36 **attend** [ə`tɛnd] (v.) 出席
My boss didn't attend the meeting.
我老闆沒有出席會議。

35 **attention** [ə`tɛnʃən] (n.) 注意力
Pay attention to what your teachers say.
老師說話要注意聽。

35 **attitude** [ˋætətjud] (n.) 態度
You should have a positive attitude about work.
你對工作應該要有積極正面的態度。

36 **attract** [əˋtrækt] (v.) 吸引
The light attracts fish to gather around at night.
這盞燈在夜間吸引了許多魚聚集。

37 **attractive** [əˋtræktɪv] (a.) 吸引人的
The offer is very attractive.
提出的條件很吸引人。

1 **audience** [ˋɔdɪəns] (n.) 觀眾，聽眾
The audience gave him a big hand.
觀眾給他如雷的掌聲。

8 **August** [ˋɔgəst] (n.) 八月
We usually have typhoons in August.
這裡八月經常有颱風。

6 **aunt** [ænt] (n.) 伯母，姑母（等女性長輩）
I live with my aunt and uncle.
我和叔叔、嬸嬸住在一起。

20 **Australia** [ɔˋstreljə] (n.) 澳洲
Koalas originated in Australia.
無尾熊原產於澳洲。

21 **Australian** [ɔˋstreljən] (n.) 澳洲人
People from Australia are called Australians.
澳洲來的人稱為澳洲人。

35 **author** [ˋɔθɚ] (n.) 作者
The author of *Pride and Prejudice* is Jane Austen.
《傲慢與偏見》的作者是珍奧斯汀。

37 **automatic** [,ɔtə`mætɪk] (a.) 自動的
The umbrella is fully automatic.
這把傘是全自動的。

18 **automobile** [`ɔtəmə,bil] (n.) 汽車（簡稱auto）
There is an increasing number of automobiles every year.
每年的汽車量一直在成長中。

8 **autumn** [`ɔtəm] (n.) 秋天
I like autumn in New York.
我喜歡紐約的秋天。

37 **available** [ə`veləbl̩] (a.) 有空的
What time are you available?
你什麼時候有空？

18 **avenue** [`ævə,njʊ] (n.) 大道
Fifth Avenue leads to the museum.
沿著第五大街走可通到博物館。

35 **average** [`ævərɪdʒ] (n.) 平均數
An average of two out of ten people gets cancer.
十人中平均有兩人會得癌症。

36 **avoid** [ə`vɔɪd] (v.) 避免
The naughty student tried to avoid teachers.
這個頑皮學生試圖躲避老師。

37 **awake** [ə`wek] (a.) 醒的
He lay awake in the bed all night.
他整夜醒著躺在床上。

36 **awaken** [ə`wekən] (v.) 意識到，弄醒
I was awaken by the sounds of people screaming “Happy Birthday!”
我被大家喊「生日快樂！」的聲音吵醒。

36 **award** [ə`wɔrd] (v.) 頒獎
The company awarded him with a free ticket to New York because he was the top sales person for this year.
公司頒給他一張去紐約的機票，因為他是今年的超級業務員。

37 **aware** [ə`wɛr] (a.) 察覺的
I am aware that this is a difficult job.
我發覺這是一個困難的工作。

38 **away** [ə`we] (adv.) 離開
My brother got in trouble when my mom was five minutes away.
我媽才離開五分鐘，我弟弟就惹了麻煩。

37 **awful** [`ɔfʊl] (a.) 可怕的
The smell is awful.
這味道好可怕。

B

1 **baby** [`bebɪ] (n.) 嬰兒
Jenny has a one- year- old baby girl.
珍妮有個一歲大的女嬰。

24 **baby sitter** [`bebɪ,sɪtɚ] (n.) 保母
Eddy's sister is a baby sitter.
艾迪的姊姊是一位保母。

3 **back** [bæk] (n.) 背部
She carried the baby on her back.
她把小孩背在背上。

12 **backpack** [`bæk,pæk] (n.) 背包
He went to the office with a backpack instead of a suitcase.
他背背包上班，而不是帶公事包。

17 **backward** [`bækwɚd] (adv.) 向後地
The man set a new world record by walking backward.
那個男人用倒退走的方式創下新的世界紀錄。

10 **bacon** [`bekən] (n.) 培根，燻豬肉
Bacon fried with eggs is my favorite.
培根炒蛋是我的最愛。

35 **bacteria** [bæk`tɪrɪə] (n.)（複數）細菌
Wash you hands after using the restroom, or you will spread bacteria.
上完廁所要洗手，不然會散布細菌。

37 **bad** [bæd] (a.) 壞的
Junk food is bad for your health.
垃圾食物對健康不好。

14 **badminton** [`bædmɪntən] (n.) 羽毛球
Jimmy is playing badminton with his friend.
吉米正在和朋友打羽毛球。

12 **bag** [bæg] (n.) 袋子
All the books are in that bag.
所有的書本都在那個袋子裡。

35 **bait** [bet] (n.) 餌
The clever fish didn't bite the bait.
這條聰明的魚不肯咬餌。

10 **bake** [bek] (v.) 烘烤
Grandma baked you a birthday cake!
奶奶烤了個生日蛋糕給你！

17 **bakery** [`bekərɪ] (n.) 麵包店
The bakery has a discount after 10 p.m.
這家麵包店晚上十點後打折。

35 **balance** [ˋbæləns] (n.) 平衡
The boy lost his balance and fell off the bike.
這男孩失去平衡從腳踏車上摔下來。

15 **balcony** [ˋbælkənɪ] (n.) 陽台
People usually dry their clothes on the balcony.
人們常在陽台上曬衣服。

35 **balloon** [bəˋlun] (n.) 氣球
She wants the purple balloon.
她想要那個紫色的氣球。

10 **banana** [bəˋnænə] (n.) 香蕉
Monkeys like bananas.
猴子喜歡香蕉。

14 **band** [bænd] (n.) 樂團，一群
The Beatles were a great rock'n' roll band.
披頭四是一個偉大的搖滾樂團。

35 **bandage** [ˋbændɪdʒ] (n.) 繃帶
The hospital is short of bandages.
這間醫院的繃帶短缺。

36 **bang** [bæŋ] (v.) 猛撞
The woman banged her head against the wall.
那女人猛力用頭撞牆。

17 **bank** [bæŋk] (n.) 銀行
I have to go to the bank tomorrow.
我明天得去銀行。

24 **banker** [ˋbæŋkɚ] (n.) 銀行業者，銀行家
He studied finance because he wants to become a banker one day.
他讀的是財務，因為他希望有朝一日能成為銀行家。

(35) **bar** [bɑr] (n.) 酒吧
They went to the bar on the corner of the street.
他們去街上轉角的酒吧。

(14) **barbecue** [ˋbɑrbɪ,kju] (n.) 烤肉
They had a barbecue in the backyard.
他們在後院烤肉。

(24) **barber** [ˋbɑrbɚ] (n.) 理髮師
The barber cut my hair way too short this time!
理髮師這次把我的頭髮剪得太短了！

(37) **bare** [bɛr] (a.) 沒有…的
This living room was almost bare of furniture.
這客廳裡原本幾乎沒有家具。

(38) **barely** [ˋbɛrlɪ] (adv.) 幾乎不
I could barely recognize my long lost friend.
我幾乎不認得失聯許久的朋友。

(27) **bark** [bɑrk] (v.) 吠叫
Her dog only barks at me so I don't think he likes me.
她的狗只對著我叫，所以我不覺得牠喜歡我。

(35) **barn** [bɑrn] (n.) 穀倉
The barn stores hay for cows.
這穀倉存放給乳牛吃的乾草。

(35) **barrel** [ˋbærəl] (n.) 木桶
The barrels of wine are stored in the cellar.
一桶桶的酒都存放在地窖裡。

(35) **base** [bes] (n.) 底部，基座
I like the base of this lamp, but the shade is ugly.
我喜歡這盞燈的基座，但整個造型很醜。

14 **baseball** [ˋbes,bɔl] (n.) 棒球
They went to see the baseball game together.
他們一起去看棒球比賽。

15 **basement** [ˋbesmənt] (n.) 地下室
My aunt is letting me live in her basement until I get my own apartment.
我阿姨讓我住她家地下室，直到我找到自己的公寓。

35 **basic** [ˋbesɪk] (n.) 基礎，基本
I learned the basics of cooking while living with grandma.
我和祖母同住時，學會烹飪的基本原理。

37 **basic** [ˋbesɪk] (a.) 基礎的，基本的
Hello and Goodbye are basic greetings in English.
你好和再見是基礎的寒暄英語。

35 **basis** [ˋbesɪs] (n.) 準則，基礎
On the basis of human rights, every child should attend school.
基於人權，每個孩子都得上學。

35 **basket** [ˋbæskɪt] (n.) 籃子
Don't put all your eggs in one basket.
不要把全部雞蛋放在同一個籃子裡。

14 **basketball** [ˋbæskɪt,bɔl] (n.) 籃球
Students like to play basketball during the breaks.
在課間休息時，學生喜歡打籃球。

27 **bat** [bæt] (n.) 蝙蝠
Bats sleep upside down.
蝙蝠倒掛著睡覺。

15 **bath** [bæθ] (n.) 洗澡
It's time to take a bath.
該去洗澡了。

36 **bathe** [beð] (v.) 洗澡
How often do you bathe your kitten?
你多久幫貓咪一次洗澡？

15 **bathroom** [ˋbæθ,rum] (n.) 浴室
There are two bathrooms in the apartment.
這間公寓有兩間廁所。

35 **battery** [ˋbætərɪ] (n.) 電池
This toy took six batteries to run!
這個玩具要六個電池才跑得動！

26 **bay** [be] (n.) 海灣
We sailed around the bay watching the sunset.
我們在海灣裡到處航行，欣賞夕陽。

26 **beach** [bitʃ] (n.) 海灘
People go swimming at the beach during the summer.
人們在夏天會到海邊游泳。

35 **beam** [bim] (n.) 光線
There is a beam of light shining through the kitchen window.
一道光線照進廚房的窗戶。

10 **bean** [bin] (n.) 豆子
They hate green beans.
他們討厭吃青豆。

27 **bear** [bɛr] (n.) 熊
We had to hide our food from the bears on our camping trip.
我們露營時必須把食物藏好，避免被熊找到。

3 **beard** [bɪrd] (n.) 鬍子
Wearing a beard makes you look old.
留鬍子使你看起來很老。

35 **beast** [bist] (n.) 野獸
The child drew pictures of the beast she saw in her dreams.
那孩子畫下她在夢裡見到的野獸。

36 **beat** [bit] (v.) 打
Junior beat Luke with his fists today.
朱尼爾今天打路克。

2 **beautiful** [`bjutəfəl] (a.) 漂亮的
My brother has a beautiful English teacher.
我哥哥有位漂亮的英語老師。

35 **beauty** [`bjutɪ] (n.) 美女
My cousin is a beauty.
我的堂妹是個美人。

33 **because** [bɪ`kɔz] (conj.) 因為
She didn't go to school because she was sick today.
她沒有去上學，因為她今天生病。

36 **become** [bɪ`kʌm] (v.) 變成
The weather is becoming colder and colder.
天氣越來越冷了。

15 **bed** [bɛd] (n.) 床
He hid all his dirty clothes under his bed.
他把髒衣服全都藏進床底下。

15 **bedroom** [`bɛd,rum] (n.) 臥室
My bedroom is my favorite place to read and study.
我最喜歡閱讀和用功的地方是我的臥室。

27 **bee** [bi] (n.) 蜜蜂
He's as busy as a bee.
他忙得像隻蜜蜂一樣。

10 **beef** [bif] (n.) 牛肉
I want some beef noodles for dinner.
我晚餐想吃牛肉麵。

10 **beer** [bɪr] (n.) 啤酒
Men love to drink beer when they watch soccer games.
男人看足球賽時喜歡喝啤酒。

32 **before** [bɪˋfor] (prep.) 在…之前
Before you eat dinner, you should wash your hands.
吃晚餐前應該先洗手。

24 **beggar** [ˋbɛgɚ] (n.) 乞丐
The underpass is full of beggars.
地下道裡都是乞丐。

36 **begin** [bɪˋgɪn] (v.) 開始
The party begins at 9 p.m.
派對晚上九點開始。

35 **beginner** [bɪˋgɪnɚ] (n.) 新手
He's just a beginner, so when he drives, he heeds someone with him.
新手開車需要有人陪伴。

35 **beginning** [bɪˋgɪnɪŋ] (n.) 開始
This is a new beginning in my life.
這是我人生新的開始。

16 **behave** [bɪˋhev] (v.) 守規矩
My little brother never behaves when we go out.
我們出門時我的弟弟從來不守規矩。

32 **behind** [bɪˋhaɪnd] (prep.) 在…之後
The umbrella is behind the door.
雨傘在門後。

35 **belief** [bɪˋlif] (n.) 信仰
He has a strong belief in God.
他對上帝有堅定的信仰。

36 **believe** [bɪˋliv] (v.) 相信
I believe you can make it.
我相信你可以做到。

35 **bell** [bɛl] (n.) 鈴
The door bell rang.
門鈴剛剛響了。

3 **belly** [ˋbɛlɪ] (n.) 肚子
My belly is aching.
我的肚子痛。

36 **belong** [bɪˋlɔŋ] (v.) 屬於
This bag belongs to me.
這個包包是我的。

32 **below** [bɪˋlo] (prep.) 在…之下，低於
The boy's IQ is below average.
那男孩的智商低於平均值。

12 **belt** [bɛlt] (n.) 皮帶
Please fasten your seat belt.
請繫緊安全帶。

15 **bench** [bɛntʃ] (n.) 長凳，長椅
It's comfortable to sit on the park bench under the winter sun.
冬天坐在公園的長椅上曬太陽很舒服。

38 **beneath** [bɪˋniθ] (adv.) 在…之下
We sat beneath the stars, talking about what we'd like to do in the future.
我們坐在星空下，聊著未來想要做什麼。

35 **benefit** [ˋbɛnəfɪt] (n.) 利潤
The benefit of a vacation is that you get to rest.
度假的好處是能讓人好好休息。

10 **berry** [ˋbɛrɪ] (n.) 漿果
Wild birds like to peck at the berries.
野鳥喜歡啄食莓果。

32 **beside** [bɪˋsaɪd] (prep.) 在…旁邊
May I sit beside you?
我可以坐你旁邊嗎？

33 **besides** [bɪˋsaɪdz] (conj.) 除了…之外
Besides two cats, I have one dog.
除了兩隻貓，我還有一隻狗。

38 **besides** [bɪˋsaɪdz] (adv.) 此外
I can't go out tonight. Besides, I don't have any money to do anything.
我今晚不能出去。此外，我也沒錢能幹嘛了。

37 **best** [bɛst] (a.) 最好的
What's your best score so far?
到目前為止，你最好的成績是？

37 **better** [ˋbɛtɚ] (a.) 較好的
Your score is so much better than mine!
你的成績比我的好多了！

32 **between** [bɪˋtwin] (prep.) 在…之間
The supermarket is between the bookstore and the park.
超級市場在書店和公園之間。

32 **beyond** [bɪˋjand] (prep.) 在…另一邊
Beyond the forest is the desert.
森林的那一邊是沙漠。

35 **Bible** [ˋbaɪbḷ] (n.) 聖經
The Bible is one of the most important books.
聖經對基督徒而言是最重要的書籍之一。

18 **bicycle** [ˋbaɪsɪkḷ] (n.) 腳踏車
He rides a bicycle to school.
他騎腳踏車上學。

19 **big** [bɪg] (a.) 大的
The jacket is too big.
那件夾克太大了。

18 **bike** [baɪk] (n.) 腳踏車
She goes to school by bike every day.
他每天騎腳踏車上學。

9 **bill** [bɪl] (n.) 帳單，紙鈔
Do you see my phone bill?
你有看到我的電話帳單嗎？

7 **billion** [ˋbɪljən] (n.) 十億
There are more than one billion people in China.
中國有超過十億人口。

35 **biography** [baɪˋɑgrəfɪ] (n.) 傳記
My favorite biography of all time is that of Benjamin Franklin.
班哲明富蘭克林的傳記是我一直都很喜歡的傳記。

16 **biology** [baɪˋɑlədʒɪ] (n.) 生物學
I passed my biology exam.
我通過生物考試了。

27 **bird** [bɝd] (n.) 鳥
She keeps a bird as a pet at home.
她在家裡養隻小鳥當寵物。

35 **birthday** [ˋbɝθ,de] (n.) 生日
I always forget my birthday.
我總是忘記我的生日。

11 **biscuit** [ˋbɪskɪt] (n.) 餅乾
The little girl fed her kitten biscuits.
小女孩餵貓咪吃餅乾。

35 **bit** [bɪt] (n.) 一點
Can I have a bit of your bread?
我可以吃一點你的麵包嗎？

36 **bite** [baɪt] (v.) 咬
Don't bite off more than you can chew.
不要自不量力。

10 **bitter** [ˋbɪtɚ] (a.) 苦的
This candy isn't sweet, it's bitter!
這顆糖不是甜的，而是苦的！

13 **black** [blæk] (a.) 黑色的
On Halloween, people get scared when they see a black cat.
萬聖節前夕，人們看到黑貓會覺得害怕。

16 **blackboard** [ˋblæk,bɔrd] (n.) 黑板
The teacher writes on the blackboard.
老師在黑板上寫字。

35 **blade** [bled] (n.) 刀片
The blade is so sharp on that knife that it could cut through anything!
那把刀的刀刃好利，什麼都能切斷！

35 **blame** [blem] (n.) 罪過
He put all the blame on me.
他將所有責備都怪在我身上。

36 **blame** [blem] (v.) 責怪
Don't blame me for your mistakes!
不要把你的錯怪到我頭上來！

35 **blank** [blæŋk] (n.) 空白處
Please fill in the blanks with the right answers.
請把空白處填入正確答案。

37 **blank** [blæŋk] (a.) 空白的
I left this one blank because I really couldn't remember the answer.
我這題空著沒寫，因為我實在想不起答案。

15 **blanket** [`blæŋkɪt] (n.) 毯子
We need a heavy blanket during the winter.
我們冬天需要一條厚毯子。

36 **bleed** [blid] (v.) 流血
My nose is bleeding.
我的鼻子流血了。

36 **blend** [blɛnd] (v.) 混合
We blended the two fruits together with milk and sugar to make a nice fruit drink.
我們把這兩種水果跟牛奶混在一起，做出一種好喝的水果飲料。

36 **bless** [blɛs] (v.) 祝福
The priest blessed all of the audience.
神父祝福所有聽講者。

2 **blind** [blaɪnd] (a.) 眼盲的
Kate's mother is blind; she can't see anything.
凱特的媽媽眼盲。她看不到任何東西。

36 **blink** [`blɪŋk] (v.) 眨眼
Don't blink while I am putting the medicine into your eye.
我在幫你點眼藥時，不要眨眼。

18 **block** [blɑk] (n.) 街區
The department store is on the second block.
百貨公司在下二個街區。

35 **blood** [blʌd] (n.) 血
He cut his hand and got blood on his shirt.
他把手割傷，上衣沾到血。

12 **blouse** [blaʊz] (n.) 短上衣(女士用)，短衫
The lady is in a black blouse.
這位女士穿的是黑色短衫。

36 **blow** [blo] (v.) 吹
This soup is too hot, so you might have to blow on it first before you taste it.
湯很燙，喝湯之前最好先吹一吹。

13 **blue** [blu] (a.) 藍色的
The sky is blue.
天空是藍色的。

2 **blush** [blʌʃ] (v.) 臉紅
He blushed when he knew he made a stupid mistake.
當他知道自己犯了個愚蠢錯誤時，他臉紅了。

35 **board** [bord] (n.) 木板，布告欄
There was a notice on the board that said we were getting a new teacher.
布告欄上有一張公告，說我們會換一位新老師。

2 **boast** [bost] (v.) 自誇，吹噓
She boasts a lot about how much money her father makes.
她很愛吹噓她爸爸多麼有錢。

18 **boat** [bot] (n.) 船
We're in the same boat. I am running out of money, too.
我們同病相憐。我也沒錢了。

3 **body** [ˋbadɪ] (n.) 身體
You must take care of your body.
你一定要好好照顧身體。

10 **boil** [bɔɪl] (v.) 煮沸
The water is boiling.
水開了。

37 **bold** [bold] (a.) 大膽的
He is so bold to talk back.
他好大的膽子敢回嘴。

35 **bomb** [bam] (n.) 炸彈
The bomb will go off in ten minutes.
炸彈將在十分鐘後爆炸。

3 **bone** [bon] (n.) 骨頭
Drinking milk will help keep your bones healthy.
喝牛奶有益骨骼健康。

16 **book** [bʊk] (n.) 書
She likes to read books.
她喜歡讀書。

15 **bookcase** [ˋbʊk,kes] (n.) 書架
That bookcase is filled with old books that I loved as a child.
那個書架擺滿我孩提時代的最愛的舊書籍。

17 **bookstore** [ˋbʊk,stor] (n.) 書店
I like to spend time at the bookstore reading new books on the weekends.
我週末喜歡待在書店裡讀新書。

35 **boot** [but] (n.) 靴子
These new boots make me look taller and thinner.
這雙新靴子讓我看起來變高又變瘦。

35 **border** [ˋbɔrdɚ] (n.) 邊境
There is a conflict at the border of the two countries.
這兩國在邊境有衝突。

36 **bore** [bor] (v.) 厭煩
The movie bores me.
這電影令我厭煩。

2 **bored** [bɔrd] (a.) 無聊的
She was bored in the history class.
她上歷史課時覺得很悶。

2 **boring** [ˋborɪŋ] (a.) 乏味的
The movie was so boring. I slept in the movie theater.
那電影好無聊。我在電影院裡睡著了。

6 **born** [bɔrn] (a.) 出生的
I was born in Japan.
我在日本出生。

36 **borrow** [ˋbɑro] (v.) 借入
I borrowed some money from my brother.
我向我弟借了些錢。

24 **boss** [bɔs] (n.) 老闆
Your boss is so bossy.
你的老闆很跋扈。

7 **both** [boθ] (pron.) 兩者，雙方
Both of them are late.
他們倆都遲到了。

36 **bother** [ˋbɑðɚ] (v.) 煩擾
Please do not bother me; I'm working.
我現在在工作，請勿打擾。

19 **bottle** [ˋbɑtḷ] (n.) 瓶子
The plastic bottles are recyclable.
塑膠瓶可回收。

35 **bottom** [ˋbɑtəm] (n.) 底部
The bottom of the bottle is leaking.
這個瓶底在漏水。

36 **bow** [baʊ] (v.) 鞠躬
Everyone bowed to him.
每個人都對他鞠躬。

11 **bowl** [bol] (n.) 碗
I was so hungry that I had two bowls of rice.
我好餓所以吃了兩碗飯。

14 **bowling** [ˋbolɪŋ] (n.) 保齡球
Let's go bowling.
我們去打保齡球吧。

35 **box** [bɑks] (n.) 盒子
What's in the box?
盒子裡有什麼？

1 **boy** [bɔɪ] (n.) 男孩
That man is forty years old but still acts like a little boy!
那個男人已經四十歲了，但行為還像個小男孩！

12 **bracelet** [ˋbreslɪt] (n.) 手鐲
The woman has several bracelets on her left wrist.
那個女士的左腕上有好幾個手鐲。

35 **brain** [bren] (n.) 頭腦
Use your brain during your exams.
考試時用點腦子。

35 **brake** [brek] (n.) 煞車
The brakes on the used car are out of order.
這輛中古車的煞車故障。

35 **branch** [bræntʃ] (n.) 樹枝
The branches on the tree broke under the weight of the snow.
樹上的枝幹因為雪的重量折斷了。

35 **brass** [bræs] (n.) 銅
The door knob is made of brass.
這門把是銅製的。

2 **brave** [brev] (a.) 勇敢的
Grandpa was a brave soldier.
爺爺過去是個勇敢的士兵。

35 **bravery** [ˋbrevərɪ] (n.) 勇敢
The soldiers showed bravery when fighting back the enemy.
士兵擊退敵人時展現出英勇氣概。

10 **bread** [brɛd] (n.) 麵包
She wants bread with butter.
她想要麵包上塗奶油。

36 **break** [brek] (v.) 打破
The glass breaks easily.
這個玻璃杯很容易破。

10 **breakfast** [ˋbrɛkfəst] (n.) 早餐
Eating breakfast is important.
吃早餐很重要。

3 **breast** [brɛst] (n.) 乳房
Breast-fed babies are healthier than bottle-fed babies.
吃母乳的小孩比喝牛奶的健康。

35 **breath** [brɛθ] (n.) 呼吸，氣息
Bungee jumping takes my breath away.
高空彈跳把我嚇死了。

36 **breathe** [brið] (v.) 呼吸
You cannot breathe in water.
在水裡不能呼吸。

36 **breed** [brid] (v.) 飼養
The aquarium knows how to breed beautiful fish.
那家水族館知道如何繁殖漂亮的魚。

35 **breeze** [briz] (n.) 微風
It's nice to walk in the cool breeze.
在涼爽微風裡散步感覺很好。

15 **brick** [brɪk] (n.) 磚塊
The hut is built with bricks, not wood.
這個小屋是用磚塊蓋的，不是用木頭。

35 **bride** [braɪd] (n.) 新娘
The bride ran away before the wedding.
新娘在婚禮前逃跑了。

18 **bridge** [brɪdʒ] (n.) 橋
The bridge is falling apart because of the heavy rain.
因為豪雨，這座橋已經快垮了。

35 **bridegroom** [`braɪ,grʊm] (n.) 新郎
The bridegroom is too nervous to dress himself properly.
那新郎緊張到連衣服都穿不好。

37 **brief** [brif] (a.) 簡略的
Can you give me a brief description of your plan?
可不可以簡略的說明你的計畫？

37 **bright** [braɪt] (a.) 明亮的
This bedroom is very bright.
這間臥室非常明亮。

37 **brilliant** [ˋbrɪljənt] (a.) 傑出的，聰明的
The brilliant boy gets good grades all the time.
這個聰明的男孩總是得到好成績。

36 **bring** [brɪŋ] (v.) 攜帶
Bring me some food.
幫我帶些食物來。

20 **Britain** [ˋbrɪtən] (n.) 英國，大不列顛
She'd like to go to Britain to study literature someday.
她未來想要到英國讀文學。

21 **British** [ˋbrɪtɪʃ] (n.) 英國人
The British are famous for their afternoon tea parties.
英國人以他們的下午茶聞名。

37 **broad** [brɔd] (a.) 廣泛的
The menu from this steak house offers broad choices of meat.
這家牛排館的菜單有各式各樣的肉類選擇。

36 **broadcast** [ˋbrɔd,kæst] (v.) 廣播，播報
The TV broadcasts the news every hour.
電視每小時都播報新聞。

25 **brook** [bruk] (n.) 小溪，小河
Fishing is not allowed in this brook.
這條小溪禁止釣魚。

35 **broom** [brum] (n.) 掃把
The new broom works very well.
新的掃把很好掃。

6 **brother** [ˋbrʌðɚ] (n.) 哥哥，弟弟
I don't have any brothers or sisters.
我沒有兄弟姐妹。

3 **brow** [braʊ] (n.) 眉毛，眉頭
He knit his brow and said nothing.
他眉頭緊鎖不發一語。

13 **brown** [braʊn] (a.) 棕色的
My sister has brown hair.
我姊姊有棕色頭髮。

10 **brunch** [brʌntʃ] (n.) 早午餐
We usually have brunch on weekends.
週末我們通常吃早午餐。

36 **brush** [brʌʃ] (v.) 刷
We must brush our teeth three times a day.
我們一天必須刷三次牙。

37 **brutal** [ˋbrutl̩] (a.) 殘忍的
The brutal combat lasted for two days.
殘忍的戰鬥持續了兩天。

35 **bubble** [ˋbʌbl̩] (n.) 泡沫
The bubbles are whirling in the bathtub.
泡沫在浴缸裡旋轉。

15 **bucket** [ˋbʌkɪt] (n.) 桶子
Grandma asked for some buckets to store water.
奶奶要了幾個水桶儲水。

35 **bud** [bʌd] (n.) 花蕾
The roses are all in buds.
所有玫瑰花都含苞待放。

35 **budget** [ˋbʌdʒɪt] (n.) 預算
We don't have a big budget to buy the house.
我們沒有足夠預算買這間房子。

27 **buffalo** [ˋbʌfə,lo] (n.) 水牛
It's difficult to see buffaloes in the fields now.
現在在草原上很難看到水牛。

17 **buffet** [bʌˋfe] (n.) 自助餐
Students like to eat at buffets.
學生喜歡吃自助餐。

27 **bug** [bʌg] (n.) 小蟲
There are bugs everywhere in the jungle.
叢林裡到處都是小蟲。

15 **build** [bɪld] (v.) 建，蓋
They built a house there.
他們在那裡蓋了間房子。

15 **building** [ˋbɪldɪŋ] (n.) 建築物
The buildings in the big cities are very tall.
大城市裡的建築物一棟比一棟高。

35 **bulb** [bʌlb] (n.) 電燈泡
That light bulb lasted two years!
那個燈泡撐了兩年沒換過！

27 **bull** [bʊl] (n.) 公牛
The bull was killed for its meat.
那頭公牛被宰來吃了。

35 **bullet** [ˋbʊlɪt] (n.) 子彈
The bullet went through his shoulder.
子彈射穿他的肩膀。

35 **bulletin** [ˋbʊlətɪn] (n.) 公告
The letter is attached on the bulletin board.
那封信被貼在布告欄上。

36 **bump** [bʌmp] (v.) 碰，撞
The car bumped into the truck.
這輛車撞上卡車。

10 **bun** [bʌn] (n.) 小圓麵包
They serve free buns before the steak.
上牛排前，他們提供免費的小麵包。

35 **bunch** [bʌntʃ] (n.) 束，串
She received a bunch of flowers on Valentine's Day.
情人節她收到了一束花。

35 **bundle** [ˋbʌndḷ] (n.) 捆，束
The police found a big bundle of lost money hiding in the ceiling.
一大包遺失的錢藏在屋頂上，被警察尋獲。

35 **burden** [ˋbɝdəṇ] (n.) 負擔，重任
The burden on his shoulders is getting heavier.
他肩上的重擔越來越重。

10 **burger** [ˋbɝgɚ] (n.) 漢堡
She loves to eat burgers.
她喜歡吃漢堡。

35 **burglar** [ˋbɝ glɚ] (n.) 強盜
The burglar went into the palace stealthily.
這個強盜偷偷跑進皇宮。

36 **burn** [bɝ n] (v.) 燃燒
Farmers are burning grass in the fields.
農人正在田裡燒雜草。

36 **burst** [bɝst] (v.) 破裂
The purple balloon burst.
紫色汽球破了。

36 **bury** [ˋbɛrɪ] (v.) 埋，使…沈浸
The professor buried his nose into his book.
這個教授埋首書堆。

18 **bus** [bʌs] (n.) 巴士
Ryan goes to school by bus.
萊恩搭公車上學。

18 **bus stop** [bʌs stɑp] (n.) 公車站
In front of the train station are many bus stops.
火車站前有很多公車站牌。

25 **bush** [bʊʃ] (n.) 灌木，灌木叢
We hid behind the bushes and watched the new neighbors as they moved in.
我們躲在樹叢後面看著新鄰居搬進來。

24 **business** [ˋbɪznɪs] (n.) 生意
He has a business trip to Canada.
他到加拿大出差。

24 **businessman** [ˋbɪznɪs,mən] (n.) 商人
Sheila's father is a businessman.
席拉的父親是生意人。

2 **busy** [ˋbɪzɪ] (a.) 忙碌的
My father is busy at work now.
我爸爸現在正在忙著工作。

33 **but** [bʌt] (conj.) 但是
I'd like to go on vacation but I don't have the time or money.
我很想去度假，但我既沒錢也沒時間。

10 **butter** [ˋbʌtɚ] (n.) 奶油
I like to use butter to stir-fry eggs.
我喜歡用奶油炒蛋。

27 **butterfly** [ˋbʌtɚ,flaɪ] (n.) 蝴蝶
Butterflies are beautiful insects.
蝴蝶是漂亮的昆蟲。

12 **button** [ˋbʌtn̩] (v.) 扣（鈕釦）
Button up your shirt.
把你的襯衫扣好。

35 **button** [ˋbʌtn̩] (n.) 鈕釦，按鈕
When you push this button, the red light will come on.
當你按下這個按鈕，紅燈就會亮。

9 **buy** [baɪ] (v.) 買
You can buy food in the convenience store.
你可以在便利商店買到食物。

35 **buzz** [bʌz] (n.) 嗡嗡聲
I heard a buzz and then saw a bee trying to eat my cake!
我聽到一陣嗡嗡聲，就看到一隻蜜蜂想吃我的蛋糕！

36 **buzz** [bʌz] (v.) 嗡嗡叫
The speaker was buzzing because it was broken.
擴音器壞掉了，所以發出嗡嗡的聲響。

32 **by** [baɪ] (prep.) 在…旁
The lamp was put on the desk by the window.
檯燈放在窗戶旁的書桌上。

C

10 **cabbage** [ˋkæbɪdʒ] (n.) 高麗菜
It's healthy to eat raw cabbage.
吃生高麗菜很健康。

15 **cabin** [ˋkæbɪn] (n.) 小屋
We have a summer cabin near the lake.
我們在湖附近有一個避暑小屋。

15 **cabinet** [ˋkæbənɪt] (n.) 櫃子
The first aid kit is in the cabinet by the TV.
急救箱在電視旁的櫃子裡。

35 **cable** [ˋkebḷ] (n.) 有線電視
We don't have cables at home.
我們家沒有第四台。

17 **cafeteria** [ˌkæfəˋtɪrɪə] (n.) 自助餐廳
He is a waiter there in the cafeteria.
他是那家自助餐廳的服務生。

35 **cage** [kedʒ] (n.) 籠子
The lions are in the cage.
獅子都在籠子裡。

10 **cake** [kek] (n.) 蛋糕
Everyone likes chocolate cake.
每個人都喜歡巧克力蛋糕。

36 **calculate** [ˋkælkjəˌlet] (v.) 計算
Mom calculated how much we spent during the trip.
媽媽算出我們這趟旅行花了多少錢。

8 **calendar** [ˋkæləndɚ] (n.) 日曆
She made a note in her calendar.
她在日曆上寫下筆記。

36 **call** [kɔl] (v.) 呼叫，打電話
I called you just now.
我剛剛才打電話給你。

36 **calm** [kɑm] (v.) 冷靜
Take a breath and calm down.
深呼吸冷靜下來。

15 **camera** [ˋkæmərə] (n.) 照相機
The digital camera has replaced the traditional camera.
數位相機已經取代傳統相機。

35 **campaign** [kæmˋpen] (n.) 活動
There is a campaign to raise funds for the homeless.
這裡有個為遊民募款的活動。

14 **camping** [ˋkæmpɪŋ] (n.) 露營
They went camping last weekend.
他們上週末去露營。

16 **campus** [ˋkæmpəs] (n.) 校園，校區
There are lots of convenience stores near the campus.
在校園附近有很多便利商店。

35 **can** [kæn] (n.) 罐頭，桶子
We put all the pens in this can for everyone to use.
我們把筆都放進這個罐子給大家用。

20 **Canada** [ˋkænədə] (n.) 加拿大
Canada is known for its beautiful scenery and comfortable lifestyle.
加拿大以風景優美和生活舒適著稱。

21 **Canadian** [kə`nedɪən] (n.) 加拿大人
You can't tell Canadians from Americans.
加拿大人和美國人很難分辨。

36 **cancel** [`kænsḷ] (v.) 取消
May I cancel my appointment with the dentist?
我可以取消和牙醫的約診嗎？

4 **cancer** [`kænsɚ] (n.) 癌症
My grandpa died of lung cancer.
我爺爺死於肺癌。

35 **candidate** [`kændədet] (n.) 候選人
All the candidates for the job didn't meet the qualification.
這個工作的所有應徵者都不符合資格。

15 **candle** [`kændḷ] (n.) 蠟燭
The number of candles on the cake stands for your age.
蛋糕上的蠟燭數量代表年齡。

10 **candy** [`kændɪ] (n.) 糖果
Candies do harm to your teeth.
糖果對你的牙齒不好。

35 **cane** [ken] (n.) 拐杖，籐條
Grandpa walks with a cane because his legs are weak.
爺爺的腿很虛弱，所以撐著一根枴杖走路。

18 **canoe** [kə`nu] (n.) 獨木舟
The Indians transferred goods by canoe.
印地安人以前用獨木舟運送貨物。

25 **canyon** [`kænjən] (n.) 峽谷
The Grand Canyon attracts many tourists every year.
每年大峽谷都吸引好多觀光客。

⑫ **cap** [kæp] (n.) 鴨舌帽
Teenagers like to wear baseball caps.
青少年喜歡戴棒球帽。

㊲ **capable** [ˋkepəbl̩] (a.) 有能力的
She isn't capable of the task.
她無法勝任這項工作。

⑫ **cape** [kep] (n.) 披肩
If you put on this cape, you'll be warmer.
披上這件披肩，你會比較暖和。

㉟ **capital** [ˋkæpətl̩] (n.) 首都
Austin is the capital of Texas.
德州的首府是奧斯汀。

㉟ **captain** [ˋkæptɪn] (n.) 隊長
She used to be the captain of the volleyball team.
她以前是排球隊的隊長。

㊱ **capture** [ˋkæptʃɚ] (v.) 捕獲
The firefighters haven't captured the wild bear.
消防隊員還沒有捕獲那隻野生的熊。

⑱ **car** [kɑr] (n.) 車
He is fond of the racing car.
他很迷賽車。

⑭ **card** [kɑrd] (n.) 卡片
I received a lot of Christmas cards.
我收到很多耶誕卡。

㊱ **care** [kɛr] (n.) 在意，關懷
I don't care if he's late, as long as he shows up!
我不在意他是不是遲到，只有他有來就好！

36 **care** [kɛr] (v.) 關心
I care about him a lot, but I don't love him.
我很關心他，但我不愛他。

24 **career** [kə`rɪr] (a.) 職業的
She's a career woman.
她是個職業婦女。

24 **career** [kə`rɪr] (n.) 職業，事業
Taking this job will be good for your career.
接受這個工作將有助於你的生涯規劃。

2 **careful** [`kɛrfəl] (a.) 小心的
You must be careful when crossing streets.
過馬路一定要小心。

2 **careless** [`kɛrlɪs] (a.) 粗心的
I failed my math test because I was so careless.
我太粗心了，所以數學考試不及格。

24 **carpenter** [`kɑrpəntɚ] (n.) 木匠
It's hard to be a skillful carpenter.
當一位技術好的木匠很難。

15 **carpet** [`kɑrpɪt] (n.) 地毯
We put a big carpet on the living room floor.
我們在起居室的地上放了一張大地毯。

10 **carrot** [`kærət] (n.) 紅蘿蔔
Rabbits like carrots.
兔子喜歡紅蘿蔔。

36 **carry** [`kɛrɪ] (v.) 攜帶
The gentleman carried the bag for the lady.
那位紳士幫那位女士拿袋子。

14 **cartoon** [kɑr`tun] (n.) 卡通動畫，漫畫
I like to watch cartoons very much.
我喜歡看卡通影片。

36 **carve** [kɑrv] (v.) 雕刻
Don't carve on the school desk.
不要在學校的書桌上刻字。

35 **case** [kes] (n.) 案例
There are a lot of murder cases in the city.
城市裡有很多兇殺案。

9 **cash** [kæʃ] (n.) 現金
I am short of cash; would you lend me some?
我缺現金，可以借我一些嗎？

15 **cassette** [kə`sɛt] (n.) 卡帶
Cassettes have been replaced by CDs.
卡帶已經被CD取代了。

36 **cast** [kæst] (v.) 投，丟
The fisherman cast the line many times, but never caught any fish.
那位漁夫拋了好幾次釣線，但都沒釣到魚。

35 **catalogue** [`kætəlɔg] (n.) 目錄
Sam likes to order items from the catalogue.
山姆喜歡從郵購目錄裡訂購東西。

35 **castle** [`kæsl̩] (n.) 城堡
Children like to build sand castles at the beach.
小孩喜歡在沙灘上蓋沙堡。

37 **casual** [`kæʒuəl] (a.) 不拘禮節的，隨意的
I dressed in casual clothes today.
我今天穿的很輕鬆。

27 **cat** [kæt] (n.) 貓
Cats and tigers are relatives.
貓和老虎是生物學上的近親。

36 **catch** [kætʃ] (v.) 接住，趕上
I didn't catch my bus this morning.
今天早上我沒趕上公車。

27 **caterpillar** [ˋkætɚ,pɪlɚ] (n.) 毛毛蟲
The caterpillar is going to transform into a beautiful butterfly.
那條毛毛蟲將會羽化成一隻漂亮的蝴蝶。

27 **cattle** [ˋkætl̩] (n.) 牛
My family raises cattle in the countryside.
我家在鄉下養牛。

35 **cause** [kɔz] (n.) 原因
The taxi driver is the cause of the accident.
這位計程車司機是這場車禍的肇事者。

14 **CD** [ˋsi ˋdi] (n.) 雷射唱片
I like to collect jazz CDs.
我喜歡收集爵士樂CD。

15 **ceiling** [ˋsilɪŋ] (n.) 天花板
There is a rat on the ceiling.
有一隻老鼠在天花板上。

23 **celebrate** [ˋsɛlə,bret] (v.) 慶祝
We celebrated Christmas together last year.
我們去年一起慶祝耶誕節。

35 **cellphone** [ˋsɛlˋfon] (n.) 手機，行動電話
Cellphones are popular now.
手機現在很普遍。

9 **cent** [sɛnt] (n.) 分

I bought the bun for fifty cents.

我花了五十分錢買這個小麵包。

35 **center** [ˋsɛntɚ] (n.) 中心

The tall building is in the center of the city.

這棟高樓位於市中心。

19 **centimeter** [ˋsɛntə,mitɚ] (n.) 公分

I am one hundred and six- five centimeters tall.

我身高一百六十五公分高。

17 **central** [ˋsɛntrəl] (a.) 中間的

The earthquake seriously hit the central part of the country.

地震重創這個國家的中部地區。

8 **century** [ˋsɛntʃərɪ] (n.) 世紀

This was the most important event of the century.

這是本世紀最重大的事件。

10 **cereal** [ˋsɪrɪəl] (n.) 穀類食品

My kids like to eat cereal with milk every morning.

我的小孩喜歡每天早上吃穀片加牛奶。

37 **certain** [ˋsɝ tən] (a.) 確定的

I'm certain that he will come tonight.

我確定他今晚會來。

38 **certainly** [ˋsɝtənlɪ] (adv.) 確實地

He certainly knows how to dress well.

他的確非常了解如何打扮。

35 **chain** [tʃen] (n.) 鏈，鎖鏈

The school gate is locked by a chain.

學校大門被鐵鏈鎖上了。

15 **chair** [tʃɛr] (n.) 椅子
The chairs are not enough for ten people.
椅子不夠十人坐。

24 **chairman** [ˋtʃɛrmən] (n.) 主席，董事長
Allen was elected as the chairman of the company.
艾倫被選為這家公司的董事長。

16 **chalk** [tʃɔk] (n.) 粉筆
Pieces of chalk are on the platform.
講台上有幾段短短的粉筆。

35 **challenge** [ˋtʃælɪŋdʒ] (n.) 挑戰
It would be a challenge to swim across the river.
游泳橫渡這條河是一大挑戰。

35 **champion** [ˋtʃæmpɪən] (n.) 優勝者，冠軍
He is the world champion in wrestling.
他是世界摔角冠軍。

35 **chance** [tʃæns] (n.) 機會
I ran across my math teacher by chance.
我意外遇到數學老師。

9 **change** [tʃendʒ] (n.) 零錢
You can keep the change.
不用找零了。

36 **change** [tʃendʒ] (v.) 改變
The magician changed the man into a frog.
魔術師把那個人變成青蛙。

37 **changeable** [ˋtʃendʒəbl̩] (a.) 易變的，不定的
The weather is changeable here.
這裡的天氣不穩定。

35 **channel** [ˋtʃænl̩] (n.) 管道，頻道

There are more than 100 channels on TV.

電視有超過一百個頻道。

16 **chapter** [ˋtʃæptɚ] (n.) 章，回

I read the first chapter of the book and decided not to buy it.

我讀了這本書的第一章後就決定不買了。

35 **character** [ˋkærɪktɚ] (n.) 角色

She's the main character in the play.

她是這齣舞台劇的主角。

2 **characteristic** [ˌkærəktəˋrɪstɪk] (n.) 特徵，特色

The old professor has strange personal characteristics.

那位老教授個性古怪。

9 **charge** [tʃɑrdʒ] (v.) 收費，索價

How much do you charge to fix my car engine?

修理我的汽車引擎你要收多少錢？

35 **charity** [ˋtʃærətɪ] (n.) 慈善

My mother gives ten percent of her salary to charity.

我媽媽將月薪十分之一捐給慈善機構。

2 **charm** [tʃɑrm] (n.) 魅力，撫媚

The charm of the lady attracts everyone's eye.

這女生的魅力吸引了大家的目光。

35 **chart** [tʃɑrt] (n.) 圖表

The teacher explained the question by drawing charts.

老師藉由畫圖表說明這個問題。

36 **chase** [tʃes] (v.) 追逐

The kids are all chasing around in the classroom.

所有的孩子都在教室裡追逐。

36 **chat** [tʃæt] (v.) 聊天，閒談
Students like to chat on the Net.
學生喜歡在網路上聊天。

9 **cheap** [tʃip] (a.) 便宜的
The car is very cheap.
這部車很便宜。

36 **cheat** [tʃit] (v.) 欺騙
Students should not cheat on the exam.
學生考試不應該作弊。

36 **check** [tʃɛk] (v.) 檢查
Can you check my mail for me when I am out traveling?
當我外出旅行時，你可否幫我看一下信件？

3 **cheek** [tʃik] (n.) 臉頰
She gave her grandpa a peck on the cheek.
她在她爺爺的臉頰上輕吻一下。

36 **cheer** [tʃɪr] (v.) 歡呼
The citizens cheered for the president.
民眾為總統歡呼。

37 **cheerful** [`tʃɪrfəl] (a.) 愉快的，歡欣的
Cheerful people make friends easily.
快樂的人容易交朋友。

16 **cheerleader** [tʃɪr`lidɚ] (n.) 啦啦隊員
The cheerleader is popular among the students.
這個啦啦隊員在學生間很受歡迎。

10 **cheese** [tʃiz] (n.) 乳酪
The French love to eat cheese every day.
法國人每天都喜歡吃乳酪。

35 **chemical** [ˋkɛmɪkḷ] (n.) 化學物品
Many cleaning products are made with dangerous chemicals.
許多清潔用品是用危險的化學藥品製成。

16 **chemistry** [ˋkɛmɪstrɪ] (n.) 化學
My favorite subject in school was chemistry.
我在學校最喜歡的科目是化學。

36 **cherish** [ˋtʃɛrɪʃ] (v.) 珍惜
You should cherish what you have in life.
你應該珍惜生命中所擁有的。

10 **cherry** [ˋtʃɛrɪ] (n.) 櫻桃
These cherries are sour.
這些櫻桃很酸。

14 **chess** [tʃɛs] (n.) 西洋棋
I don't know how to play chess.
我不知道如何下西洋棋。

3 **chest** [tʃɛst] (n.) 胸膛
The water level is up to his chest.
這裡水深到達他的胸部高度。

36 **chew** [tʃu] (v.) 咬，嚼
Chew your food slowly, and you will probably eat less.
慢慢咀嚼食物，你就可能會吃少一點。

27 **chicken** [ˋtʃɪkɪn] (n.) 雞
The old man runs a chicken farm in the countryside.
那個老人在鄉下經營一間養雞場。

24 **chief** [tʃif] (a.) 等級最高的，主要的
Amanda was appointed to be the chief secretary in her company.
亞曼達在公司裡被指派為主任祕書。

1 **child** [tʃaɪld] (n.) 小孩
The missing child was found dead.
那個失蹤的小孩被發現已經死亡。

35 **childhood** [ˋtʃaɪld,hʊd] (n.) 童年時期
I had a wonderful childhood.
我有個美好的童年。

2 **childish** [ˋtʃaɪldɪʃ] (a.) 幼稚的
Her voice sounds so childish on the phone.
她在電話裡的聲音很幼稚。

2 **childlike** [ˋtʃaɪld,laɪk] (a.) 天真的，像小孩子的
Tim is 30 years old now but still has a childlike look.
提姆目前已經三十歲，不過還是一張娃娃臉。

35 **chill** [tʃɪl] (n.) 寒顫
A chill went up my spine as she told me the ghost story.
她跟我說鬼故事時，我覺得背脊發涼。

36 **chill** [tʃɪl] (v.) 凍結，凝結
Chill this meat and you can use it later.
把這塊肉冰起來，以後再用。

37 **chilly** [ˋtʃɪlɪ] (a.) 冷颼颼的
The weather outside is getting chilly.
外面的天氣越來越冷了。

35 **chimney** [ˋtʃɪmnɪ] (n.) 煙囪
The thief was trapped in the chimney.
小偷被卡在煙囪裡。

3 **chin** [tʃɪn] (n.) 下巴
She rested her chin on her hands.
她用手撐著下巴。

20 **China** [ˋtʃaɪnə] (n.) 中國
China is becoming the most popular tourist destination in the world.
中國正在成為全球最受歡迎的旅遊目的地。

21 **Chinese** [tʃaɪˋniz] (n.) 中文
Chinese is easy for me to learn.
學中文對我來說很簡單。

21 **Chinese** [tʃaɪˋniz] (n.) 中國人
Chinese enjoy eating many dishes at each meal.
中國人喜歡一餐吃很多道菜。

36 **chip** [tʃɪp] (v.) 形成缺口、瑕疵
I fell down and chipped my tooth!
我跌了一跤，牙齒撞缺了一角！

10 **chocolate** [ˋtʃakəlɪt] (n.) 巧克力
My favorite kind of chocolate is white chocolate.
我最喜歡的一種巧克力是白巧克力。

35 **choice** [tʃɔɪs] (n.) 選擇
You have to be careful with your choice.
你必須當心自己的選擇。

36 **choke** [tʃok] (v.) 使窒息，窒息
The victim was choked by the heavy smoke.
這個受害者被濃煙窒息了。

36 **choose** [tʃuz] (v.) 選擇
I don't know which color to choose.
我不知道要選哪個顏色。

36 **chop** [tʃap] (v.) 砍，劈，剁
Mom is chopping vegetables.
媽媽在切菜。

11 **chopsticks** [ˋtʃɑp,stɪks] (n.) 筷子
Using chopsticks is more difficult than using a fork.
用筷子比用叉子難。

35 **chore** [tʃor] (n.) 雜事
I have to do chores every day after school.
每天放學後我都得做家事。

23 **Christmas** [ˋkrɪsməs] (n.) 耶誕節
Christmas is on December 25th.
耶誕節是十二月二十五日。

2 **chubby** [ˋtʃʌbɪ] (a.) 圓胖的，嬰兒肥的
My younger sister is getting chubby now.
我妹妹現在變得越來越圓了。

17 **church** [tʃɝtʃ] (n.) 教堂
We go to church on Wednesday nights and Sunday mornings.
我們星期三晚上和星期天早上去教堂。

35 **cigar** [sɪˋgɑr] (n.) 雪茄
The old man likes to smoke expensive cigars.
那老人喜歡抽昂貴的雪茄。

35 **cigarette** [,sɪgˋrɛt] (n.) 香菸
Teenagers shouldn't buy cigarettes.
青少年不准買香菸。

35 **circle** [ˋsɝkḷ] (n.) 圓圈
Please draw a circle on the paper.
請在紙上畫個圓圈。

36 **circulate** [ˋsɝkjə,let] (v.) 循環
Blood circulates in the body.
血液在人體裡循環。

35 **circus** [ˋsɝkəs] (n.) 馬戲團
The circus is well- known for its clowns.
這馬戲團以小丑馳名。

21 **citizen** [ˋsɪtəzn̩] (n.) 公民
I will soon become a citizen of Canada.
我即將成為加拿大公民。

17 **city** [ˋsɪtɪ] (n.) 都市
Hong Kong is a great city for eating and shopping.
香港是個飲食和購物勝地。

37 **civil** [ˋsɪvl̩] (a.) 公民的
Citizens should have their civil rights.
公民應享有公民權。

36 **claim** [klem] (v.) 要求
You can claim the money back from the insurance.
你可以申請保險給付。

36 **clap** [klæp] (v.) 鼓掌
All of the audience are clapping their hands.
所有聽眾都在鼓掌。

16 **class leader** [klæs ˋlidɚ] (n.) 班長
The hard- working student has been the class leader for 3 years.
那個用功的學生當了三年的班長。

16 **class** [klæs] (n.) 班級
Don't fall asleep in class.
上課時不要睡覺。

37 **classic** [ˋklæsɪk] (a.) 經典的，古典的
The old lady wears a classic dress.
這位老太太穿一件古典的洋裝。

37 **classical** [ˋklæsɪkḷ] (a.) 古典的
The lady likes to listen to classical music.
這位女士喜歡聽古典樂。

36 **classify** [ˋklæsəfaɪ] (v.) 分類
The students classified the books into three piles.
學生們把書分三堆。

16 **classmate** [ˋklæs,met] (n.) 同班同學
We are classmates.
我們是同班同學。

16 **classroom** [ˋklæs,rum] (n.) 教室
The student is in the classroom.
那個學生在教室裡。

15 **clean** [klin] (a.) 乾淨的
The bathroom is very clean.
這間浴室很乾淨。

25 **clear** [klɪr] (a.) 清楚的，晴朗的
The sky is so clear.
天空好晴朗。

24 **clerk** [klɝk] (n.) 店員
The clerk works from nine to five.
那個店員從早上九點工作到下午五點。

2 **clever** [ˋklɛvɚ] (a.) 聰明的
Shelly is so clever; she always gets good grades on her tests.
雪莉真聰明，她考試總是得到好成績。

36 **click** [klɪk] (n.) 卡嗒聲，喀嚓聲
The lock of the car opened with a click.
這車子的鎖卡嗒一聲就開了。

35 **client** [ˋklaɪənt] (n.) 客戶
The store is losing its clients.
這家店的客戶正在流失。

25 **climate** [ˋklaɪmɪt] (n.) 氣候
The climate here is not suitable for people to live in.
這裡的氣候不適合人居住。

35 **climax** [ˋklaɪmæks] (n.) 頂點，高潮
The movie came to its climax when the murderer was hanged.
這部電影在兇手被吊死時，到達整部片的最高潮。

36 **climb** [klaɪm] (v.) 攀登
The little girl likes to climb trees.
那個小女孩喜歡爬樹。

35 **clinic** [ˋklɪnɪk] (n.) 診所
The dental clinic provides good service.
這家牙醫診所提供很好的服務。

35 **clip** [klɪp] (n.) 迴紋針
I need more paper clips to organize my desk.
我需要多一點迴紋針來整理書桌。

8 **clock** [klɑk] (n.) 鐘
There is a huge clock on the wall.
牆上有個大時鐘。

36 **close** [kloz] (v.) 關
Remember to close the lid of the trash can.
記得要將垃圾筒的蓋子蓋上。

15 **closet** [ˋklɑzɪt] (n.) 衣櫥
Put away your clothes into the closet.
把衣服放入衣櫃裡。

12 **clothes** [kloz] (n.) 衣服
My sister is always buying new clothes and giving me her old ones.
我老姊老是在買新衣服，再把她的舊衣服給我。

25 **cloud** [klaʊd] (n.) 雲
There are no clouds in the sky.
天空萬里無雲。

25 **cloudy** [`klaʊdɪ] (a.) 陰天的
It is a cloudy day.
今天是陰天。

35 **club** [klʌb] (n.) 俱樂部，社團
The health club isn't open today.
健身中心今天不營業。

35 **clue** [klu] (n.) 線索，跡象
I don't have a clue why he didn't come to the office.
我不知道他為什麼沒來辦公室。

2 **clumsy** [`klʌmzɪ] (a.) 笨手笨腳的
The clumsy student searched for his pencil in the bag.
那個笨手笨腳的學生在書包裡找鉛筆。

24 **coach** [kotʃ] (n.) 教練
He is a soccer coach.
他是一個足球教練。

26 **coast** [kost] (n.) 海岸
There are many restaurants along the coast.
沿著海岸有許多餐廳。

12 **coat** [kot] (n.) 大衣
It's snowy; put on a heavy coat.
下雪了，穿上厚外套。

27 **cockroach** [ˋkɑk,rotʃ] (n.) 蟑螂
Mother saw a cockroach in the kitchen sink.
媽媽在廚房水槽裡看到一隻蟑螂。

10 **cocktail** [ˋkɑk,tel] (n.) 雞尾酒
We enjoyed cocktails on the beach.
我們在海灘上享用雞尾酒。

10 **coconut** [ˋkokə,nət] (n.) 椰子
Coconuts are used a lot in Thai cooking.
泰式烹調經常運用椰子。

10 **coffee** [ˋkɔfɪ] (n.) 咖啡
I need a cup of black coffee every morning.
我都每天早上需要一杯黑咖啡。

35 **code** [kod] (n.) 密碼
The specialist can't break the code.
那專家無法破解密碼。

9 **coin** [kɔɪn] (n.) 硬幣
I need some coins to make a phone call.
我需要一些硬幣打電話。

10 **Coke** [kok] (n.) 可口可樂
Coke is not very healthy, but it's still the world's favorite drink.
可口可樂對健康不太好，但依然是全球最受歡迎的飲料。

25 **cold** [kold] (a.) 寒冷的
The winters in Japan are cold.
日本的冬天很冷。

36 **collapse** [kəˋlæps] (v.) 坍塌，（情緒）崩潰
The old lady collapsed after hearing of her only son's death.
老婦人聽到她獨子的死訊就崩潰了。

35 **collar** [ˋkɑlɚ] (n.) 衣領
She likes to wear her collar up.
她穿衣服喜歡把領子立起來。

14 **collect** [kəˋlɛkt] (v.) 收集
Daddy has been collecting stamps for years.
爸爸已經集郵好幾年。

14 **collection** [kəˋlɛkʃən] (n.) 收集，收藏
He has a huge collection of Jazz CDs.
他的爵士樂CD收藏很可觀。

16 **college** [ˋkɑlɪdʒ] (n.) 大學
The college student fooled around too much and failed to pass the exams.
那個大學生太混了，沒有通過考試。

35 **colony** [ˋkɑlənɪ] (n.) 殖民地
Vietnam used to be a French colony.
越南曾經是法國殖民地。

13 **color** [ˋkʌlɚ] (n.) 顏色
The color of clothes can express one's emotions.
衣服的顏色可以反映一個人的心情。

13 **colorful** [ˋkʌlɚfəl] (a.) 鮮豔的
Cathy is wearing a colorful Halloween costume.
凱西穿著一件鮮豔的萬聖節服裝。

35 **column** [ˋkɑləm] (n.) 專欄
He writes columns for newspapers.
他為報紙寫專欄。

12 **comb** [kom] (n.) 梳子
She combs her hair with a comb.
她用梳子梳頭髮。

36 **combine** [kəm`baɪn] (v.) 使結合，使聯合
Don't combine these two chemicals.
不要把這兩種化學物品混合在一起。

35 **combination** [,kɑmbə`neʃən] (n.) 組合
The thief couldn't open the safe because he didn't know the combination.
小偷不知道密碼，打不開保險箱。

36 **come** [kʌm] (v.) 來，到
The teacher asked me to come.
老師叫我過來。

36 **comfort** [`kʌm,fɚt] (v.) 安慰，慰問
Everyone tried to comfort the widow.
每個人都試著要安慰這名寡婦。

4 **comfortable** [`kʌmfɚtəbl̩] (a.) 舒服的
This bed is very comfortable to sleep on.
這床睡起來很舒服。

14 **comic book** [`kɑmɪk bʊk] (n.) 漫畫書
Students like to read comic books.
學生喜歡看漫畫書。

35 **comma** [`kɑmə] (n.) 逗號
The sentence needs another comma in the middle.
這句子中間需要再加一個逗號。

36 **command** [kə`mænd] (v.) 命令，指揮
He commanded his soldiers to stay up all night.
他命令士兵通宵待命。

36 **comment** [`kɑmɛnt] (n.) 評論
Do you have any comments about our plan?
對於我們的計畫，你有任何評論嗎？

36 **commercial** [kə`mɝʃəl] (n.) 廣告

Sometimes the commercials are better than the TV shows.

有時候廣告比電視節目還好看。

35 **committee** [kə`mɪtɪ] (n.) 委員會

The building committee refused the tenant.

這棟大樓的委員會拒絕了這名租戶。

37 **common** [`kɑmən] (a.) 常見的，普遍的

It's common for girls in Mexico to get married before they turn twenty.

墨西哥女孩在二十歲前結婚是很普遍的

36 **communicate** [kə`mjʊnə,ket] (v.) 傳達，傳遞，溝通

They communicate in French.

他們用法語溝通。

24 **company** [`kʌmpənɪ] (n.) 公司

Peggy works for an electronics company.

佩姬在一家電子公司上班。

36 **compare** [kəm`pɛr] (v.) 比較

My parents like to compare me with other students.

我爸媽喜歡拿我和其他學生比較。

35 **comparison** [kəm`pærəsən] (n.) 比照，比喻，對照

By comparison, France is more well- known than Portugal.

相較之下，法國比葡萄牙有名。

36 **compete** [kəm`pit] (v.) 競爭，比賽，對抗

I'd like to compete in the English speech competition, but I'm afraid I won't have enough time to prepare.

我想在英文演講比賽中參賽，但我恐怕沒有足夠時間準備。

36 **complain** [kəm`plen] (v.) 抱怨

This student often complains about her math teacher.

這個學生常常抱怨她的數學老師。

35 **complaint** [kəm`plent] (n.) 抗議，怨言
The loser accepted the result without complaint.
敗方無異議接受結果。

36 **complete** [kəm`plit] (v.) 完成
Did you complete your homework?
你的回家作業完成了嗎？

35 **complex** [`kampleks] (n.) 複合物，集合住宅
A huge complex including a mall, market, and theater is going to be built here.
這裡將興建一座包含購物中心、市場和電影院的大型複合式建築。

35 **composition** [,kampə`zɪʃən] (n.) 作文
His English composition was so good that people thought it was written by a native speaker.
他的英文作文好到讓人以為是英文母語人士寫的。

16 **computer** [kəm`pjutɚ] (n.) 電腦
The computer has played an important role in daily life.
在現今日常生活中，電腦扮演很重要的角色。

14 **computer game** [kəm`pjɪtɚ gem] (n.) 電腦遊戲
Many of the new computer games are too violent for young children.
許多新電腦遊戲對幼童而言太過暴力。

36 **concentrate** [`kansɛn,tret] (v.) 專心
Please concentrate in class.
上課請集中精神。

36 **concern** [kən`sɜn] (v.) 關心
The boss is very concerned about this matter.
老闆非常的關心此事。

35 **concert** [`kansɚt] (n.) 音樂會，演唱會
The concert tonight was a big success.
今晚的演唱會非常成功。

36 **conclude** [kən`klud] (v.) 斷定，決定
The committee concluded that the proposal was to be rejected.
委員會決定不採用這提議。

35 **conclusion** [kən`kluʒən] (n.) 推論，結論
They were in the meeting for hours without reaching any conclusion.
他們開會好幾個鐘頭，最後仍然沒有結論。

35 **condition** [kən`dɪʃən] (n.) 情況，症狀
The patient is in critical condition.
這位病人情況危急。

2 **confident** [`kɑnfədənt] (a.) 自信的
Sarah is so confident that she will pass the exam.
莎拉很有信心能通過這次考試。

36 **confirm** [kən`fɝm] (v.) 確認
I confirmed my booking with the receptionist.
我向接待人員確定過我的訂位。

35 **conflict** [`kɑnflɪkt] (n.) 衝突
The conflict between the two countries was resolved through peace talks.
兩國之間的衝突已透過和談化解。

35 **Confucius** [kən`fjuʃəs] (n.) 孔子
Confucius' Day is also known as Teacher's Day.
孔子紀念日也是教師節。

36 **confuse** [kən`fjuz](v.) 使困惑
The math question confused me.
那個數學題目把我弄糊塗了。

35 **congratulation** [kən,grætʃə`leʃən] (n.) 恭喜
Congratulations on your excellent performance!
恭喜你傑出的表現！

36 **connect** [kə`nɛkt] (v.) 連接，連結
The two laptops are connected by a wireless connection.
這兩台筆記型電腦利用無線傳輸連結。

35 **connection** [kə`nɛkʃen] (n.) 關聯，關係
He had many good business connections in Europe because he had worked there for ten years.
他在歐洲有許多很好的商業人脈，因為他已經在那邊工作十年。

37 **conscious** [`kɑnʃəs] (a.) 有知覺的，神智清醒的
He's not conscious of his bad habits.
他沒有發覺自己的惡習。

36 **consider** [kən`sɪdɚ] (v.) 考慮
I will consider taking a second job to earn more money.
我會考慮接第二份工作好多賺點錢。

37 **considerable** [kən`sɪdərəbl̩] (a.) 相當大的
They lost a considerable amount of money on gambling.
他們賭博輸了一大筆錢。

2 **considerate** [kən`sɪdərɪt] (a.) 體貼的
It was considerate of you to help the elderly people.
你能幫助老人真是體貼。

35 **consideration** [kənsɪdəre`ʃən] (n.) 考慮
I am sending you a catalog and a pricelist for your consideration.
我會寄一份目錄和價目表供您參考。

37 **constant** [`kɑnstənt] (a.) 固定的，不變的
The patient needs constant visits to the doctor.
這個病人需要定期去看醫生。

35 **contact** [`kɑntækt] (n.) 接觸
I haven't made contact with him for a long time.
我已經好久沒跟他聯絡了。

⓬ **contact lens** [ˋkɑntækt ˌlɛnz] (n.) 隱形眼鏡
Wearing contact lenses too long will damage your eyes.
隱形眼鏡戴太久會傷害你的眼睛。

❷ **contain** [kənˋten] (v.) 包含
This travel package contains two nights at a five star hotel.
這個套裝行程包含五星級飯店住宿兩晚。

⓯ **container** [kənˋtenɚ] (n.) 容器
We need some containers to store noodles.
我們需要一些容器來裝麵條。

㉖ **continent** [ˋkɑntənənt] (n.) 大陸，陸地，洲
There are seven continents on the surface of the Earth.
地球表面上有七大洲。

㊱ **continue** [kənˋtɪnju] (v.) 繼續
She continued her studies after she graduated from university.
她大學畢業後繼續深造。

㉟ **contract** [ˋkɑntrækt] (n.) 契約書，合同
They signed a contract to rent a flat.
他們簽約租了一層公寓。

㉟ **control** [kənˋtroll] (n.) 控制
He lost control of his car and hit the car in front of him.
他開車失控撞上前面那輛車。

㊱ **control** [kənˋtroll] (v.) 控制
Please try to control your child in the restaurant.
在餐廳裡請試著控制你的孩子。

㉟ **convenience** [kənˋvinjəns] (n.) 便利
We prefer the convenience of living in the city.
我們比較喜歡在城市生活的便利性。

17 **convenience store** [kən`vinjəns stor] (n.) 便利商店
There is a convenience store on the corner.
在街角有一間便利商店。

37 **convenient** [kən`vinjənt] (a.) 方便的
The transportation in Taiwan is very convenient.
台灣的交通很方便。

35 **conversation** [,kɑnvɚ`seʃən] (n.) 對話
We had a short conversation yesterday.
我們昨晚有簡短交談。

36 **convince** [kən`vɪns] (v.) 說服
Please convince Tom not to quit his job.
請說服湯姆不要辭職。

24 **cook** [kʊk] (n.) 廚師
They have the most wonderful cook here in this restaurant.
這家餐廳有最棒的廚師。

10 **cookie** [`kʊkɪ] (n.) 餅乾
We usually have cookies and coffee in the afternoon.
我們經常在下午喝咖啡、吃餅乾。

14 **cooking** [`kʊkɪŋ] (n.) 烹飪
We don't have cooking class at school.
我們學校沒有烹飪課。

25 **cool** [kul] (a.) 涼爽的
It is cool in this room.
在這個房間裡很涼爽。

36 **copy** [`kɑpɪ] (v.) 抄襲，複製
Cindy copied answers from my book.
辛蒂從我的課本抄襲答案。

10 **corn** [kɔrn] (n.) 玉米
Corn soup is my favorite soup!
玉米湯是我最喜歡的湯！

35 **corner** [ˋkɔrnɚ] (n.) 角落
The bank is on the corner of First and Main.
那間銀行在第一街和主要大道交叉口轉角。

36 **correct** [kəˋrɛkt] (v.) 修正
The teacher told me to correct my answers.
老師叫我要訂正我的答案。

37 **correct** [kəˋrɛkt] (a.) 正確的
I don't have the correct address of your apartment.
我沒有你住處的正確地址。

9 **cost** [kɔst] (v.) 花費
This book cost me one hundred dollars.
這本書花了我一百元。

12 **cotton** [ˋkɑtn̩] (n.) 棉花
I miss the cotton candy in the night market.
我懷念夜市的棉花糖。

15 **couch** [kaʊtʃ] (n.) 長沙發，躺椅
The boy is lying on the couch.
這個男孩躺在長沙發上。

4 **cough** [kɔf] (n.) 咳嗽
You have a bad cough.
你咳得很嚴重。

36 **count** [kaʊnt] (v.) 計算
My little brother knows how to count.
我弟弟會算數。

17 **country** [ˋkʌntrɪ] (n.) 國家
China is a developing country.
中國是個發展中國家。

35 **countryside** [ˋkʌntɪ,saɪd] (n.) 鄉村
The air in the countryside is much better than that in the cities.
鄉下的空氣比都市好多了。

35 **county** [ˋkaʊntɪ] (n.) 郡，縣
We live in Taipei County.
我們住在台北縣。

1 **couple** [ˋkʌpl̩] (n.) 夫妻，一對情侶
The young couple over there just got married.
那對年輕夫婦才剛結婚。

35 **courage** [,kɝɪdʒ] (n.) 勇氣
Being a firefighter takes courage.
當一位消防人員需要勇氣。

16 **course** [kors] (n.) 課程
She took a course in history.
她選了一門歷史的課。

35 **court** [kort] (n.) 法庭
He went to court because of too many speeding tickets.
他因為收到太多超速罰單上法庭。

6 **cousin** [ˋkʌzn̩] (n.) 堂、表親（兄弟姊妹）
Tommy is my cousin.
湯米是我的表哥。

36 **cover** [ˋkʌvɚ] (v.) 遮蓋
He covered his ears when he heard the scream.
他一聽到尖叫就把耳朵摀住。

27 **cow** [kaʊ] (n.) 母牛
The cow produces milk.
母牛生產牛乳。

35 **coward** [ˋkaʊɚd] (n.) 懦夫，膽怯者
People called him a coward for not fighting, but I think he was brave.
大家因為他不打架就說他是懦夫，但我覺得他很勇敢。

24 **cowboy** [ˋkaʊ,bɔɪ] (n.) 牛仔
The cowboy lives in the country, where he takes care of the cattle.
那位牛仔住在野外照顧牲畜。

27 **crab** [kræb] (n.) 螃蟹
The little crabs are crawling here and there on the beach.
小螃蟹在海灘上到處爬。

35 **cradle** [ˋkredl̩] (n.) 搖籃
The baby in the cradle is sleeping soundly.
搖籃裡的嬰兒睡得很安穩。

36 **crash** [kræʃ] (v.) 碰擊
The plane crashed into the ocean in the middle of the night.
這架飛機在半夜墜落海裡。

36 **crawl** [krɔl] (v.) 爬行，蠕動
The baby is crawling on the floor.
這個小嬰兒在地上爬行。

16 **crayon** [ˋkreən] (n.) 蠟筆
The school kids are drawing pictures with crayons.
小學生們正在用蠟筆畫畫。

2 **crazy** [ˋkrezɪ] (a.) 瘋狂的
My boss is driving me crazy.
我老闆快把我逼瘋了。

10 **cream** [krim] (n.) 鮮奶油，乳脂
He likes lots of cream in his ice coffee.
他喜歡在冰咖啡上加很多鮮奶油。

36 **create** [krɪ`et] (v.) 創造
Artists create beautiful things.
藝術家創造漂亮的東西。

37 **creative** [krɪ`etɪv] (a.) 創造的，創造性的
He is a creative artist.
他是一位有創意的藝術家。

35 **creator** [krɪ`etɚ] (n.) 創造者，創作者
The creator of the drama is productive.
這齣劇的作者產量很大。

35 **creature** [`kritʃɚ] (n.) 生物
There are millions of tiny creatures in a drop of water.
一滴水裡有幾百萬個微小生物。

9 **credit card** [`krɛdɪt kɑrd] (n.) 信用卡
The credit card is also called plastic money.
信用卡又被稱作塑膠貨幣。

35 **credit** [`krɛdɪt] (n.) 榮譽，信譽
I wrote the report, but he took all the credit.
那份報告是我寫的，他卻占去所有功勞。

36 **creep** [krip] (v.) 躡手躡腳，爬行
The little boy was creeping into the kitchen for some candy.
這個小男孩躡手躡腳溜進廚房找糖果。

35 **crew** [kru] (n.) 人員，一群
All of the rescue crew are missing.
所有的救難人員團都失蹤了。

27 **cricket** [ˋkrɪkɪt] (n.) 蟋蟀
I can hear the crickets chirping outside my window.
我可以聽到蟋蟀在我窗外發出唧唧聲。

35 **crime** [kraɪm] (n.) 罪
The crime rate is getting high in this country.
這國家的犯罪率越來越高。

35 **criminal** [ˋkrɪmənl̩] (n.) 罪犯
The mean criminal was finally sentenced to death.
這名殘酷的罪犯最後被宣判死刑。

35 **crisis** [ˋkraɪsɪs] (n.) 危機
An oil crisis impacts our daily life very much.
石油危機嚴重衝擊我們的日常生活。

37 **crispy** [ˋkrɪspɪ] (a.) 脆的，酥的，鬆脆的
The cookies are so crispy.
這些餅乾真是酥脆。

36 **criticize** [ˋkrɪtɪ,saɪz] (v.) 批評
Don’t criticize people behind their back.
不要在背後批評人。

18 **cross** [krɔs] (v.) 越過
The little boy crosses the road without noticing the cars.
這個小男孩沒注意車輛就橫越馬路。

35 **crowd** [kraʊd] (n.) 一群人
The crowd on the street was out of control when they lost the game.
比賽落敗，街上的群眾便失去控制。

37 **crowded** [ˋkraʊdɪd] (a.) 擁擠的
It is crowded everywhere during Chinese New Year.
農曆新年時到處都很擁擠。

35 **crown** [kraʊn] (n.) 王位，王冠
All the ladies in the beauty contest compete for the crown.
參加選美比賽的佳麗都在爭取后冠。

2 **cruel** [ˋkruəl] (a.) 殘忍的
It's cruel to abuse animals.
虐待動物真是殘忍。

37 **crunchy** [ˋkrʌntʃɪ] (a.) 酥脆的
The chocolate biscuit in his mouth is crunchy.
他嘴裡的巧克力餅乾很脆。

35 **crutch** [krʌtʃ] (n.) 拐杖
The weak young man walks with crutches.
這個虛弱的年輕人用柺杖走路。

36 **cry** [kraɪ] (v.) 哭
The baby cried very loudly on the train.
這個嬰兒在火車上哭得很大聲。

23 **cultural** [ˋkʌltʃərəl] (a.) 文化的
There are many cultural differences among the different ethnic groups in China.
中國不同民族間有許多文化差異。

23 **culture** [ˋkʌltʃɚ] (n.) 文化
Asians have their own unique cultures.
亞洲人有其特殊的文化。

11 **cup** [kʌp] (n.) 杯子
Give me a cup of coffee.
給我一杯咖啡。

15 **cupboard** [ˋkʌbɚd] (n.) 食櫥，碗櫃
The cookies are hidden in the cupboard.
餅乾藏在碗櫃裡。

4 **cure** [kjʊr] (v.) 治療
The medicine cured him of his illness.
這藥治好了他的病。

2 **curiosity** [ˌkjʊrɪˋɑsətɪ] (n.) 好奇
I asked you the question just out of curiosity.
我是出於好奇才問你這問題。

2 **curious** [ˋkjʊrɪəs] (a.) 好奇的
Little kids are always curious about new things.
小孩對新事物總是感到好奇。

8 **current** [ˋkɝənt] (a.) 當前的
Mini skirts are in current fashion now.
迷你裙現在正流行。

15 **curtain** [ˋkɝtn̩] (n.) 窗簾
The chair is by the curtain.
窗簾旁邊有一張椅子。

35 **curve** [kɝv] (n.) 彎曲、彎道
Beware of the dangerous curve ahead.
小心前面的危險彎道。

23 **custom** [ˋkʌstəm] (n.) 習俗
It is a custom for Taiwanese to have rice cakes during Chinese New Year.
農曆新年吃年糕是台灣人的習俗。

1 **customer** [ˋkʌstəmɚ] (n.) 顧客
The customers is always right.
顧客永遠是對的。

36 **cut** [kʌt] (v.) 剪，切割
Can I borrow some candles? My power is cut off.
我能借些蠟燭嗎？我的電源被切斷了。

2 **cute** [kjʊt] (a.) 可愛的
I have a cute and sweet cat.
我有隻可愛甜美的小貓。

35 **cycle** [ˋsaɪkl̩] (n.) 週期，循環
The cycle is four months long.
一次循環週期是四個月。

D

6 **dad** [dæd] (n.) 爸爸（亦稱daddy [ˋdædɪ]）
Her dad is not at home now.
她爸現在不在家。

8 **daily** [ˋdeli] (a.) 日常的
My daily schedule includes going to school.
我每天的行程就是上學。

10 **dairy** [ˋdɛrɪ] (n.) 乳製品，牛奶的
The milk is in the dairy section.
牛奶在乳製品區。

35 **dam** [dæm] (n.) 水壩
They are building the largest dam in the world.
他們正在建造全世界最大的水壩。

35 **damage** [ˋdæmɪdʒ] (v.) 傷害
The storm damaged the bridge.
暴風雨把橋摧毀了。

25 **damp** [dæmp] (a.) 潮溼的
It is damp and cold in winter here.
這裡冬天又冷又溼。

14 **dancing** [ˋdænsɪŋ] (n.) 舞蹈
Dancing is a way to lose weight.
跳舞是減肥的方法之一。

35 **danger** [ˋdendʒɚ] (n.) 危險
The driver in the car accident is still in danger.
出車禍的駕駛依然生命垂危。

37 **dangerous** [ˋdendʒərəs] (a.) 危險的
It's dangerous to exceed the speed limit.
超速是非常危險的。

36 **dare** [dɛr] (v.) 敢，膽敢，竟敢
How dare you drive dad's car?
你竟敢開爸爸的車？

37 **dark** [dɑrk] (a.) 黑暗的
It is getting darker and darker.
天越來越黑了。

35 **darling** [ˋdɑrlɪŋ] (n.) 心愛的，寵兒
He calls his girlfriend "darling."
他稱呼他女朋友「心愛的」。

35 **dash** [dæʃ] (n.) 破折號
Some words are connected by a dash.
有些字是用破折號連結。

35 **data** [ˋdetə] (n.) 資料
Do you have any data on the products?
你有任何這些產品的資料嗎？

36 **date** [det] (v.) 約會
My brother is dating a beautiful girl.
我哥哥正在和一位漂亮女孩交往。

6 **daughter** [ˋdɔtɚ] (n.) 女兒
My daughter is five years old.
我的女兒五歲了。

8 **dawn** [dɔn] (n.) 黎明
Most people are still asleep at dawn.
大部分人清晨都還在睡。

8 **day** [de] (n.) 天，白天
We are not home during the day.
我們白天不在家。

37 **dead** [dɛd] (a.) 死的
We saw a dead rat in the garden.
我們在花園裡看到一隻死老鼠。

2 **deaf** [dɛf] (a.) 聾的
The old woman has been deaf for twenty years.
那老婦人已經耳聾二十年了。

36 **deafen** [ˋdɛfn̩] (v.) 使聾，使聽不見
The blaring horn deafened my ears.
那聲巨響令我震耳欲聾。

8 **deadline** [ˋdɛd,laɪn] (n.) 最後期限
I can't finish the work by the deadline.
我無法如期完成工作。

36 **deal** [dil] (v.) 處理
The young salesman doesn't know how to deal with this tough problem.
這年輕的推銷員不知如何處理這個棘手的問題。

24 **dealer** [ˋdilɚ] (n.) 業者，商人
The car dealer helped me find the right car for my family.
車商幫我找出適合我家的車。

37 **dear** [dɪr] (a.) 親愛的
They are my dear parents.
他們是我親愛的父母親。

4 **death** [dɛθ] (n.) 死亡
The death of my grandma made me feel so sad.
我奶奶去世讓我好傷心。

35 **debate** [dɪ`bet] (n.) 辯論
They held a debate on the war in Iraq.
他們為伊拉克戰爭辦過一場辯論。

35 **debt** [dɛt] (n.) 借款
I have a lot of debts to pay by the end of the month.
我在月底前有好多債得付。

8 **decade** [`dɛked] (n.) 十年
After a decade, the case is still unsolved.
十年之後，這個案子仍未解決。

8 **December** [dɪ`sɛmbɚ] (n.) 十二月
Christmas is in December.
耶誕節在十二月。

36 **decide** [dɪ`saɪd] (v.) 決定
He decided to take a rest.
他決定要休息一下。

35 **decision** [dɪ`sɪʒən] (n.) 決定
I have to make a decision about my career.
我必須為我的職業生涯做個決定。

35 **deck** [dɛk] (n.) 甲板，一副（紙牌）
The police found a bomb on the upper deck.
警察在上層甲板找到一顆炸彈。

15 **decorate** [ˋdɛkə,ret] (v.) 裝飾
Mother decorated the Christmas tree with colorful balls.
媽媽用彩球裝飾耶誕樹。

36 **decrease** [dɪˋkris] (v.) 減少
The temperature decreased from ten degrees to zero.
氣溫從十度降到零度。

35 **deed** [did] (n.) 行動，契約
If we all did a good deed every day, the world would be a better place.
如果我們每天都做好事，世界會是個更美好的地方。

19 **deep** [dip] (a.) 深的
The hunter went into the deep forest.
那個獵人進入森林深處。

36 **deepen** [ˋdipən] (v.) 使變深，使加深
The river deepens at this point.
這條河在這邊變得更深。

27 **deer** [dɪr] (n.) 鹿
Be careful driving on this road, as many deer cross here at night.
在這邊開車要小心，夜裡有許多鹿會橫越這條路。

36 **defeat** [dɪˋfit] (v.) 擊敗
We defeated the other team ten to one.
我們以十比一打敗另一隊。

36 **defend** [dɪˋfɛnd] (v.) 防守
We study Karate to be able to defend ourselves from attackers.
我們學空手道以自衛防身。

36 **define** [dɪˋfaɪn] (v.) 解釋，給…下定義
Our relationship is defined by trust, support and love.
我們的關係稱得上是信任、支持和愛的結合。

35 **definition** [ˌdɛfəˋnɪʃen] (n.) 定義，解譯
You can find the definition in the dictionary.
你可以在字典裡找到字義。

25 **degree** [dɪˋgri] (n.) 度數
It's 30 degrees Celsius today.
今天攝氏三十度。

36 **delay** [dɪˋle] (v.) 延期
The plane was delayed due to the typhoon.
班機因為颱風延期了。

10 **delicious** [dɪˋlɪʃəs] (a.) 美味的
The delicious pancake attracts lots of people.
可口的煎餅吸引許多人。

2 **delighted** [dɪˋlaɪtɪd] (a.) 高興的
I'm delighted that you decided to come see me.
真高興你決定來看我。

36 **deliver** [dɪˋlɪvɚ] (v.) 傳遞
Can you deliver the message to my parents?
你可以帶這個訊息給我父母嗎？

35 **delivery** [dɪˋlɪvərɪ] (n.) 投遞，傳送
The mail was sent by special delivery.
這封信是用限時專送寄的。

36 **demand** [dɪˋmænd] (v.) 要求
The student president demands to see the principal.
學生會主席要求見校長。

35 **democracy** [dɪˋmɑkrəsɪ] (n.) 民主，民主主義
Our democracy has been ruined by the political conflicts.
我們的民主已被政治鬥爭破壞了。

37 **democratic** [dɛmə`krætɪk] (a.) 民主政治的，民主黨的
The Democratic Party won the election.
民主黨派贏得了這場選舉。

24 **dentist** [`dɛntɪst] (n.) 牙醫
I have an appointment with my dentist.
我和牙醫有約。

36 **deny** [dɪ`naɪ] (v.) 否認
She denied stealing the money, even after she was caught on tape.
縱使被錄影帶拍到，她依然否認偷錢。

17 **department store** [dɪ`pɑrtmənt stor] (n.) 百貨公司
I went shopping at the department store.
我去百貨公司購物。

36 **depend** [dɪ`pɛnd] (v.) 依賴
Your grades will depend on your test scores.
你的成績將由考試分數決定。

36 **deposit** [dɪ`pɑsɪt] (v.) 儲存，存放
You have to deposit the money in the bank.
你必須把錢存在銀行。

36 **depress** [dɪ`prɛs] (v.) 使沮喪
The news always depresses me.
新聞報導總是讓我沮喪。

37 **depressed** [dɪ`prɛst] (a.) 沮喪的
I was so depressed when I saw my score.
看到成績時，我很沮喪。

36 **deserve** [dɪ`zɝv] (v.) 應得
You deserve better than that!
你應該得到更好的對待！

36 **describe** [dɪˋskraɪb] (v.) 描寫
Please describe what happened yesterday.
請描述一下昨晚發生的事。

35 **description** [dɪsˋkrɪpʃən] (n.) 描寫，敘述，形容
This tour guide's description is not very clear.
這本導遊手冊的敘述並不清楚。

26 **desert** [ˋdɛzɚt] (n.) 沙漠
The country is in the middle of the desert.
這個國家在沙漠中間。

36 **design** [dɪˋzaɪn] (v.) 設計
The lady designed lots of popular dresses.
那位女士設計了許多受歡迎的洋裝。

24 **designer** [dɪˋzaɪnɚ] (n.) 設計師
We hired a designer to help us decorate our house.
我們雇了一位設計師幫我們裝潢房子。

37 **desirable** [dɪˋzaɪrəbl̩] (a.) 值得嚮往的
He got a desirable job at the big company.
他在那間大公司得到一個令人嚮往的工作。

35 **desire** [dɪˋzaɪr] (n.) 慾望
Angel has a great desire to be a model.
安琪非常渴望成為模特兒。

15 **desk** [dɛsk] (n.) 書桌
He sat at his desk writing for eighteen hours.
他坐在書桌前寫了十八個小時。

32 **despite** [dɪˋspaɪt] (prep.) 儘管
Despite his illness, he still works very hard.
儘管身上有病痛，他還是很努力工作。

10 **dessert** [dɪ`zɜt] (n.) 點心
You can choose cake, cookies, or ice cream for dessert.
你可以選蛋糕、餅乾或冰淇淋當點心。

36 **destroy** [dɪ`strɔɪ] (v.) 毀壞，破壞
The typhoon destroyed the house.
颱風把房子給毀了。

36 **detail** [`ditel] (v.) 詳述，詳細說明
Please detail this report and have it on my desk tomorrow morning.
請詳細說明份報告，明天早上交到我桌上。

36 **detect** [dɪ`tɛkt] (v.) 察覺
She detected my anger on the phone.
她在電話中察覺到我的憤怒。

24 **detective** [dɪ`tɛktɪv] (n.) 偵探
The wife hires a private detective to spy on her husband.
那位太太雇用一名私家偵探監視她的先生。

35 **determination** [dɪˏtɚmə`neʃən] (n.) 決心
Success lies in great determination.
成功來自於堅毅的決心。

36 **determine** [dɪ`tɜmɪn] (v.) 決定，使下定決心
My mom determined to send me to the military.
我媽下定決心送我去從軍。

36 **develop** [dɪ`vɛləp] (v.) 發展
Drawing helps children to develop their own imagination.
畫圖幫助孩子們發展想像力。

35 **devil** [`dɛvl̩] (n.) 惡魔
Some people believe that earthquakes are the work of the devil.
有些人認為地震是惡魔所為。

36 **devote** [dɪ`vot] (v.) 將…奉獻給，致力於
The teacher devotes herself to education.
那位老師獻身於教育。

36 **dial** [`daɪəl] (v.) 撥號，打（電話）
Dial 911 for help, if you get in trouble.
假如遇上麻煩，就打九一一求救。

35 **dialogue** [`daɪə,lɔg] (n.) 對話
Their dialogue is meaningless.
他們的對話毫無意義。

12 **diamond** [`daɪmənd] (n.) 鑽石
I never met a woman who didn't like diamonds.
我從沒見過不喜歡鑽石的女人。

16 **diary** [`daɪərɪ] (n.) 日記
I have a habit of keeping a diary every day.
我有每天寫日記的習慣。

16 **dictionary** [`dɪkʃən,ɛrɪ] (n.) 字典
Look the word up in the dictionary.
在字典裡查出這個字。

36 **die** [daɪ] (v.) 死亡
The young lady died at the age of twenty.
這位年輕小姐二十歲就死了。

10 **diet** [`daɪət] (n.) 節食
My sister went on a diet before getting married.
我的姊姊在結婚前開始節食。

35 **difference** [`dɪfərəns] (n.) 差別，差異
What's the difference between these two things?
這兩者之間有何不同？

37 **different** [ˋdɪfərənt] (a.) 不同的
There are many different types of mushrooms.
蕈類有很多不同種類。

37 **difficult** [ˋdɪfə,kəlt] (a.) 困難的
Some customers are difficult to communicate with.
有些顧客實在很難溝通。

35 **difficulty** [ˋdɪfə,kʌltɪ] (n.) 困難
My younger sister has learning difficulties.
我的妹妹有學習障礙。

36 **dig** [dɪg] (v.) 挖
The dog is digging a hole in the backyard.
小狗正在後院挖一個洞。

36 **digest** [daɪˋdʒɛst] (v.) 消化
The meat is not easy to digest.
這肉不好消化。

2 **diligent** [ˋdɪlədʒənt] (a.) 勤勉的
He's very diligent in his work.
他工作很勤勉。

37 **dim** [dɪm] (a.) 微暗，暗淡
I can't see a thing in this dim light.
在這黯淡的燈光下，我什麼也看不到。

35 **dime** [daɪm] (n.) 一角硬幣
A dime is a coin worth ten cents.
一角硬幣價值十分錢。

10 **dine** [daɪn] (v.) 進餐，用餐
Jean left the office and dined with her boyfriend at the restaurant.
珍離開辦公室跟男友在餐廳用餐。

15 **dining room** [ˋdaɪnɪŋrum] (n.) 飯廳
We have dinner in the dining room every evening
我們每晚都在飯廳裡用餐。

10 **dinner** [ˋdɪnɚ] (n.) 晚餐
My family goes out for dinner every Saturday night.
我家每週六晚上都到外面吃晚餐。

27 **dinosaur** [ˋdaɪnə,sɔr] (n.)恐龍
Many boys love dinosaurs.
許多男孩喜愛恐龍。

36 **dip** [dɪp] (v.) 浸，泡
The little girl dipped her toes into the lake.
小女孩將腳趾泡進湖裡。

24 **diplomat** [ˋdɪpləmæt] (n.) 外交官
Dad wanted to be a diplomat when he was young.
爸爸年輕時想當外交官。

36 **direct** [dəˋrɛkt] (v.) 導演，執導
This film was directed by a famous director.
這部電影由一位知名導演執導。

35 **direction** [dəˋrɛkʃən] (n.) 方向
Is this the direction to the zoo?
這是往動物園的方向嗎？

24 **director** [dəˋrɛktɚ] (n.) 導演
The director of the film is from England.
這部電影的導演來自英國。

35 **dirt** [dɝt] (n.) 灰塵，泥
A great deal of dirt is on the table.
桌上的灰塵好多。

37 **dirty** [ˋdɜtɪ] (a.) 骯髒的
This dog is so dirty.
這隻狗好髒。

36 **disappear** [ˌdɪsəˋpɪr] (v.) 消失
She has disappeared for a week.
她已經失蹤一個星期了。

35 **disappointment** [ˌdɪsəˋpɔɪntmənt] (n.) 失望
The movie turned out to be a disappointment.
這部電影令人失望。

35 **disaster** [dɪˋzæstɚ] (n.) 災難
The earthquake was a disaster.
這場地震是場災難。

14 **disco** [ˋdɪsko] (n.) 迪斯可舞廳
Teens are not allowed to stay at disco after midnight.
午夜十二點後，青少年不准在迪斯可舞廳裡逗留。

9 **discount** [ˋdɪskaʊnt] (n.) 折扣
Could you give me a discount?
你可以給我打個折嗎？

36 **discourage** [dɪsˋkɜɪdʒ] (v.) 勸阻
Mom discouraged me from going hiking alone in the mountains.
媽媽勸阻我不要單獨去山裡健行。

36 **discover** [dɪˋskʌvɚ] (v.) 發現
I discovered him stealing money from the teacher.
我發現他偷老師的錢。

35 **discovery** [dɪsˋkɑvərɪ] (n.) 發現
The discovery of gold in California led many people to move there, looking to become rich.
加州發現金礦讓許多人遷往當地，尋求致富。

36 **discuss** [dɪˋskʌs] (v.) 討論
I have to discuss my situation with you.
我必須跟你討論我的狀況。

35 **discussion** [dɪˋskʌʃən] (n.) 討論
They had a serious discussion over the issue.
他們針對這個議題做過嚴肅的討論。

4 **disease** [dɪˋziz] (n.) 疾病
The disease is fatal.
這個疾病能致命。

36 **disguise** [dɪsˋɡaɪz] (v.) 偽裝
The robber was disguised as a policeman.
搶匪偽裝成警察。

11 **dish** [dɪʃ] (n.) 盤子
Would you help me do the dishes?
你可以幫我洗碗盤嗎？

2 **dishonest** [dɪsˋɑnɪst] (a.) 不誠實的
He was fired for being dishonest with all his customers.
他因為對所有客戶說謊而被辭退。

35 **disk** [dɪsk] (n.) 磁碟
He inserted the disk into the computer.
他把磁碟片放進電腦。

36 **dislike** [dɪsˋlaɪk] (v.) 不喜歡，討厭
I dislike eating eggplants.
我不喜歡吃茄子。

36 **dismiss** [dɪsˋmɪs] (v.) 解散，下課
We were dismissed early because of the holiday.
我們今天因為節日提早下課。

35 **dispute** [dɪ`spjʊt] (n.) 爭論
The two men had dispute over the result of the football game.
那兩個男人為了美式足球比賽的結果而爭吵。

19 **distance** [`dɪstəns] (n.) 距離
I travel a long distance to work every day.
我每天通勤很遠去上班。

19 **distant** [`dɪstənt] (a.) 遠的
We sailed to a distant island and enjoyed lunch there.
我們航行到遠處的小島，在那邊吃午飯。

37 **distinct** [dɪs`tɪŋkt] (a.) 明顯的
The differences between the two copies are distinct.
這兩份拷貝的差異相當明顯。

36 **disturb** [dɪs`tɝb] (v.) 打擾
Don't disturb me while I am studying.
我在讀書時不要打擾我。

35 **ditch** [dɪtʃ] (n.) 溝
The ditch is full of trash.
這條水溝都是垃圾。

14 **dive** [daɪv] (v.) 跳水，潛水
The lifeguard dived into the pool to save a boy.
救生員跳入游泳池內救一個男孩。

36 **divide** [də`vaɪd] (v.) 分配
Mother divided the cake in half.
媽媽將蛋糕分成兩半。

35 **division** [də`vɪʒən] (n.) 部門
The secretary is appointed to another division.
這名祕書被派到另一個部門。

6 **divorce** [də`vors] (v.) 離婚
They divorced after their first wedding anniversary.
結婚一週年之後，他們就離婚了。

4 **dizzy** [`dɪzɪ] (a.) 頭暈的
Mother felt dizzy this morning.
媽媽今天早上覺得頭暈。

35 **dock** [dɑk] (n.) 碼頭，港區
The ship is at the dock and will be leaving soon.
那艘船停在碼頭，很快就會離開。

24 **doctor** [`dɑktɚ] (n.) 醫師
My father is a doctor.
我的爸爸是醫生。

35 **document** [`dɑkjəmənt] (n.) 文件
The envelope contains a secret document.
這個信封內含一份祕密文件。

36 **dodge** [dɑdʒ] (v.) 閃開，躲開
The president dodged all the questions.
總統迴避了所有問題。

14 **dodge ball** [`dɑdʒ,bɔl] (n.) 躲避球
Most elementary school students love to play dodge ball.
多數小學生都喜歡玩躲避球。

27 **dog** [dɔg] (n.) 狗
My neighbor has fifteen dogs.
我的鄰居有十五隻狗。

14 **doll** [dɑl] (n.) 洋娃娃
I gave her a doll as a birthday present.
我送她一個洋娃娃當作生日禮物。

9 **dollar** [ˋdɑlɚ] (n.) 元（美金）
This house cost me one million dollars!
這棟房子花了我一百萬美金！

27 **dolphin** [ˋdɑlfɪn] (n.) 海豚
We can go to Kenting for the dolphin show.
我們可以去墾丁看海豚秀。

37 **domestic** [dəˋmɛstɪk] (a.) 家庭的，家事的
No child likes to do domestic chores.
沒有小孩喜歡做家事。

27 **donkey** [ˋdɑŋkɪ] (n.) 驢
He is as stupid as a donkey.
他笨的跟頭驢一樣。

15 **door** [dɔr] (n.) 門
He wants to paint the door blue.
他想要將門漆成藍色。

35 **dose** [doz] (n.) 一劑，一服
A little dose of the poison can kill a bull.
這種毒藥只要一點點就可以殺死一隻公牛。

19 **dot** [dɑt] (n.) 點
There's a red dot on the tags of all the sale items.
所有拍賣物品標籤上都有一個紅點。

7 **double** [ˋdʌbl̩] (a.) 雙的
She will pay me double if I work overtime.
如果我加班，她會付我雙倍工資。

36 **doubt** [daʊt] (v.) 懷疑
I doubt I will ever see him again.
我懷疑是否會再見到他。

37 **doubtful** [ˋdaʊtfəl] (a.) 疑惑，懷疑
I am doubtful about his sincerity.
我懷疑他的誠意。

10 **doughnut** [ˋdonət] (n.) 甜甜圈
I always have doughnuts in the afternoon.
我每到下午就會吃甜甜圈。

32 **down** [daʊn] (adv.) 向下
Grandma fell down the stairs.
祖母從樓梯上摔下來。

15 **downstairs** [daʊnˋstɛrz] (adv.) 在樓下
I went downstairs for dinner.
我下樓吃晚餐。

17 **downtown** [ˌdaʊnˋtaʊn] (n.) 市區，市中心
The shopping mall is a mile away from downtown.
這間購物中心位在離市中心一英里處。

36 **doze** [doz] (v.) 打瞌睡
I dozed off when I was on the bus.
我搭公車時打起瞌睡來。

19 **dozen** [ˋdʌzn̩] (n.) 一打
Grandma needs a dozen eggs to bake a cake.
奶奶需要一打雞蛋來烤蛋糕。

24 **doctor** [ˋdɑktɚ] (n.) 醫生（縮寫為Dr.）
I've made an appointment with Dr. Peterson this Friday night.
本週五晚上我已經和彼德森醫師約好時間。

27 **dragon** [ˋdrægən] (n.) 龍
We have dragon boat races during at Dragon Boat Festival.
我們在端午節時有龍舟比賽。

35 **drain** [dren] (n.) 下水道，排水溝
The drain of the sink is clogged.
水槽的排水管塞住了。

14 **drama** [ˋdrɑmə] (n.) 戲劇
He studies computers and drama at university.
他在大學裡主修電腦與戲劇。

37 **dramatic** [drəˋmætɪk] (a.) 戲劇性的
The climax of the movie is very dramatic.
這部電影的高潮很富戲劇性。

14 **draw** [drɔ] (v.) 畫圖
Tina is busy drawing.
蒂娜正忙著畫圖。

15 **drawer** [ˋdrɔɚ] (n.) 抽屜
My grandpa keeps his money in the drawer.
我爺爺將他的錢存放在抽屜。

14 **drawing** [ˋdrɔɪŋ] (n.) 畫圖，圖畫
My teacher saw my drawings and noticed that I had talent.
我的老師看到我的畫，發現我有天分。

35 **dream** [drim] (n.) 夢
I had a dream last night.
我昨晚做了一個夢。

12 **dress** [drɛs] (n.) 洋裝
Mother got a purple dress for me.
媽媽買了一件紫色洋裝給我。

15 **dresser** [ˋdrɛsɚ] (n.) 化妝台
Mom needs a dresser in her bedroom.
媽媽需要在她的房間放一個化妝台。

⑮ **drier** [ˋdraɪɚ] (n.) 烘乾機，吹風機
The hair drier doesn't work.
這台吹風機壞了。

⑩ **drink** [drɪŋk] (n.) 飲料
Coffee is the most popular drink in New York City cafés.
咖啡是紐約市餐廳中最受歡迎的飲料。

㊱ **drip** [drɪp] (v.) 留下，滴下
The rain is dripping down the wall.
雨水從牆壁流下來。

⑱ **drive** [draɪv] (v.) 開（車、船等）
I learned how to drive at the age of fifteen.
我十五歲學會開車。

㉔ **driver** [ˋdraɪvɚ] (n.) 司機
Taxi drivers always drive fast.
計程車司機開車一向很快。

㊱ **drop** [drɑp] (v.) 使掉下
Be careful not to drop that box!
小心不要讓箱子掉下來！

㊱ **drown** [draʊn] (v.) 淹死，淹沒
The boy swimming in the river was drowned.
在河裡游泳的男孩淹死了。

㊲ **drowsy** [ˋdraʊzɪ] (a.) 昏昏欲睡的，睏倦的
The boring class made me drowsy.
這堂無聊的課讓我昏昏欲睡。

④ **drug** [drʌg] (n.) 藥物，毒品
Stay away from drugs.
遠離毒品。

17 **drugstore** [ˋdrʌg,stor] (n.) 藥局
Some drugstores are not allowed to sell certain medicines.
有些藥局不准販賣特定藥品。

14 **drum** [drʌm] (n.) 鼓，鼓聲
My brother plays the drums in a rock band.
我哥哥在樂隊裡打鼓。

37 **drunk** [drʌŋk] (a.) 喝醉的
He was dead drunk after the party.
派對過後他喝得爛醉如泥。

25 **dry** [draɪ] (v.) 把…弄乾
Will this jacket dry by tomorrow?
這件夾克明天之前會乾嗎？

27 **duck** [dʌk] (n.) 鴨子
There is a duck in the lake.
湖中有一隻鴨子。

37 **due** [djʊ] (a.) 由於，因為
Due to the heavy rain, lots of students were late to school.
因為這場大雨，很多學生上學遲到。

2 **dumb** [dʌm] (a.) 啞的
The dumb old lady lives alone in the village.
那名瘖啞老太太獨自住在村裡。

36 **dump** [dʌmp] (v.) 傾倒，拋棄
Don’t dump the garbage on the street.
別在街道上丟垃圾。

10 **dumpling** [ˋdʌmplɪŋ] (n.) 餃子
Many people like to eat dumplings.
很多人喜歡吃餃子。

32 **during** [ˋdʊrɪŋ] (prep.) 在…的期間
I have to work during the holidays.
我在假日時必須工作。

35 **dust** [dʌst] (n.) 灰塵，塵土
The factory is filled with dust.
這間工廠到處都是灰塵。

35 **duty** [ˋdjutɪ] (n.) 責任
It is her duty to clean the house.
打掃這間房子是她的責任。

36 **dye** [daɪ] (v.) 染色
Don't dye your hair blue.
不要把頭髮染成藍色。

E

29 **each** [itʃ] (pron.) 每一個
Each one of you must go home now.
你們現在全都得回家。

37 **eager** [ˋigɚ] (a.) 熱心的，渴望的
The boy is eager to see his parents.
這個男孩渴望見他的父母親。

27 **eagle** [ˋigl̩] (n.) 鷹
Eagles are circling in the sky.
老鷹正在天空盤旋。

3 **ear** [ɪr] (n.) 耳朵
She wears an earring on her left ear.
她的左耳戴著耳環。

8 **early** [ˋɜlɪ] (adv.) 早
I like to get to work half an hour early to organize my desk.
我喜歡提早半小時到公司去整理桌面。

9 **earn** [ɜn] (v.) 賺取
The old man earns a living by selling second hand books.
那老人以賣二手書為生。

12 **earnings** [ˋɜnɪŋz] (n.) 收入
My earnings increase every year by ten percent.
我的收入每年成長百分之十。

25 **earth** [ɜθ] (n.) 地球
We should protect our earth.
我們應該保護我們的地球。

25 **earthquake** [ˋɜθ,kwek] (n.) 地震
A large earthquake struck Japan early this morning.
今天早晨一個大地震侵襲日本。

36 **ease** [iz] (v.) 舒緩
The young lady took some pills to ease her headache.
那個年輕小姐吃了一些藥丸來舒緩頭痛。

17 **east** [ist] (n.) 東方
The sun rises in the east.
太陽從東方升起。

23 **Easter** [ˋistɚ] (n.) 復活節
Children like to paint Easter eggs on Easter Day.
小朋友喜歡在復活節彩繪復活節蛋。

17 **eastern** [ˋistɚn] (a.) 東方的，東部的
She's from eastern London.
她來自倫敦東部。

37 **easy** [ˋizɪ] (a.) 簡單的
Learning English is easy.
學英文很簡單。

10 **eat** [it] (v.) 吃
I eat five meals a day.
我每天吃五餐。

36 **echo** [ˋɛko] (v.) 產生回音
The girls' voices echo in the building.
這些女孩的噪音在大樓裡迴盪著。

9 **economic** [,ikəˋnɑmɪk] (a.) 經濟的
The shop was shut down because of the economic problem.
這家店因經濟問題而停止營業。

35 **edge** [ɛdʒ] (n.) 邊緣
The diver jumped down the cliff edge into the ocean.
那個潛水夫從懸崖邊跳入海中。

36 **edit** [ˋɛdɪt] (v.) 編輯，剪接
I spent all morning editing the book.
我花了一整個早上編這本書。

35 **edition** [əˋdɪʃən] (n.) 版，版本
This edition of the book is not available now.
這本書的這一版現在買不到。

24 **editor** [ˋɛdɪtɚ] (n.) 編輯
She's an editor at this newspaper.
她在這家報社擔任編輯。

16 **educate** [ˋɛdʒə,ket] (v.) 教育，培養
I was educated at this university.
我在這所大學接受教育。

35 **education** [,ɛdʒʊˋkeʃən] (n.) 教育
Education is the primary concern for all countries.
對所有國家來說，教育皆為首要考量。

37 **educational** [,ɛdʒʊˋkeʃən!] (a.) 教育的
We gave Timmy educational software for his computer.
我們送提米教育軟體安裝在他的電腦上。

35 **effect** [ɪˋfɛkt] (n.) 影響
Nelson Mandela had a great effect on South Africa.
曼德拉在過去對南非有極大的影響。

37 **effective** [ɪˋfɛktɪv] (a.) 有效的
The heater is effective at keeping you warm.
這暖爐有效地讓人保持溫暖。

37 **efficient** [ɪˋfɪʃənt] (a.) 有能力，能勝任的
That man is efficient at managing the hotel.
那位男士有能力擔任管理旅館的職務。

35 **effort** [ˋɛfɚt] (n.) 努力
We should put more effort into our studies.
我們應該更加努力用功。

10 **egg** [ɛg] (n.) 蛋
I don't eat meat, but I do eat eggs.
我不吃肉，但我吃蛋。

7 **eight** [et] (a.) 八個
There are eight people in the classroom.
教室裡有八個人。

7 **eighteen** [ˋeˋtin] (n.) 十八
She bought eighteen eggs.
她買了十八顆蛋。

7 **eighteenth** [`e`tinθ] (a.) 第十八的
She was born on August eighteenth.
她生於八月十八日。

7 **eighth** [eθ] (a.) 第八的
He was the eighth runner to finish the marathon.
他在這場馬拉松賽跑第八名。

7 **eighty** [`etɪ] (n.) 八十
Forty times two is eighty.
四十乘二等於八十。

37 **either** [`iðɚ] (a.) 兩者之一
You can choose either one.
你可以兩者擇其一。

3 **elbow** [`ɛlbo] (n.) 肘部
The boy's elbow was hurt and in bandages.
這男孩的手肘受傷裹著繃帶。

6 **elder** [`ɛldɚ] (a.) 年紀大的
Her elder sister is a famous singer.
她的姊姊是有名的歌手。

6 **elderly** [`ɛldɚlɪ] (a.) 年老的，上了年紀的
The elderly men are experienced in life.
上了年紀的人有人生閱歷。

36 **elect** [ɪ`lɛkt] (v.) 選舉
People elect the president every four years.
人民每四年選一次總統。

35 **election** [ɪ`lɛkʃən] (n.) 選舉
The opposite party won this election.
反對黨贏得了這場選舉。

37 **electric** [ɪ`lɛktrɪk] (a.) 電的
Mother got an electric shock from the hair drier.
媽媽被吹風機電到了。

37 **electric** [ɪ`lɛktrɪk] (a.) 導電的，電的
Computers needs electric power to run.
電腦需要電力才能啟動。

37 **electrical** [ɪ`lɛktrɪkl̩] (a.) 電力學的，電的
There was an electrical problem with the airplane and it wasn't allowed to take off.
飛機由於發生電力問題，不准起飛。

35 **electricity** [,ilɛk`trɪsətɪ] (n.) 電力
Did you pay my electricity bill?
你有幫我繳電費嗎？

37 **electronic** [ɪlɛk`trɑnɪk] (a.) 電子的
Many students rely heavily on electronic dictionaries now.
現在許多學生非常依賴電子辭典。

elegant [`ɛləgənt] (a.) 優雅的
The elegant bride walks into the aisle, accompanied by her father.
那個優雅的新娘由爸爸陪伴著走上紅毯。

35 **element** [`ɛləmənt] (n.) 成分
There are some chemical elements in this medicine.
這種藥裡有些化學成分。

16 **elementary school** [,ɛlə`mɛntərɪ skul] (n.) 小學
His mother teaches in an elementary school.
他的媽媽在小學教書。

27 **elephant** [`ɛləfənt] (n.) 大象
Elephants have huge bodies.
大象的身體很大。

7 **eleven** [ɪˋlɛvn̩] (a.) 十一個
There are eleven desks in this room.
這間房間裡有十一張桌子。

7 **eleventh** [ɪˋlɛvn̩θ] (a.) 第十一的
The apartment on the eleventh floor is for rent.
十一樓的公寓要出租。

eliminate [ɪˋlɪmə,net] (v.) 消除，消滅
The cockroaches in the kitchen are all eliminated.
廚房裡的蟑螂全被消滅了。

37 **else** [ɛls] (adv.) 其他
I don’t have anything else to say to him.
我沒有其他話要跟他說了。

35 **e-mail** [ˋɪ,mel] (n.) 電子郵件
People seldom write letters now; they send e-mails.
人們現在很少寫信了，都在寄電子郵件。

36 **embarrass** [ɪmˋbærəs] (v.) 尷尬
The girl was embarrassed.
這女孩覺得很尷尬。

36 **emerge** [ɪˋmɝdʒ] (v.) 浮現
The submarine emerges out of the sea level.
潛水艇從海平面下浮出來。

35 **emergency** [ɪˋmɝdʒənsɪ] (n.) 緊急狀況
In case of emergency, please contact my wife at this number.
要是發生緊急狀況，請打這個電話號碼通知我太太。

35 **emotion** [ɪˋmoʃən] (n.) 情感
I was filled with emotion after hearing her speech.
聽完她的演說，我心中充滿感動。

35 **emperor** [`ɛmpərə] (n.) 皇帝

The emperor is murdered on the bed.

這皇帝在床上被謀殺了。

35 **emphasis** [`ɛmfəsɪs] (n.) 強調

The politician put emphasis on the importance of people's freedom.

那位政治家強調人民自由的重要性。

36 **emphasize** [`ɛmfə,saɪz] (v.) 強調

He emphasizes the main point by underlining with a red pen.

他用紅筆畫底線來強調重點。

24 **employ** [ɪm`plɔɪ] (v.) 雇用

We need to employ another part- time worker.

我們需要再雇一位兼差的人員。

36 **employment** [ɪm`plɔɪmənt] (n.) 聘雇

The jobless young man turned to the employment agency for help.

那個失業的年輕人向職業介紹所求助。

35 **employee** [,ɛmplɔɪ`i] (n.) 員工，受雇者

There are few employees in this firm.

這家公司的員工沒幾個。

35 **employer** [ɪm`plɔɪə] (n.) 雇主

The employer laid off lots of workers.

這名雇主遣散了很多員工。

37 **empty** [`ɛmptɪ] (a.) 空的

The bottle is empty.

這個瓶子是空的。

36 **enable** [ɪn`ebl̩] (v.) 使能夠

The medicine enables you to sleep better.

此藥可以讓你睡得比較好。

36 **encourage** [ɪn`kɝɪdʒ] (v.) 鼓勵
My mother encourages me to go swimming.
我媽媽鼓勵我去游泳。

36 **end** [ɛnd] (v.) 結束
The movie has a happy ending.
這部電影有個快樂結局。

35 **enemy** [`ɛnəmɪ] (n.) 敵人
We have no enemies.
我們沒有敵人。

2 **energetic** [,ɛnɚ`dʒɛtɪk] (a.) 有活力的
The energetic boy sits restlessly at the desk.
這個精力充沛的男孩坐在書桌後面動來動去。

35 **energy** [`ɛnɚdʒɪ] (n.) 精力
I lost all my energy after the ball game.
球賽過後，我完全沒體力了。

36 **enforce** [ɪn`fors] (v.) 實施執行
The law should be enforced to protect people's property.
應該執行此法來保護人民的財產。

36 **engage** [ɪn`gedʒ] (v.) 從事
He is engaged in studying English literature.
他致力於研究英文文學。

36 **engagement** [ɪn`gedʒmənt] (n.) 婚約，承諾
Their engagement was kept a secret until one month before the wedding.
他們對於的事訂婚一直保密，直到結婚前一個月才公布。

35 **engine** [`ɛndʒən] (n.) 引擎
My new car has a large and powerful engine.
我的新車有大型強力引擎。

24 **engineer** [ˌɛndʒə`nɪr] (n.) 工程師

The engineer can't figure out what happened to the machine.

這工程師搞不清這部機器出了什麼問題。

20 **England** [`ɪŋglənd] (n.) 英國，英格蘭

Mr. Blair is from England.

布萊爾先生來自英國。

21 **English** [`ɪŋglɪʃ] (n.) 英文

English isn't my favorite subject.

英語不是我最愛的科目。

21 **Englishman** [`ɪŋglɪʃˌmən] (n.) 英國人

The Englishman worked as a doctor in India, helping the poor.

那位英國人在印度行醫，幫助窮人。

36 **enjoy** [ɪn`dʒɔɪ] (v.) 喜愛

Michael enjoyed his steak very much.

麥克吃牛排吃得很高興。

37 **enjoyable** [ɪn`dʒɔɪəbl̩] (a.) 有趣的，有樂趣的

Having a picnic on Sunday morning is enjoyable

星期天上午去郊遊很有趣。

37 **enormous** [ɪ`nɔrməs] (a.) 巨大的

The Golden Gate Bridge is an enormous structure.

金門大橋是一座雄偉的建築結構體。

37 **enough** [ɪ`nʌf] (a.) 足夠的

I think the food will be enough for sixty people.

我想這些食物夠六十個人吃。

36 **enter** [`ɛntɚ] (v.) 進入

The thief entered the house from the window.

小偷從窗戶進入屋子。

36 **entertain** [ˌɛntɚˋten] (v.) 使歡樂
The purpose of the movie is to entertain people.
電影的目的就是娛樂大眾。

35 **enthusiasm** [ɪnˋθjuzɪˌæzəm] (n.) 熱心
The volunteer helps the patients with great enthusiasm.
這位志工很熱心地幫助病患。

37 **entire** [ɪnˋtaɪr] (a.) 全部的
This book took him an entire summer to finish.
這本書花了他整個夏天才完成。

35 **entrance** [ˋɛntrəns] (n.) 入口
Where's the entrance to the restaurant?
戲院的入口在哪裡？

35 **entry** [ˋɛntrɪ] (n.) 進入，入口
The entry of the stadium is on Fifth Avenue.
這座體育場的入口在第五街。

16 **envelope** [ˋɛnvəˌlop] (n.) 信封
The envelope was addressed to my neighbor, but it was delivered to my house.
信封上的地址是我鄰居的，信卻寄到我家來。

26 **environment** [ɪnˋvaɪrəmənt] (n.) 環境
We have to protect our environment.
我們必須保護我們的環境。

2 **envy** [ˋɛnvɪ] (v.) 嫉妒，羨慕
All the students envy his opportunity to dine with a movie star.
學生們無不羨慕他有機會與一個電影明星共進晚餐。

37 **equal** [ˋikwəl] (a.) 相同的
All of you have an equal chance.
你們每個人都有相同的機會。

36 **erase** [ɪˋrez] (v.) 擦掉，抹去
Could you erase all the words on the blackboard?
請把黑板上所有的字都擦掉好嗎？

16 **eraser** [ɪˋresɚ] (n.) 橡皮擦，板擦
Please hand me the eraser so I can change these answers.
請把橡皮擦遞給我，我才能改這些答案。

35 **error** [ˋɛrɚ] (n.) 錯誤
She made an error on her test.
她在考試時犯了個錯誤。

18 **escalator** [ˋɛskə,letɚ] (n.) 電扶梯
Take good care of your children when on the escalator.
搭乘電扶梯時，要看好你的小孩。

36 **escape** [əˋskep] (v.) 逃出，脫逃
The killer escaped from prison and is somewhere in the state of California.
殺人犯逃出監獄，藏身加州某處。

38 **especially** [əˋspɛʃəlɪ] (adv.) 特別
This song is especially for you.
這首歌是特別獻給你的。

37 **essential** [ɪˋsɛnʃəl] (a.) 必要的，不可或缺的
To pass the exam, it is essential to study hard.
要通過考試，用功念書是免不了的。

36 **establish** [əˋstæblɪʃ] (v.) 建立
The foundation was established one year ago.
這個基金會於一年前創立。

20 **Europe** [ˋjʊrəp] (n.) 歐洲
Spain is in Europe.
西班牙位於歐洲。

⑳ **European** [ˏjʊrəˋpiən] (a.) 歐洲的
European culture is much different from American.
歐洲文化和美國文化大不相同。

⑧ **eve** [iv] (n.) 前夕
They will go to church on Christmas Eve.
他們耶誕夜會上教堂。

㊳ **even** [ˋivən] (adv.) 甚至
This baby can't even walk.
這個嬰兒連走路都不會走。

⑧ **evening** [ˋivnɪŋ] (n.) 晚間
Father works from morning till evening.
爸爸從早到晚工作。

㉟ **event** [ɪˋvɛnt] (n.) 事件
This is a front- page event!
這是一個頭條事件！

㊳ **ever** [ˋɛvɚ] (adv.) 在任何時候，至今
She's the prettiest girl I've ever seen.
她是我見過最漂亮的女孩。

㉘ **every** [ˋɛvrɪ] (a.) 每一個
It is a new day every day.
每天都是新的一天。

㉙ **everybody** [ˋɛvrɪˏbadɪ] (n.) 每人
Everybody has to be here on Sunday.
每個人星期天都得來這裡。

㉙ **everyone** [ˋɛvrɪˏwʌn] (pron.) 每一個人
Everyone in the class has a locker.
班上每個人都有一個置物櫃。

29 **everything** [ˋɛvrɪ,θɪŋ] (pron.) 每一件事
Everything is under control. Don't worry.
一切都在掌握之中。別擔心。

38 **everywhere** [ˋɛvrɪ,hwɛr] (pron.) 每一個地方
I've been everywhere in Taiwan.
我到過台灣的每個地方。

38 **evidence** [ˋɛvədəns] (n.) 證據
There is no evidence of his committing any crimes.
沒有任何他犯罪的證據。

2 **evil** [ˋivḷ] (n.) 邪惡，罪惡
Greed is the root of all evils.
貪婪為萬惡之源。

2 **evil** [ˋivḷ] (a.) 邪惡的
Cinderella has an evil step mother.
灰姑娘有一個邪惡的繼母。

37 **exact** [ɪgˋzækt] (a.) 精確的
Here is the exact amount of one million dollars.
這裡剛好是一百萬。

16 **exam** [ɪgˋzæm] (n.) 考試
We have an exam tomorrow.
我們明天有考試。

4 **examine** [ɪgˋzæmɪn] (v.) 檢查
I have to go to the hospital to examine my health.
我必須去醫院檢查我的健康狀況。

16 **examinee** [ɪg,zæməˋni] (n.) 應試者
The examinees can not wear any electronic devices.
考生不得佩戴任何電子儀器。

16 **examiner** [ɪgˋzæmɪnɚ] (n.) 主考官
The examiner explained the regulations to the students.
那個主考官向學生解釋規定。

16 **example** [ɪgˋzæmpḷ] (n.) 範例
You may read the example sentences.
請念例句。

35 **excellence** [ˋɛksələns] (n.) 傑出，卓越
The excellence of his performance won him an award.
他傑出的表現讓他贏得了個獎。

37 **excellent** [ˋɛksələnt] (a.) 傑出的
You had an excellent performance on your test.
你的測驗成績非常傑出。

32 **except** [ɪkˋsɛpt] (prep.) 除…之外
All the students failed the exam except Kelly.
除了凱莉，所有學生都沒通過考試。

37 **exchange** [ɪksˋtʃendʒ] (a.) 交換
I'm the exchange student from Japan.
我是日本來的交換學生。

36 **excite** [ɪkˋsaɪt] (v.) 刺激
Dancing excites Emily.
跳舞讓艾蜜莉很興奮。

2 **excited** [ɪkˋsaɪtɪd] (a.) 興奮的
I'm so excited about the trip to Japan this weekend.
我好興奮這個週末要去日本旅行。

2 **exciting** [ɪkˋsaɪtɪŋ] (a.) 令人激動的
The baseball game was really exciting last night.
昨晚的棒球賽真的很刺激。

35 **excuse** [ɪk`skjuz] (n.) 藉口
There is no excuse for being late.
遲到是沒有藉口的。

14 **exercise** [`ɛksə,saɪz] (n.) 運動
I do exercises every day to stay healthy.
我每天做運動保持健康。

16 **exercise** [`ɛksə,saɪz] (n.) 練習，習題
The math exercise is on page ten.
數學習題在第十頁。

35 **exhibition** [,ɛksə`bɪʃən] (n.) 展覽會，展覽
I went to a book exhibition today.
我今天去了一個書展。

36 **exist** [ɪg`zɪst] (v.) 存在
Do you think ghosts exist in the world?
你認為世界上有鬼嗎？

35 **existence** [ɪg`zɪstəns] (n.) 存在
I believe in the existence of ghosts and angels.
我相信鬼魂和天使的存在。

35 **exit** [`ɛksɪt] (n.) 出口
There is no emergency exit in the movie theater.
那間電影院沒有緊急出口。

36 **expand** [ɪk`spænd] (v.) 擴大
My boss hopes to expand his business.
我的老闆希望擴大他的事業版固。

36 **expect** [ɪk`spɛkt] (v.) 預期
Mother expects me to be at home by five.
媽媽希望我在五點前到家。

35 **expectation** [ˌɛkspɛkˋteʃən] (n.) 期望，期待
His grades didn't meet his parents' expectations.
他的成績沒有達到父母親的期望。

9 **expense** [ɪkˋspɛns] (n.) 費用，開支
The office expense is beyond the budget.
辦公室的開銷超出預算。

9 **expensive** [ɪkˋspɛnsɪv] (a.) 昂貴的
I bought an expensive TV.
我買了一台昂貴的電視。

35 **experience** [ɪkˋspɪrɪəns] (n.) 經驗
He has lots of experiences in teaching.
他有很多教學經驗。

35 **experiment** [ɪkˋspɛrəmənt] (n.) 實驗
The experiment proved the theory impossible.
此實驗證明這個理論不可行。

1 **expert** [ˋɛkspɚt] (n.) 專家
Mother is an expert at shopping.
媽媽是個購物高手。

16 **explain** [ɪkˋsplen] (v.) 解釋
I can't explain his strange behavior.
我無法解釋他的詭異行徑。

35 **explanation** [ˌɛkspləˋneʃən] (n.) 解釋
You owe me an explanation.
你欠我一個解釋。

36 **explode** [ɪkˋsplod] (v.) 爆炸，爆發
The bomb exploded in ten minutes.
這顆炸彈十分鐘後爆炸了。

36 **explore** [ɪk`splor] (v.) 探險
This is the area that no one has explored before.
這是無人探索過的區域。

36 **export** [ɪks`port] (v.) 出口
The company exports goods to Japan.
這間公司外銷商品到日本。

36 **express** [ɪk`sprɛs] (v.) 表達
It's hard sometimes for a man to express his feelings.
對男人來說，有時表達情感是困難的。

35 **expression** [ɪk`sprɛʃən] (n.) 表達，表示
The teacher's expression is clear and reasonable.
這老師的表達方式清楚又有道理。

37 **expressive** [ɪk`sprɛsɪv] (a.) 表現的，表達的
The smile on his face is expressive of his gratitude.
他臉上的微笑表達出他的感激。

19 **extra** [`ɛkstrə] (a.) 額外的
We need extra help.
我需要再多一點幫助。

35 **extreme** [ɪk`strim] (n.) 極端
He goes from one extreme to the other, not eating one week, and eating too much the next.
他吃東西很極端，先是一星期不吃不喝，下星期又暴飲暴食。

3 **eye** [aɪ] (n.) 眼睛
Her eyes are green.
她的眼睛是綠色的。

F

35 **fable** [ˋfebl̩] (n.) 寓言，虛構
Aesop's fables are famous all over the world.
伊索寓言舉世皆知。

3 **face** [fes] (n.) 臉
I have a big smile on my face.
我臉上笑容洋溢。

35 **fact** [fækt] (n.) 事實
In fact, I didn't pass the exam.
其實我沒有通過考試。

35 **factor** [ˋfæktɚ] (n.) 因素，原因
The factor that caused the experiment to fail is still unknown.
造成實驗失敗的因素至今不明。

17 **factory** [ˋfæktərɪ] (n.) 工廠
The factory is polluting the river.
這間工廠正在污染河流。

36 **fade** [fed] (v.) 枯萎，褪去
The color faded away after washing.
顏色在洗過之後褪了。

16 **fail** [fel] (v.) 失敗，不及格
I failed my math test this morning.
我今天早上數學考不及格。

35 **failure** [ˋfeljɚ] (n.) 失敗，失敗者
Our efforts ended in failure.
我們的努力終告失敗。

A B C D E F G H I J K L M N O P Q R S T U V W X Y Z

35 **faint** [fent] (v.) 昏倒，暈倒
After a long walk, Jimmy fainted.
走了很長一段路後，吉米昏到了。

19 **fair** [fɛr] (a.) 公平的
The teacher is fair to all the students.
這位老師公平對待所有學生。

37 **fairy** [ˋfɛrɪ] (a.) 幻想中的
She is fascinated by fairy stories.
她很迷奇幻故事。

35 **faith** [feθ] (n.) 信任，信念
We don't have faith in the new government.
我們對新政府沒有信心。

2 **faithful** [ˋfeθfəl] (a.) 忠實，忠誠
The soldier is faithful to his king.
這名士兵忠於他的國王。

35 **fake** [fek] (n.) 仿冒品
That diamond watch is a fake.
那支鑽錶是仿冒品。

8 **fall** [fɔl] (n.) 秋天
Fall is my favorite season.
秋天是我最愛的季節。

36 **fall** [fɔl] (v.) 掉下
The kid fell down the stairs.
這小孩子從樓梯上跌下來。

37 **false** [fɔls] (a.) 不正確的
Eva doesn't want them to get a false impression.
伊娃不想給他們錯誤的印象。

35 **fame** [fem] (n.) 名氣
Nowadays teenagers only run after fame.
現在青少年只想出名。

37 **familiar** [fə`mɪljɚ] (a.) 熟悉的
I am not familiar with the neighborhood.
我跟附近鄰居不熟。

6 **family** [`fæməlɪ] (n.) 家庭
The Brown family is going to move this week.
布朗一家人這星期要搬家。

2 **famous** [`feməs] (a.) 出名的，有名的
The skillful doctor is very famous.
那個技術高超的醫生非常出名。

15 **fan** [fæn] (n.) 扇子，電扇
Did you turn on the fan?
你有打開電扇嗎？

14 **fan** [fæn] (n.) 迷
The popular singer has many fans.
這個受歡迎的歌手有好多歌迷。

37 **fancy** [`fænsɪ] (a.) 別緻的，花俏的
I am looking for a fancy dress.
我在找一件別緻的洋裝。

37 **fantastic** [fæn`tæstɪk] (a.)（好到）難以置信的，棒的
The movie turned out to be fantastic.
這部電影實在太棒了！

35 **fantasy** [`fæntəsɪ] (n.) 空想，夢想
Your diet is only fantasy, not practical.
妳的減重計畫只是空想，並不實際。

⑲ **far** [fɑr] (a.) 遙遠的
The missing child didn't go very far.
那個失蹤的小孩並沒有跑很遠。

⑱ **fare** [fɛr] (n.) 票價
The ticket fare to New York is not cheap.
到紐約的票價並不便宜。

㊲ **farewell** [`fɛr`wɛl] (a.) 再會，別了
They threw a farewell party for me.
他們為我舉行了一場歡送派對。

⑰ **farm** [fɑrm] (n.) 農場
He has many farms.
他有很多農場。

㉔ **farmer** [`fɑrmɚ] (n.) 農夫
Grandpa used to be a farmer.
祖父以前是個農夫。

㊲ **farther** [`fɑrðɚ] (adv.) 更遠的，更往前
My new school is farther than my old school.
我的新學校比原來的學校遠。

㉟ **fashion** [`fæʃən] (n.) 流行樣式，時尚
One of the latest fashions is wearing miniskirts with boots.
穿迷你裙配長靴是最新流行。

㊲ **fashionable** [`fæʃənəbl̩] (a.) 流行的，時髦的
She always wears a pair of fashionable glasses.
她總是戴著一副時髦的眼鏡。

⑩ **fast food** [fæst fud] (n.) 速食
Most fast food is junk food.
大部分的速食都是垃圾食物。

17 **fast food restaurant** [fæst fud `rɛstərənt] (n.) 速食店
Most children like to have meals at the fast food restaurant.
小孩大多喜歡在速食店用餐。

18 **fast** [fæst] (adv.) 快速地
The train runs faster than the motorcycle.
火車的速度比摩托車快。

36 **fasten** [`fæsn̩] (v.) 紮牢，繫緊
Please fasten your seat belt.
請繫好安全帶。

2 **fat** [fæt] (a.) 胖
He is too fat to play basketball.
他胖到沒辦法打籃球。

37 **fatal** [`fetl̩] (a.) 致命的
He witnessed a fatal accident.
他親眼目睹一場死亡車禍。

35 **fate** [fet] (n.) 命運
It was his fate to become famous around the world.
他命中註定會聞名全球。

6 **father** [`fɑðɚ] (n.) 父親
His father is a doctor.
他的爸爸是醫生。

15 **faucet** [`fɔsɪt] (n.) 龍頭
The faucet is leaking.
水龍頭在漏水。

35 **fault** [fɔlt] (n.) 錯誤
It's not your fault.
不是你的錯。

35 **favor** [`fevɚ] (n.) 恩惠
Can I ask you a favor?
我可以請你幫個忙嗎？

37 **favorite** [`fevərɪt] (a.) 最愛的
Pizza is my favorite food.
披薩是我最愛的食物。

36 **fax** [fæks] (v.) 傳真
Could you fax me the document?
你可以傳真那份文件給我嗎？

2 **fear** [fɪr] (n.) 害怕
He was trembling with fear.
他怕得直發抖。

35 **feast** [fist] (n.) 大餐，大吃大喝
We had a huge Christmas feast at grandmother's house.
我們在祖母家吃了一頓耶誕大餐。

27 **feather** [`fɛðɚ] (n.) 羽毛
My bird is sick and is losing its feathers.
我的鳥病了，正在掉毛。

35 **feature** [`fitʃɚ] (n.) 特徵，特色
The Internet has become an important feature of modern society.
網路已經成為現代社會的一項重要特色。

8 **February** [`fɛbrʊ,ɛrɪ] (n.) 二月
February is the shortest month of the year.
二月是一年裡最短的月份。

9 **fee** [fi] (n.) 費用
I am afraid that I won't be able to pay the fee.
我恐怕付不起這個費用。

36 **feed** [fid] (v.) 餵食
The mother feeds her child with milk.
媽媽餵她的小孩喝牛奶。

36 **feel** [fil] (v.) 感覺
How do you feel today?
你今天感覺如何？

35 **feeling** [ˋfilɪŋ] (n.) 感覺，情感
She has no feelings for my brother.
她對我哥哥沒有感覺。

1 **fellow** [ˋfɛlo] (n.)（口）夥伴，傢伙
A bunch of fellows went out for a drink.
一群朋友出去喝酒。

17 **female** [ˋfimel] (n.) 女性的，雌的
We have one female dog and one male dog.
我們養了一隻母狗和一隻公狗。

15 **fence** [fɛns] (n.) 籬笆
The fence needs fixing.
籬笆需要修補了。

18 **ferry** [ˋfɛrɪ] (n.) 渡輪
We took the ferry at the port.
我們在港口搭渡輪。

23 **festival** [ˋfɛstəvl̩] (n.) 節日
Taiwan has a Dragon Boat Festival.
台灣有端午節。

36 **fetch** [fɛtʃ] (v.) 拿來，去拿…給
Could you fetch me the salt, please?
可以請你去拿鹽巴來給我嗎？

4 **fever** [ˋfivɚ] (n.) 發燒
You are running a fever now, so you should take a good rest.
你在發燒，所以應該好好休息。

7 **few** [fjʊ] (a.) 很少的
There were only a few people here yesterday.
昨天這裡只有幾個人。

35 **fiction** [ˋfɪkʃən] (n.) 小說
That book in the fiction section is increasingly popular.
小說區的那本書越來越熱門。

17 **field** [fild] (n.) 田野
We will have a field trip tomorrow.
我們明天有校外教學。

37 **fierce** [fɪrs] (a.) 兇猛的，殘酷的
The storm was fierce and caused a lot of damage.
暴風雨非常劇烈，造成嚴重損害。

7 **fifteen** [ˋfɪfˋtin] (a.) 十五個
The boy is fifteen years old.
那男孩十五歲了。

7 **fifteenth** [ˋfɪfˋtinθ] (a.) 第十五的
She was born on November fifteenth.
她在十一月十五號出生。

7 **fifth** [fɪfθ] (a.) 第五的
He's in the fifth grade now.
他現在五年級。

7 **fifty** [ˋfɪftɪ] (n.) 五十
His grandma is fifty years old.
他祖母現年五十歲。

36 **fight** [faɪt] (v.) 打架
Don't fight with your sister.
別和你姊姊打架。

35 **figure** [ˋfɪgjɚ] (n.) 外型
She has a great figure.
她的身材很棒。

36 **file** [faɪl] (v.) 把…歸檔
Could you file these documents away?
你可以將這些文件歸檔嗎？

36 **fill** [fɪl] (v.) 充滿
The theater is filled with people.
電影院滿是人潮。

14 **film** [fɪlm] (n.) 影片
The film is worth seeing.
這部電影值得一看。

16 **final** [ˋfaɪnl̩] (a.) 最終的
The final exam will start next week.
期末考從下星期開始。

38 **finally** [ˋfaɪnəlɪ] (adv.) 最後
You finally show up!
你終於出現了！

36 **finance** [faɪˋnæns] (v.) 供資金給…，為…籌措資金
We took out a loan to finance the house.
我們貸了一筆錢買房子。

37 **financial** [faɪˋnænʃəl] (a.) 財政的，金融的
The firm was in financial difficulties.
這間公司有財務困難。

36 **find** [faɪnd] (v.) 發現
I can never find the answers!
我老是找不到答案！

3 **finger** [ˋfɪŋgɚ] (n.) 手指
She has long and thin fingers.
她有修長纖細的手指。

36 **finish** [ˋfɪnɪʃ] (v.) 完成
I will finish my work on time.
我會準時完成我的工作。

17 **fire station** [faɪr ˋsteʃən] (n.) 消防局
There is a fire station next to the gas station.
加油站旁邊有間消防局。

35 **fire** [faɪr] (n.) 火
The supermarket is on fire.
這間超市失火了。

35 **firecracker** [ˋfaɪr,krækɚ] (n.) 爆竹，鞭炮
We set off firecrackers on Chinese New Year's Eve.
我們會在除夕夜放鞭炮。

35 **fireplace** [ˋfaɪr,ples] (n.) 壁爐
He placed lots of pictures on the fireplace.
他在壁爐上放了很多張照片。

35 **firework** [ˋfaɪr,wɝk] (n.) 煙火，煙火大會
We went to a fireworks display yesterday.
我們昨天去看煙火表演。

37 **firm** [fɝm] (a.) 堅固的
This building is tall and firm.
這棟建築物又高又堅固。

7 **first** [fɝst] (a.) 第一的
It was her first day of school.
今天是她第一天上學。

27 **fish** [fɪʃ] (n.) 魚
Cats like to eat fish.
貓喜歡吃魚。

24 **fisherman** [ˋfɪʃɚmən] (n.) 漁夫
The fisherman has stayed on the boat for 3 days.
這個漁夫已經待在船上三天了。

14 **fishing** [ˋfɪʃɪŋ] (n.) 釣魚
My family goes fishing every Sunday.
每週日我們家都會去釣魚。

3 **fist** [fɪst] (n.) 拳打，拳
The nurse told me to make a fist so that she could give me a shot.
護士叫我握緊拳頭，她才能幫我打針。

36 **fit** [fɪt] (v.) 適合
The necktie fits his suit very well.
這條領帶很配他的西裝。

7 **five** [faɪv] (a.) 五個
Two and three are five.
二加三等於五。

15 **fix** [fɪks] (v.) 修理，安排
Ian fixed me a drink.
伊恩準備了一杯飲料給我。

35 **flag** [flæg] (n.) 旗幟
We are holding our country's flag.
我們拿著我們的國旗。

35 **flame** [flem] (n.) 發火焰，燃燒
Don't put oil on the flame.
不要火上加油。

15 **flashlight** [ˋflæʃ,laɪt] (n.) 手電筒
The flashlight is running out of power.
這支手電筒快沒電了。

37 **flat** [flæt] (a.) 平坦的
She has a really flat tummy!
她有非常平坦的小腹！

18 **flat tire** [flæt taɪr] (n.) 爆胎
It's terrible to have a flat tire on the freeway.
在高速公路上爆胎很可怕。

36 **flatter** [ˋflætɚ] (v.) 使感到滿意，諂媚
Don't try to flatter me!
別想拍我馬屁！

35 **flavor** [ˋflevɚ] (n.) 味道，風味
Many children don't like the flavor of eggplants.
很多小孩不喜歡茄子的味道。

27 **flea** [fli] (n.) 跳蚤
The fleas were gathering around the food.
食物上都是跳蚤。

36 **flee** [fli] (v.) 消失，逃走
All the gangsters fled when the police came.
警察來的時候，盜匪全跑光了。

35 **flesh** [flɛʃ] (n.) 肉，肌肉
The burning flesh smelled terrible.
燒焦皮肉的味道很可怕。

37 **flexible** [ˋflɛksəbl̩] (a.) 可彎曲的，有彈性的
The plastic hose is flexible.
塑膠水管是有彈性的。

18 **flight** [flaɪt] (n.) 班機
The flight is delayed because of the typhoon.
因為颱風，班機誤點了。

36 **float** [flot] (v.) 飄，漂泊
I learned how to float on my back in swim class.
我在游泳課上學會怎麼仰著漂浮。

27 **flock** [flɑk] (n.)（飛禽、牲畜等的）群
A flock of seagalls are eating on the shore.
一群海鷗在岸上覓食。

15 **floor** [flor] (n.) 地板
We'll mop the floor twice a week.
我們一個星期拖地兩次。

10 **flour** [flaʊr] (n.) 麵粉
The bread is made of flour.
麵包是麵粉製的。

36 **flow** [flo] (v.) 流動
Water flows from high points to low points.
水從高處往低處流。

25 **flower** [ˋflaʊɚ] (n.) 花
His father gave his mother some flowers.
他爸爸送他媽媽一些花。

17 **flower shop** [ˋflaʊɚ ʃɑp] (n.) 花店
The flower shop made a fortune on Valentine's Day.
這間花店在情人節大撈一筆。

4 **flu** [flu] (n.)（口）流行性感冒
Ian had a bad case of the flu .
伊恩患了嚴重的流行性感冒。

37 **fluent** [ˋfluənt] (a.) 流利，流暢
She can speak fluent Spanish.
她的西班牙語說得很流利。

16 **flunk** [flʌŋk] (v.)（口）不及格
I flunked in my math examination.
我數學考不及格。

36 **flush** [flʌʃ] (v.) 沖洗
Don't forget to flush the toilet.
別忘了沖馬桶。

14 **flute** [flut] (n.) 長笛
She plays the flute very well.
她長笛吹得很好。

18 **fly** [flaɪ] (v.) 飛
If I were a bird, I could fly.
假如我是隻鳥，我就能飛。

36 **focus** [ˋfokəs] (v.) 聚焦，集中
I have trouble focusing on one thing at a time.
我很難一次專心做一件事。

25 **fog** [fɑg] (n.) 霧
I can not see clearly in this heavy fog.
在這片濃霧中，我看不清楚。

25 **foggy** [ˋfɑgɪ] (a.) 多霧的
It is always foggy in the mountains.
山區一向多霧。

36 **fold** [fold] (v.) 折疊，對折
He folded the letter neatly.
他把信件整齊對折。

35 **folk** [folk] (n.)（口）家屬，親屬
My brother writes letters to my folks regularly.
我哥哥定期寫信給我的家人。

36 **follow** [ˋfɑlo] (v.) 跟隨
The dog followed me home.
這隻狗跟著我回家。

35 **follower** [ˋfɑləwɚ] (n.) 追隨者，部下
The criminal's followers were all caught.
這名罪犯的手下全都被抓到了。

37 **following** [ˋfɑləwɪŋ] (a.) 接著的，下面的
Please answer the following questions.
請回答以下問題。

37 **fond** [fɑnd] (a.) 喜歡的，愛好的
He isn't fond of going hiking in the mountains.
他不喜歡到山區健行。

10 **food** [fud] (n.) 食物
The food mother cooked was delicious.
媽媽做的菜很美味。

1 **fool** [ful] (n.) 傻瓜
You are such a fool.
你真是個傻瓜。

2 **foolish** [ˋfulɪʃ] (a.) 愚笨的
You've made a foolish mistake.
你犯了一個愚蠢的錯誤。

19 **foot** [fʊt] (n.) 英尺（複數形為feet）
This building is 60 feet high.
這棟建築物有六十英尺高。

3 **foot** [fʊt] (n.) 腳（複數形為feet）
I broke my foot in cheerleading practice.
我練啦啦隊時摔斷腳。

14 **football** [ˋfʊt,bɔl] (n.) 美式足球
We play football every week.
我們每個星期都會打美式足球。

32 **for** [fɔr] (prep.) 為了
The present is for you.
這是給你的禮物。

36 **forbid** [fɚˋbɪd] (v.) 阻止，妨礙
Dad fordbade us to go out on Halloween.
萬聖節前夕，爸爸不准我們出門。

35 **force** [fors] (n.) 力量
The force of the earthquake was huge.
地震的力量很大。

36 **forecast** [ˋfor,kæst] (v.) 預測，預報
The weather forecast nowadays is accurate.
現在的天氣預測都很準確。

3 **forehead** [ˋfɔr,hɛd] (n.) 額頭，前額
The father kissed his baby girl on the forehead.
那個爸爸親吻他小女兒的額頭。

20 **foreign** [ˋfɔrɪn] (a.) 外國的
I like to collect foreign coins.
我喜歡蒐集外國錢幣。

❶ **foreigner** [ˋfɔrɪnɚ] (n.) 外國人
There are many foreigners visiting Japan every year.
每年有許多外國人造訪日本。

㉖ **forest** [ˋfɔrɪst] (n.) 森林
We hiked through the forest all afternoon.
我們整個下午都在森林裡健行。

❽ **forever** [fɚˋɛvɚ] (adv.) 永遠，老是
I don't want to work here forever, but I'm not quitting anytime soon.
我不打算在這裡工作一輩子，但我暫時不會離職。

㊱ **forget** [fɚˋgɛt] (v.) 忘記
I forgot to lock the door.
我忘了鎖門。

㊱ **forgive** [fɚˋgɪv] (v.) 原諒
Please forgive me for lying.
請原諒我說謊。

⓫ **fork** [fɔrk] (n.) 叉子
He's not used to the knife and fork.
他不習慣拿刀叉。

㊱ **form** [fɔrm] (v.) 形成，組成
The parade formed a beautiful pattern.
遊行隊伍排成一個漂亮的圖案。

㊲ **formal** [ˋfɔrml̩] (a.) 正式的
Father's secretary will write a formal letter for him.
爸爸的祕書會幫他寫一封正式信函。

㊲ **former** [ˋfɔrmɚ] (a.) 前者
He was the former president of the U.S.
他是前美國總統。

35 **formula** [ˋfɔrmjələ] (n.) 慣例，配方
The formula for weight loss is a healthy diet and exercise.
減重的良方就是健康的飲食和運動

38 **forth** [fɔrθ] (adv.) 向前，向前方
He came forth and told the teacher he had cheated on the test.
他走上前去，告訴老師他考試作弊。

37 **fortunate** [ˋfɔrtʃənɪt] (a.) 幸運的，僥倖的
We are very fortunate to be able to live near the ocean.
我們很幸運能住在海邊。

35 **fortune** [ˋfɔrtʃən] (n.) 財產，財富
It cost me a fortune to buy the house.
買那間房子花了我一大筆錢。

7 **forty** [ˋfɔrtɪ] (n.) 四十
My father is forty years old.
我爸爸現年四十歲。

17 **forward** [ˋfɔrwɚd] (adv.) 向前地
Please move forward.
請向前移動。

25 **fossil** [ˋfɑsl̩] (n.) 化石
I found a fossil on the beach.
我在海灘上找到一個化石。

36 **found** [faʊnd] (v.) 設立
The building was founded in 1968.
那棟建築物建於一九六八年。

35 **foundation** [faʊnˋdeʃən] (n.) 地基，基礎
The foundation of the skyscraper is not stable.
那棟摩天樓的地基不穩。

24 **founder** [ˋfaʊndɚ] (n.) 創立者，奠基者
My father is the founder of Texas Light Company.
我爸是德州燈具公司的創辦人

35 **fountain** [ˋfaʊtɪn] (n.) 噴水池，噴泉
There is a fountain in the center of the park.
公園中央有一個噴水池。

7 **four** [for] (n.) 四
My sister raises four cats in her apartment.
我姊姊在她家裡養了四隻貓。

7 **fourteen** [ˋforˋtin] (n.) 十四
I got that dress on sale for fourteen dollars.
我趁打折時用十四美元買到這件洋裝。

7 **fourteenth** [ˋforˋtinθ] (a.) 第十四
I got a puppy for my fourteenth birthday.
我十四歲生日時得到一隻狗。

7 **fourth** [fɔrθ] (a.) 第四的
The fourth season is winter.
第四個季節是冬天。

27 **fox** [fɑks] (n.) 狐狸
The hunters are hunting the foxes in the forest.
獵人在森林中獵捕狐狸。

35 **fragrance** [ˋfregrəns] (n.) 香味，香氣
I like light fragrances that smell like flowers.
我喜歡聞起來像花香的淡雅香味。

37 **fragrant** [ˋfregrənt] (a.) 香的，芳香的
The temple is filled with the fragrant incense.
整間廟宇充滿了焚香的香氣。

35 **frame** [frem] (n.) 框架，框子
The frame of the picture is crooked.
這張照片的相框歪了。

20 **France** [fræns] (n.) 法國
I learned to speak French in France.
我在法國學會法語。

2 **frank** [fræŋk] (a.) 坦白的，直率的
To be frank, I am not interested in you as a girlfriend.
坦白說，我無意把你當女朋友。

39 **free** [fri] (a.) 自由的，空閒的
I'm free to go after my English class.
上完英文課後我就可以走了。

35 **freedom** [ˋfridəm] (n.) 自由
I am enjoying the freedom of single life.
我很喜歡單身生活的自由自在。

18 **freeway** [ˋfri,we] (n.) 高速公路
If you use the freeway, you will get here in ten minutes.
如果走高速公路，十分鐘就可以到這邊了。

36 **freeze** [friz] (v.) 凍僵，凍結
That cola will freeze if you leave it in the car.
如果你把可樂留在車上，它會結冰。

15 **freezer** [ˋfrizɚ] (n.) 冰箱，冷藏庫
The freezer is packed.
這台冰箱塞得滿滿的。

25 **freezing** [ˋfrizɪŋ] (a.) 寒冷的
It's freezing in New York now.
現在紐約冷極了。

21 **French** [frɛntʃ] (n.) 法國人
Most French don't like to speak English.
多數法國人不喜歡說英語。

10 **French fries** [frɛntʃ fraɪz] (n.) 薯條
French fries make you fat.
薯條會讓你發胖。

35 **frequency** [`frikwənsɪ] (n.) 頻繁，屢次
The frequency of earthquakes is increasing.
地震愈來愈頻繁。

37 **frequent** [`frikwənt] (a.) 時常發生的
Storms are frequent in the summer.
夏天時常有暴風雨。

37 **fresh** [frɛʃ] (a.) 新鮮的
The seafood in this restaurant is fresh.
這家餐廳的海鮮很新鮮。

35 **freshman** [`frɛʃmən] (n.) 一年級生，新生
He is happy to be a freshman in the university.
他很高興成為大學新鮮人。

8 **Friday** [`fraɪde] (n.) 星期五
Friday is my favorite day.
星期五是我最愛的日子。

16 **friend** [frɛnd] (n.) 朋友
Andy has a lot of friends.
安迪有許多朋友。

2 **friendly** [`frɛndlɪ] (a.) 友善的
The most important thing at this job is to be friendly and helpful.
做這個工作最重要的就是待人和善、樂於助人。

35 **friendship** [ˋfrɛnʃɪp] (n.) 友誼
Their friendship lasted for twenty years.
他們的友誼維持了二十年之久。

36 **frighten** [ˋfraɪtn̩] (v.) 使害怕
The horrible story frightened me.
這個恐怖的故事嚇死我了。

14 **Frisbee** [ˋfrɪzbi] (n.) 飛盤
We usually go to the park and play Frisbee on weekends.
我們週末經常去公園玩飛盤。

27 **frog** [frɑg] (n.) 青蛙
I found a frog in the swimming pool.
我在游泳池裡發現一隻青蛙。

32 **from** [frɑm] (prep.) 從
The new student comes from Canada.
那個新同學來自加拿大。

17 **front** [frʌnt] (n.) 前面，正面
There is a big tree in front of my house.
我家前面有棵大樹。

35 **frost** [frɑst] (n.) 冰凍，霜
The field is covered with frost.
原野被霜覆蓋著。

36 **frown** [fraʊn] (v.) 皺眉額，對…表示不滿
Are you frowning because the food doesn't taste good?
你皺眉頭是因為東西不好吃嗎？

10 **fruit** [frʊt] (n.) 水果
She has fruit for breakfast.
她早餐吃水果。

36 **frustrate** [ˋfrʌs,tret] (v.) 挫敗，阻撓
The confusing math question frustrates me.
這題難解的數學題讓我深感挫敗。

35 **frustration** [,frʌsˋtreʃən] (n.) 挫折，失敗
I yelled at my boss out of frustration.
我深感挫折，才對老闆大吼大叫。

36 **fry** [fraɪ] (v.) 煎，炸，炒
He fried some bacon and eggs for breakfast.
他煎培根蛋當早餐。

35 **fuel** [ˋfjʊəl] (n.) 燃料
We are running out of fuel.
我們的燃料快用光了。

36 **fulfill** [fʊlˋfɪl] (v.) 達到，滿足
We fulfilled the child's wishes and took him to swim with dolphins.
我們達成了那孩子的願望，帶他去和海豚一起游泳。

36 **fulfillment** [fʊlˋfɪlmənt] (n.) 實現，成就（感）
I get a lot of fulfillment from my job as a doctor.
身為醫師，我從工作中得到極大的成就感。

10 **full** [fʊl] (a.) 滿的
The bottle is full of water.
這個瓶子裝滿了水。

35 **fun** [fʌn] (a.) 有趣的
It was fun to go hiking.
健行很有趣。

35 **fun** [fʌn] (n.) 樂趣
What do you like to do for fun?
你喜歡找什麼樂子？

35 **function** [ˋfʌŋkʃən] (n.) 功能
This cell phone has many functions.
這支手機有許多功能。

9 **fund** [fʌnd] (n.) 資金，基金
They raise funds to help the poor.
他們募集資金來幫助窮人。

35 **funeral** [ˋfjunərəl] (n.) 喪葬，葬儀
The funeral was held on Sunday morning.
葬禮已於星期天上午舉行。

2 **funny** [ˋfʌnɪ] (a.) 好笑的
I saw a funny movie yesterday.
我昨天看了一部好笑的電影。

27 **fur** [fɝ] (n.) 毛皮，軟毛
People shouldn't buy animal fur.
人們不應該購買動物的毛皮。

37 **furious** [ˋfjʊərɪəs] (a.) 狂怒的，猛烈的
The furious bus driver crashed the bus into a taxi.
那位憤怒的公車司機開公車去撞計程車。

15 **furniture** [ˋfɝnɪtʃɚ] (n.) 家具
The furniture in this room is exotic.
這間房間裡的家具富有異國情調。

37 **further** [ˋfɝðɚ] (a.) 另外的，進一步的
If you have further questions, please call me.
如果還有其他問題，請打電話給我。

38 **furthermore** [ˋfɝðɚˋmɔr] (adv.) 而且，此外
David is not a careful worker; furthermore, he is always late.
大衛不是一位謹慎的員工；而且，他老是遲到。。

8 **future** [`fjutʃɚ] (n.) 未來
I want to be famous in the future.
未來我想要出名。

G

36 **gain** [gen] (v.) 增加
Sally gained five pounds in a week.
莎莉一星期內胖了五磅。

17 **gallery** [`gælərɪ] (n.) 畫廊
Her paintings are displayed in the gallery.
她的畫正在畫廊裡展示。

19 **gallon** [`gælən] (n.) 加侖
I bought a gallon of milk at the grocery store.
我們在雜貨店買了一加侖牛奶。

14 **gamble** [`gæmbl̩] (v.) 賭掉，賭博
My uncle gambled all his money away when he was young.
我父年輕時賭博，把錢輸光了。

14 **game** [gem] (n.) 遊戲
Tommy likes to play video games after school.
湯米放學後喜歡玩電動玩具。

35 **gang** [gæŋ] (n.) 一幫，一群
The police caught a gang of thieves inside the bank.
警方在銀行內抓到一幫盜賊。

35 **gap** [gæp] (n.) 間隔，空隙
Beware of the gap when you get on the MRT.
上捷運列車時，要當心月台間隙。

35 **garage** [gəˋraʒ] (n.) 車庫

The car is parked in the garage.

車子停在車庫裡。

35 **garbage** [ˋgarbɪdʒ] (n.) 垃圾

Please throw the garbage away.

請把垃圾丟掉。

15 **garden** [ˋgardṇ] (n.) 花園

We grow some tomatoes in the garden.

我們在花園種了一些番茄。

10 **garlic** [ˋgarlɪk] (n.) 大蒜

The chef chopped up some garlic and added it to the sauce.

廚師剁碎一些大蒜加到醬汁裡。

35 **gas** [gæs] (n.) 汽油

There is a gas station on the street.

這條街上有一間加油站。

18 **gasoline** [ˋgæsə,lin] (n.) 汽油

Gasoline is getting more and more expensive.

汽油越來越貴。

15 **gate** [get] (n.) 大門

The main gate is shut at night.

大門晚上是關上的。

36 **gather** [ˋgæðɚ] (v.) 聚集

The writer is gathering new sources for his new novel.

那位作家正在為他的新小說收集新資料。

36 **gaze** [gez] (v.) 注視

The policeman gazed at the dark corner in the distance.

那位警察注視著遠方漆黑的角落。

37 **general** [ˋdʒɛnərəl] (a.) 一般的
This is a general exam question.
這題是一般考題。

9 **generation** [ˌdʒɛnəˋreʃən] (n.) 世代
This tradition has existed for many generations.
這種傳統已經延續很多代了。

2 **generosity** [ˌgɛnəˋrɑsətɪ] (n.) 慷慨
Jane was praised by everyone for her generosity.
珍的慷慨受到大家的稱讚。

2 **generous** [ˋdʒɛnərəs] (a.) 大方的
Paul is always generous with compliments when he meets someone for the first time.
保羅跟人第一次見面時，總大方問候對方。

1 **genius** [ˋdʒinjəs] (n.) 天才
Beethoven was a musical genius.
貝多芬是音樂天才。

2 **gentle** [ˋdʒɛntḷ] (a.) 溫和的
Aunt Mary is a gentle woman.
瑪麗嬸嬸是一位溫柔的女士。

1 **gentleman** [ˋdʒɛntḷmən] (n.) 紳士
My grandfather is a real gentleman
我爺爺是真正的紳士。

16 **geography** [dʒiˋɑgrəfɪ] (n.) 地理學
She is good at geography.
她地理很好。

21 **German** [ˋdʒɝmən] (n.) 德國人
The Germans are famous for their engineering skills.
德國人以他們的工程技術聞名。

20 **Germany** [ˋdʒɝmənɪ] (n.) 德國，德語
I would like to visit the Black Forest in Germany.
我想去看看德國的黑森林。

35 **gesture** [ˋdʒɛstʃɚ] (n.) 姿勢，手勢
Sometimes you can use gestures to express your thoughts.
有時候你可以用手勢來表達你的想法。

36 **get** [gɛt] (v.) 獲得，得到
Ivy got the candy from her teacher.
艾薇從老師那裡得到糖果。

35 **ghost** [gost] (n.) 鬼
We don't believe in ghosts.
我們不相信有鬼。

1 **giant** [ˋdʒaɪənt] (n.) 巨人
Standing next to tiny Anita, Karl looked like a giant.
站在小不點艾妮塔旁邊，卡爾看起來像個巨人。

35 **gift** [gɪft] (n.) 禮物
Jasmine got a gift for her birthday.
茉莉收到一個生日禮物。

2 **gifted** [ˋgɪftɪd] (a.) 有天賦的
He is a gifted artist.
他是有天賦的藝術家。

19 **gigantic** [dʒaɪˋgæntɪk] (a.) 巨大的
There's a gigantic bug crawling across the kitchen floor!
有一隻超大的蟲在廚房地板上爬啦！

36 **giggle** [ˋgɪgḷ] (v.) 咯咯地笑
All the girls giggled when the newly- wed teacher came in.
新婚的老師進來時，所有女孩都在咯咯笑。

10 **ginger** [ˋdʒɪndʒɚ] (n.) 薑

Fresh ginger is used in many Chinese medicines.

中藥常會用到新鮮的薑。

1 **girl** [gɝl] (n.) 女孩

The girl is thin and beautiful.

那個女孩又苗條又漂亮。

36 **give** [gɪv] (v.) 給

She gave the teacher a hug.

她給老師一個擁抱。

37 **glad** [glæd] (a.) 高興的

I'm so glad to see you on the stage.

我很高興看到你站上舞臺。

35 **glance** [glæns] (n.) 一瞥，掃視

I gave a quick glance at the passerby.

我匆匆看了那個路人一眼。

19 **glass** [glæs] (n.) 玻璃

My brother broke the glass.

我弟弟打破玻璃。

16 **glasses** [ˋglæsɪz] (n.) 眼鏡

His glasses are new.

他的眼鏡是新的。

36 **glide** [glaɪd] (v.) 滑行，划水前行

The swan is gliding in the lake.

那隻天鵝在湖上划水前行。

36 **glimpse** [ˋglɪmps] (n.) 一瞥

I caught a glimpse of the thief.

我有看到小偷一眼。

A B C D E F G H I J K L M N O P Q R S T U V W X Y Z

37 **global** [ˋglobḷ] (a.) 全世界的，總體的
The world is becoming a global village.
世界正逐漸變成一個地球村。

35 **glory** [ˋglorɪ] (n.) 光榮，榮譽
The glory belongs to those who died in the battle.
榮譽屬於戰死沙場的人。

12 **glove** [glʌv] (n.) 手套
Gloves will keep your hands warm.
手套會讓你的手保持溫暖。

36 **glow** [glo] (v.) 發光，灼熱
The street lights glowed in the rain.
街燈在雨中發出光亮。

35 **glue** [glu] (n.) 黏膠
The child attached the poster on the wall with glue.
那小孩用膠水把海報黏在牆上。

36 **go** [go] (v.) 去
Do you want to go to the department store?
你想去百貨公司嗎？

35 **goal** [gol] (n.) 目標
My goal in life is to be a famous teacher.
我的人生目標是成為一位名師。

27 **goat** [got] (n.) 山羊
Goats are different from sheep.
山羊和綿羊不同。

35 **god** [gɑd] (n.) 神明，上帝
We all believe in God.
我們都相信上帝。

12 **gold** [gold] (n.) 金子
Gold is very valuable.
黃金很有價值。

13 **golden** [`goldn̩] (a.) 金色的
Mila has bright golden hair.
米拉有一頭亮麗的金髮。

14 **golf** [gɑlf] (n.) 高爾夫球
The former president likes to play golf.
前任總統喜歡打高爾夫球。

2 **good** [gʊd] (a.) 好的
Jason got good grades on his tests.
傑森考試成績很好。

34 **good-bye** [gʊd`baɪ] (n.) 再見
Say good-bye to your teacher.
跟你的老師說再見。

35 **goodness** [`gʊdnɪs] (n.)（感嘆語）天啊
My goodness! You added pepper to the ice- cream!
我的天啊！你竟然在冰淇淋上面加胡椒粉！

27 **goose** [gus] (n.) 鵝
There are two geese in the pond.
池塘裡有二隻鵝。

36 **gossip** [`gɑsəp] (v.) 閒話，聊天
School girls like to gossip.
學校女生喜歡聊八卦。

35 **government** [`gʌvənmənt] (n.) 政府
This car is owned by the government.
這部車為政府所有。

24 **governor** [ˋgʌvənɚ] (n.) 州長

Arnold was recently elected to a second term as governor of California.

阿諾最近獲選為加州州長。

12 **gown** [gaʊn] (n.)（女用）長禮服，睡袍

Bernice arrived at the party wearing a beautiful evening gown.

貝妮絲抵達舞會現場時穿了件很美的晚禮服。

36 **grab** [græb] (v.) 攫取，抓取

The shoppers grabbed at the shoes being sold for 70% off.

購物人群搶著買打三折的鞋子。

16 **grade** [gred] (n.) 成績

I always get good grades in school.

我的學校成績向來很好。

37 **gradual** [ˋgrɛdʒʊəl] (a.) 逐漸的，逐步的

We can see a gradual improvement in his grades.

我們可以看到他的成績逐漸進步。

36 **graduate** [ˋgrædʒʊ,et] (v.) 畢業

I graduated from this university.

我畢業於這所大學。

10 **grain** [gren] (n.) 穀物，穀類

Lots of grains are stored in the barn.

這間穀倉儲存了很多穀物。

19 **gram** [græm] (n.) 公克

One thousand grams is equal to one kilogram.

一千公克相當於一公斤。

16 **grammar** [ˋgræmɚ] (n.) 文法

Students need to learn English grammar for the exam.

學生需要為考試學習英文文法。

37 **grand** [grænd] (a.) 雄偉的
They live in a grand house.
他們住在一棟富麗堂皇的房子裡。

6 **granddaughter** [ˋgrænd,dɔtɚ] (n.)（外）孫女
She misses her granddaughter a lot.
她很想念她的孫女。

6 **grandfather** [ˋgrænd,fɑðɚ] (n.)（外）祖父
Her grandfather is still well and healthy.
她爺爺還很健康。

6 **grandmother** [ˋgræn,mʌðɚ] (n.)（外）祖母
My grandmother cares about me very much.
我祖母很關心我。

6 **grandson** [ˋgrænd,sʌn] (n.)（外）孫子
The old man has ten grandsons in total.
那個老人總共有十個孫子。

10 **grape** [grep] (n.) 葡萄
Wine is made from grapes.
葡萄酒是葡萄製成的。

36 **grasp** [græsp] (v.) 抓牢，握緊
She grasped me by my arm.
她緊握抓我的手臂。

25 **grass** [græs] (n.) 草
The cows were fat after eating grass all summer.
乳牛吃了一夏天的草都胖了。

27 **grasshopper** [ˋgræs,hɑpɚ] (n.) 蚱蜢，蝗蟲
The grasshoppers like to hide in the grass.
蚱蜢喜歡藏在草叢裡。

2 **grateful** [ˋgretfəl] (a.) 感激的
I am grateful that you can give me a hand.
很感激你幫我的忙。

17 **grave** [grev] (n.) 墓穴
The thieves dug the grave and stole the gold.
盜賊挖開墳墓，偷走金子。

13 **gray** [gre] (a.) 灰色的
It is going to rain because the sky is gray.
要下雨了，因為天空灰灰的。

37 **great** [gret] (a.) 非常好的
She felt great after winning first place in a piano contest.
她贏得鋼琴比賽冠軍，覺得很開心。

2 **greedy** [ˋgridɪ] (a.) 貪心的
The greedy gambler ended up losing all his money.
那個貪心的賭徒最後輸掉所有的錢。

13 **green** [grin] (a.) 綠色的
Looking at the green grass is good for your eyes.
多看綠油油的草地對你的眼睛有益。

17 **greenhouse** [ˋgrin,haus] (n.) 溫室，暖房
They grow tomatoes in the greenhouse.
他們在溫室裡種番茄。

36 **greet** [grit] (v.) 問候
I greeted my parents this morning.
我早上問候過父母了。

2 **grief** [grɪf] (n.) 悲痛
The heart- broken lady cries with grief.
那個心碎的女士悲傷痛哭。

36 **grin** [gɪn] (v.) 露齒而笑
Susan had a big grin on her face after she won the race.
蘇珊贏得賽跑獲勝後笑容滿面。

36 **grind** [graɪnd] (v.) 磨碎
The cook ground some pepper into the noodles.
那廚師磨了些胡椒粉到麵裡。

17 **grocery** [ˋgrosərɪ] (n.) 食品雜貨，雜貨店
Buy some milk from the grocery downstairs.
到樓下雜貨店買些牛奶。

17 **ground** [graʊnd] (n.) 地面
All the money is scattered on the ground.
所有的錢散落一地。

35 **group** [grup] (n.) 群
They are in a group.
他們是同一組的。

36 **grow** [gro] (v.) 生長
Sean grows so fast; he is even taller than his father.
尚恩長得好快，甚至比他的父親還高了。

35 **growth** [groθ] (n.) 成長
Exercise is important for the growth of a child.
運動對孩子的成長很重要。

24 **guard** [gɑrd] (n.) 警衛
The bank is protected by armed guards.
這家銀行由武裝警衛保護。

1 **guardian** [ˋgɑrdɪən] (n.) 監護人
The little boy needs a guardian before he's 18.
這個小男孩在十八歲以前需要一名監護人。

10 **guava** [ˋgwɑvə] (n.) 番石榴

Guavas carry lots of vitamin C.

芭樂含有大量維他命C。

36 **guess** [gɛs] (v.) 猜測

The math teacher guessed most of the questions.

數學老師猜到了大部分題目。

1 **guest** [gɛst] (n.) 客人

We will have 50 guests tonight for my birthday party.

我的生日派對今晚將有五十個客人參加。

35 **guidance** [ˋgaɪdəns] (n.) 輔導，諮詢

I need guidance when I do the research alone.

我單獨做研究時需要輔導。

24 **guide** [gaɪd] (n.) 嚮導，導遊

The guide will show you around the city.

導遊會帶你們到城裡到處逛逛。

2 **guilty** [ˋgɪltɪ] (a.) 有罪的

The judge sentenced the guilty man to three years in prison.

法官判這個罪犯三年有期徒刑。

14 **guitar** [gɪˋtɑr] (n.) 吉他

John knows how to play the guitar.

約翰曉得怎麼彈吉他。

10 **gum** [gʌm] (n.) 口香糖（chewing gum的簡稱）

Gum is not allowed on the MRT.

捷運上禁止吃口香糖。

35 **gun** [gʌn] (n.) 槍

My grandfather collects antique guns from World War I.

我爺爺蒐集第一次世界大戰時的古董槍枝。

1 **guy** [gaɪ] (n.) 傢伙（指男性），各位
There were more guys than girls at the club.
夜店裡的男生比女生多。

16 **gym** [dʒɪm] (n.) 體育館，健身房
The gym is packed with students.
體育館裡擠滿學生。

H

35 **habit** [ˋhæbɪt] (n.) 習慣
Most children have a bad habit of throwing toys around.
多數小孩有亂丟玩具的壞習慣。

3 **hair** [hɛr] (n.) 毛髮
My mother has beautiful long hair.
我媽媽有一頭漂亮的長髮。

35 **haircut** [ˋhɛr,kʌt] (n.) 理髮
He needs a haircut before he goes back to school.
他在開學前需要理個頭髮。

24 **hairdresser** [ˋhɛr,drɛsɚ] (n.) 美髮師
The hairdressing salon needs an extra hairdresser to help.
這家美髮沙龍還需要一名美髮師幫忙。

7 **half** [hæf] (n.) 一半
She ate half of the cake.
她吃了半個蛋糕。

15 **hall** [hɔl] (n.) 大廳
There are some comfortable sofas in the hall.
大廳內有幾張舒適的沙發。

23 **Halloween** [,hælo`in] (n.) 萬聖節前夕
Halloween is on October 31.
十月三十一號是萬聖節前夕。

17 **hallway** [`hɔl,we] (n.) 玄關，走廊
Don't run in the hallway.
別在走廊上奔跑。

10 **ham** [hæm] (n.) 火腿
We had ham with toast for breakfast.
我們早餐吃了火腿吐司。

10 **hamburger** [`hæmbɝgɚ] (n.) 漢堡
My little brother likes hamburgers very much.
我弟弟非常喜歡漢堡。

15 **hammer** [`hæmɚ] (n.) 鐵鎚
The workers arrived with a hammer, some nails, and lots of wood.
工人帶著一枝鐵鎚、一些釘子和許多木材前來。

3 **hand** [hænd] (n.) 手
You have beautiful hands.
你的手很漂亮。

35 **handful** [`hænd,ful] (n.) 一把，少量
The boy has a handful of candy.
這男孩手上有一把糖果。

12 **handkerchief** [`hæŋkɚ,tʃif] (n.) 手帕
Students nowadays seldom bring handkerchiefs.
現在的學生很少帶手帕。

36 **handle** [`hændḷ] (v.) 處理
Mother knows how to handle the problem.
媽媽知道如何處理這個問題。

2 **handsome** [ˋhænsəm] (a.) 英俊的，好看的
Tom is a very handsome boy.
湯姆是個非常英俊的男孩。

35 **handwriting** [ˋhænd,raɪtɪŋ] (n.) 筆跡
The signature on the check isn't my handwriting.
這張支票上的簽名不是我的筆跡。

37 **handy** [ˋhændɪ] (a.) 就手的，方便的
The restaurant is near by, so it's quite handy to have a bite.
餐廳就在附近，吃東西很方便。

36 **hang** [hæŋ] (v.) 把…掛起
Could you hang up the phone?
你可以把電話掛了嗎？

15 **hanger** [ˋhæŋɚ] (n.) 衣架
I like to keep all of my dress clothes on clothes hangers.
我喜歡用衣架把我全部的洋裝掛起來。

36 **happen** [ˋhæpən] (v.) 發生
What happened to you this morning?
你今天早上怎麼了？

2 **happy** [ˋhæpɪ] (a.) 高興的
My younger sister is always happy.
我妹妹總是很快樂。

18 **harbor** [ˋhɑrbɚ] (n.) 港灣，海港
Pearl Harbor was attacked in 1941.
珍珠港於一九四一年遭到攻擊。

37 **hard** [hɑrd] (a.) 困難的
The math exam was very hard.
數學考試很難。

38 **hardly** [ˋhardlɪ] (adv.) 幾乎不…
I hardly talk to my teacher.
我幾乎沒和老師說過話。

14 **harmonica** [harˋmanɪkə] 口琴
The little boy can play the harmonica well.
這個小男孩口琴吹得很好。

35 **hardship** [ˋhardʃɪp] (n.) 艱難，困苦
He fears no hardship.
他無懼任何艱難。

2 **hard-working** [ˏhardˋwɜkɪŋ] (a.) 努力的，勤勉的
Leo is a hard-working student.
里奧是用功的學生。

36 **harm** [harm] (v.) 損害，危害
Cigarettes will do you harm.
香菸會危害你的健康。

37 **harmful** [ˋharmfəl] (a.) 有害的
Smoking is harmful to your health.
抽菸對你的健康有害。

35 **harmony** [ˋharmənɪ] (n.) 和諧，協調
The two tribes live together in harmony.
這兩個部落和諧地居住在一起。

37 **harsh** [harʃ] (a.) 嚴厲的，惡劣的
Dad had harsh words for me.
爸爸對我說了很嚴厲的話。

36 **harvest** [ˋharvɪst] (n.) 收穫
The farmer has had good harvests for three successive years.
這個農夫連續三年來都有很好的豐收。

36 **haste** [hest] (n.) 急忙，迅速
She scolded her son in haste, before she heard the whole story.
她不分青紅皂白就罵了兒子一頓，根本沒聽完整件事的經過。

37 **hasty** [ˋhestɪ] (a.) 匆忙的，急忙的
Don't be hasty; we still have plenty of time.
別急，我們還有很多時間。

12 **hat** [hæt] (n.) 帽子
I don't like to wear hats.
我不喜歡戴帽子。

36 **hatch** [hætʃ] (v.) 孵化
The farmer tried to hatch the eggs by light bulb.
這個農夫試著用燈泡孵蛋。

36 **hate** [het] (v.) 討厭
Teachers hate students for not paying attention during class.
老師討厭學生上課時不認真。

35 **hatred** [ˋhetrɪd] (n.) 憎恨，增惡
His hatred for his parents is still strong.
他對父母親的恨意仍然強烈。

27 **hawk** [hɔk] (n.) 鷹
You can see the hawks circling in the sky.
你可以看見老鷹在天空上盤旋。

25 **hay** [he] (n.) 牧草，乾草
The farmer fed fresh hay to his horse every morning
那個農夫每天早上餵他的馬吃新鮮的牧草。

3 **head** [hɛd] (n.) 頭
Emily injured her head badly during the car crash.
愛蜜莉在車禍中頭部受重傷。

4 **headache** [ˋhɛd,ek] (n.) 頭痛
She is suffering from a terrible headache.
她頭痛得很厲害。

35 **headline** [ˋhɛd,laɪn] (n.) 頭條，大標題
The singer was in the headlines of all the newspapers.
這位歌手登上所有報紙的頭條。

35 **headphone(s)** [ˋhɛd,fon] (n.) 頭戴式耳機
You can see many people wearing headphones and listening to music on the MRT.
在捷運車上可以看到很多人戴耳機聽音樂。

17 **headquarters** [ˋhɛdˋkwɔrtɚz] (n.) 總部，總公司
The police headquarters is right down the road from where I live.
警政署就位於我住的那條路上。

36 **heal** [hil] (v.) 治癒，使恢復健康
The wound on my back has already healed.
我背部的傷口已癒合。

4 **health** [hɛlθ] (n.) 健康
Health is more important than wealth.
健康比財富重要。

4 **healthful** [ˋhɛlθfəl] (a.) 有益健康的
Jogging every morning for a half hour is healthful.
每天振跑半小時有益健康。

4 **healthy** [ˋhɛlθɪ] (a.) 健康的，有益健康的
Fruits and vegetables are healthy foods.
蔬果是有益健康的食物。

35 **heap** [hip] (n.) 堆積，積聚
There was a heap of dirty clothes next to John's bed.
約翰床邊有一堆髒衣服。

36 **hear** [hɪr] (v.) 聽見
Mother heard me talking on the phone.
媽媽聽見我在講電話。

3 **heart** [hɑrt] (n.) 心
SHe broke my heart.
她傷了我的心。

35 **heat** [hit] (n.) 熱
The heat during the summer in Taiwan is hard to bear.
台灣夏天熱得讓人受不了。

15 **heater** [ˋhitɚ] (n.) 暖氣
Could you turn down the heater? It's hot here.
可以把暖氣調弱嗎？這裡太熱了。

17 **heaven** [ˋhɛvən] (n.) 天堂
May his soul rest in Heaven.
願他的靈魂在天堂安息。

37 **heavy** [ˋhɛvɪ] (a.) 沉重的
Those books are too heavy for her.
這些書對她來說太重了。

12 **heel** [hil] (n.) 高跟鞋
High heels are not good for your feet.
穿高跟鞋對腳不好。

19 **height** [haɪt] (n.) 高度
She's about four feet in height.
她的身高約四呎。

18 **helicopter** [ˋhɛlɪ,kɑptɚ] (n.) 直昇機
I learned to fly a helicopter when I was in my 20s.
我二十幾歲時學會開直昇機。

17 **hell** [hɛl] (n.) 地獄
Many old people believe there is a hell.
許多老人相信有地獄。

34 **hello** [ˋhɛlo] (int.) 哈囉
Please say hello to your parents for me.
請幫我問候你的父母。

12 **helmet** [ˋhɛlmɪt] (n.) 安全帽
Put on your helmet while riding the scooter.
騎乘機車時要戴安全帽。

36 **help** [hɛlp] (v.) 幫助
She helped her mother clean the house.
她幫媽媽打掃房子。

37 **helpful** [ˋhɛlpfəl] (a.) 有幫助的
You have been very helpful these days!
這些日子以來你幫了很大的忙！

27 **hen** [hɛn] (n.) 母雞
Hens can lay eggs.
母雞會生蛋。

17 **here** [hɪr] (adv.) 這裡
Here comes the bus.
公車來了。

1 **hero** [ˋhɪro] (n.) 英雄
The firefighter became a hero.
那名消防員成了英雄。

29 **herself** [hɝˋsɛlf] (pron.) 她自己
The poor mom raised five children by herself.
那可憐的媽媽獨力扶養五個小孩。

36 **hesitate** [`hɛzə,tet] (v.) 躊躇，猶豫
Don't hesitate to call me if you have any questions.
有問題就打電話給我，不要不好意思。

35 **hesitation** [,hɛzə`teʃən] (n.) 躊躇，猶豫
The firefighter ran into the fire without hesitation to save the boy.
消防員毫不猶豫跑進火場救那個男孩。

36 **hide** [haɪd] (v.) 藏
Jade is hiding behind the door.
傑德躲在門後。

19 **high** [haɪ] (a.) 高的
I can't reach the top; it's too high for me.
我搆不到上面；那對我來說太高了。

18 **highway** [`haɪ,we] (n.) 公路
Motorbikes are not allowed on the highway.
摩托車禁止騎上高速公路。

36 **hike** [haɪk] (v.) 健行
My dad likes to go hiking along the river.
我爸爸喜歡在河畔健行。

14 **hiking** [`haɪkɪŋ] (n.) 健行，遠足
Hiking can relax you body and mind.
健行可以讓你身心放鬆。

26 **hill** [hɪl] (n.) 丘陵，小丘
The village was surrounded by a number of small hills.
村莊被幾個小山丘環繞。

29 **himself** [hɪm`sɛlf] (pron.) 他自己
He cut himself accidentally when he was cutting vegetables.
他切菜時不小心割傷自己。

36 **hint** [hɪnt] (v.) 暗示，示意
The lady hinted that she wouldn't accept the offer.
那個女士暗示她不會接受條件。

3 **hip** [hɪp] (n.) 髖部，臀部
Grandma fell down on her hip.
奶奶摔倒時臀部著地。

27 **hippo** [ˋhɪpo] (n.) 河馬
Hippos are larger than deer.
河馬的體型比鹿大。

24 **hire** [haɪr] (v.) 雇用
We hired a tour guide to show us around.
我們雇了一個導遊帶我們到處參觀。

35 **historian** [hɪsˋtorɪən] (n.) 歷史學家
The historian is an expert who quite understands history.
歷史學家是嫻熟歷史的專家。

37 **historic** [hɪsˋtɔrɪk] (a.) 歷史上著名的
The historic events aren't recorded in the book.
這些歷史重大事件並未記錄在這本書裡。

37 **historical** [hɪsˋtɔrɪkl̩] (a.) 歷史的，史學的
He is an expert of historical research.
他是史學研究的專家。

16 **history** [ˋhɪstərɪ] (n.) 歷史
China has a recorded history of over 5,000 years.
中國有記載的歷史超過五千年。

36 **hit** [hɪt] (v.) 打，擊中
The batter hit the ball hard.
打擊者用力擊出這球。

35 **hive** [haɪv] (n.) 蜂窩
There is a bee hive under the porch—be careful when walking near there.
門廊下有一個蜂窩——經過附近要小心。

14 **hobby** [ˋhɑbɪ] (n.) 嗜好
Reading is one of her hobbies.
閱讀是她的嗜好之一。

36 **hold** [hold] (v.) 握住
My dad held my mom's hand.
我爸爸握住我媽媽的手。

35 **hole** [hol] (n.) 洞
There is a hole in the wall.
牆上有一個洞。

23 **holiday** [ˋhɑlə,de] (n.) 假日，節日
Many Western holidays, like Christmas, are also celebrated in Taiwan.
台灣也慶祝許多西洋節日，如耶誕節。

37 **hollow** [ˋhɑlo] (a.) 空的，中空
I hid the money inside a hollow tree.
我把錢藏在一棵中空的樹裡。

37 **holy** [ˋholɪ] (a.) 神聖的，獻身於宗教的
It's a holy job to serve in the church.
在教堂裡服務是神聖的工作。

15 **home** [hom] (n.) 家
There is no place like home.
沒有地方比得上家。

17 **homeland** [ˋhom,lænd] (n.) 祖國，故國
Many refugees are eager to return to their homeland.
許多難民渴望回到祖國。

37 **homesick** [ˋhom,sɪk] (a.) 想家的
I was homesick when I lived in the U.S.
我住在美國的時候很想家。

17 **hometown** [ˋhomˋtaʊn] (n.) 故鄉，家鄉
His hometown only has about 2,500 people in it.
我的家鄉只有大約兩千五百人。

16 **homework** [ˋhom,wɝk] (n.) 功課，家庭作業
She has a lot of homework to do.
她有很多功課要做。

2 **honest** [ˋɑnɪst] (a.) 誠實的
He is honest, and never lies to anyone.
他很誠實，從來不說謊。

2 **honesty** [ˋɑnɪstɪ] (n.) 誠實
Honesty is the first quality we look for in employees.
誠實是我們招募員工最重視的品格。

10 **honey** [ˋhʌnɪ] (n.) 蜂蜜
The tea will taste better if you add a little honey.
那杯茶加點蜂蜜會更好喝。

35 **honeymoon** [ˋhʌnɪ,mun] (n.) 蜜月旅行
The newlywed couple went to L.A. for their honeymoon.
這對新婚夫婦到洛杉磯度蜜月。

35 **honor** [ˋɑnɚ] (n.) 榮譽，名譽
Those players fought for the honor of their team.
這些選手為了團隊榮譽而戰。

2 **honorable** [ˋɑnərəbl̩] (a.) 可敬的，正直的
Samuel was elected as the association president because everyone thought he was an honorable man.
山姆被選為協會理事長，因為大家覺得他是一個可敬的人。

(35) **hook** [hʊk] (n.) 掛鉤
Can you hang my keys on the hook?
可以幫我把鑰匙吊在掛鉤上嗎？

(36) **hop** [hɑp] (v.) 單腳跳，躍過
The dancers hopped up and down to the beat of the music.
舞者隨著音樂節拍上下跳躍。

(36) **hope** [hop] (v.) 希望
I hope I can see you soon.
希望可以很快見到你。

(37) **hopeful** [ˋhopfəl] (a.) 抱有希望的，充滿希望的
He has a hopeful future.
他的未來大有可為。

(35) **horizon** [həˋraɪzn̩] (n.) 地平線
We are here to see the sun rise above the horizon.
我們在這裡等著看太陽從地平線升起。

(35) **horn** [hɔrn] (n.) 角，觸角
That bull has very sharp horns—be careful.
那頭公牛的角很尖——要小心。

(37) **horrible** [ˋhɔrəbl̩] (a.) 可怕的
It was horrible to see the car accident.
目睹那場車禍真是可怕。

(36) **horrify** [ˋhɔrə,faɪ] (v.) 使恐懼，使驚懼
She was very horrified when the car ran into the tree.
車撞上樹的時候，她嚇壞了。

(35) **horror** [ˋhɔrɚ] (n.) 恐怖，震驚
I watched with horror as the man tripped and fell in front of the bus.
我看著那個人被絆倒摔在公車前面，看得我心驚膽戰。

27 **horse** [hɔrs] (n.) 馬
She's learning how to ride a horse.
她正在學騎馬。

17 **hospital** [ˋhɑspɪtl̩] (n.) 醫院
The victim was dead in the hospital.
那個受害者在醫院過世了。

1 **host** [host] (n.) 主人
The host gave a short speech to welcome all the guests.
主人發表一個簡短的演說歡迎所有賓客。

10 **hot dog** [ˋhɑt,dɔg] (n.) 熱狗
The hot dogs from that vendor are delicious.
從那個攤販買來的熱狗很好吃。

25 **hot** [hɑt] (a.) 熱
You shouldn't exercise outside when it's so hot.
天氣這麼熱，你不該在外面運動。

17 **hotel** [hoˋtɛl] (n.) 旅館
We stayed at a hotel near the beach.
我們下榻於一間海灘附近的旅館。

8 **hour** [aʊr] (n.) 小時
Mother works twelve hours a day.
媽媽一天工作十二小時。

37 **hourly** [ˋaʊrlɪ] (a.) 每小時的
The lawyer charges on an hourly basis.
這名律師是根據鐘點時數計費。

15 **house** [haʊs] (n.) 房子
They own a few houses in the countryside.
他們在鄉下有幾棟房子。

24 **housekeeper** [ˋhaʊs,kipɚ] (n.)（女）管家
The housekeeper takes charge of everything in the house.
這個女管家負責屋內大小事。

24 **housewife** [ˋhaʊs,waɪf] (n.) 家庭主婦
Her mother is a housewife.
她的媽媽是家庭主婦。

15 **housework** [ˋhaʊs,wɝk] (n.) 家事
Aunt Maria is busy doing housework.
瑪麗亞阿姨忙著做家事。

30 **how** [haʊ] (adv.) 如何
Do you know how to get there?
你知道如何去那裡嗎？

33 **however** [haʊˋɛvɚ] (conj.) 不過
He wants to buy that computer. However, he has to ask his dad first.
他想買那部電腦。不過，他得先問他爸爸。

36 **hug** [hʌg] (v.) 擁抱
They hugged each other at the airport.
他們在機場互相擁抱。

37 **huge** [hjudʒ] (a.) 龐大的
I saw a huge balloon in the sky.
我在天空中看到了一個巨大的汽球。

35 **human** [ˋhjumən] (n.) 人類
Some humans believe there are aliens in space.
有些人相信外太空有外星人。

2 **humble** [ˋhʌmbl̩] (a.) 謙遜的
Dr. Brown became very famous, but he remained as humble as ever.
布朗博士變得很有名，但他依然保持謙遜的態度。

25 **humid** [ˋhjumɪd] (a.) 潮溼的
Taipei is very hot and humid in the summer.
台北的夏天炎熱潮濕。

2 **humor** [ˋhjumɚ] (n.) 幽默
Dad has a good sense of humor.
爸爸很有幽默感。

2 **humorous** [ˋhjʊmərəs] (a.) 幽默的，詼諧的
His humorous speech made everyone laugh.
他幽默的演説讓大家開懷大笑。

7 **hundred** [ˋhʌndrɪd] (n.) 一百
This school is one hundred years old.
這間學校一百歲了。

10 **hunger** [ˋhʌŋgɚ] (n.) 飢餓
Many people in Africa suffer from hunger.
非洲很多人受飢餓之苦。

10 **hungry** [ˋhʌŋgrɪ] (a.) 飢餓的
I'm so hungry I'm going to die.
我快餓死了。

36 **hunt** [hʌnt] (v.) 打獵
Dad and uncle went hunting yesterday.
爸爸和叔叔昨天去打獵。

24 **hunter** [ˋhʌntɚ] (n.) 獵人
The hunter caught a lion.
這個獵人捉到一隻獅子。

36 **hurry** [ˋhɜɪ] (v.) 趕緊
We need to hurry in order to make it to the airport on time.
我們得加緊速度趕快才能準時抵達機場。

36 **hurt** [hɜt] (v.) 使受傷
Doug hurt his ankle while playing soccer.
道格踢足球時傷到膝蓋。

6 **husband** [ˋhʌzbənd] (n.) 丈夫
Many husbands start to gain weight after being married for several years.
許多丈夫結婚幾年之後就開始發福。

36 **hush** [hʌʃ] (v.) 安靜下來，沈默
Mother tried to hush the crying baby.
媽媽試圖讓哭泣的嬰兒安靜下來。

35 **hut** [hʌt] (n.) 小屋
A family of four lives in that tiny hut on the hill.
那一家四口住在山上那棟小屋裡。

I

10 **ice cream** [ˋaɪs,krim] (n.) 冰淇淋
Chocolate is my favorite flavor of ice cream.
巧克力是我最喜歡的冰淇淋。

10 **ice** [aɪs] (n.) 冰
I want some ice in my beer.
我想要在啤酒裡加點冰塊。

37 **icy** [ˋaɪsɪ] (a.) 結冰的，覆蓋著冰的
Don't walk on the icy lake; it's dangerous.
別在結冰的湖面上行走，那是很危險的。

35 **idea** [aɪˋdiə] (n.) 想法
She has so many good ideas.
她有很多好的點子。

37 **ideal** [aɪˋdil] (a.) 理想的，完美的
The handsome, tall man is her ideal husband.
那個又帥又高的男人是她理想中的老公。

37 **identical** [aɪˋdɛntɪkḷ] (a.) 相同的
The false document is identical to the real one.
這份假文件跟真的一模一樣。

35 **identity** [aɪˋdɛntətɪ] (n.) 身分，本身
I lost my identity card.
我弄丟了我的身分證。

8 **idle** [ˋaɪdḷ] (v.) 虛度光陰
The salesman idles his afternoon away.
這個推銷員混了整個下午。

33 **if** [ɪf] (conj.) 如果
If she comes in time, we can go to the movies.
如果她準時抵達，我們就可以去看電影。

35 **ignorance** [ˋɪgnərəns] (n.) 愚昧，無知
The only way to fight ignorance is with education.
戰勝無知唯有教育一途。

36 **ignore** [ɪgˋnor] (v.) 忽略
He ignored his girlfriend when he was working.
他工作時忽略了他的女朋友

4 **ill** [ɪl] (a.) 生病的
I was too ill to go on the company trip last weekend.
我病得太嚴重，上週無法參加公司旅遊。

36 **illustrate** [ˋɪləstret] (v.) 用圖說明
Please illustrate the question with pictures.
請用圖片來說明這個問題。

35 **image** [`ɪmɪdʒ] (n.) 形象，肖像
The writer's image is printed on the bill.
這位作家的肖像被印在紙鈔上。

35 **imagination** [ɪ,mædʒə`neʃən] (n.) 想像力，創造力
The artist's imagination enriches his paintings.
這名藝術家的想像力豐富了他的畫作。

36 **imagine** [ɪ`mædʒɪn] (v.) 想像
Can you imagine the earth without water?
你可以想像地球沒有水的景象嗎？

36 **imitate** [`ɪmə,tet] (v.) 模仿
The monkey imitates people eating.
那隻猴子模仿人類吃飯。

37 **immediate** [ɪ`midɪɪt] (a.) 立即的，即刻的
You can give me an immediate answer by sending me an email.
你可以立刻寄電子郵件給我答覆。

20 **immigrate** [`ɪmə,gret] (v.) 遷入
My family immigrated to Canada in 1989.
我家在一九八九年移民加拿大。

35 **impact** [`ɪmpækt] (n.) 衝擊，影響
Exercising daily will have a positive impact on your health.
每天運動會為健康帶來正面的影響。

2 **impolite** [,ɪmpə`laɪt] (a.) 無禮的
Kenny is very impolite to everyone.
肯尼對每個人都很沒禮貌。

36 **import** [ɪm`port] (v.) 進口，輸入
They import furniture from England.
他們從英國進口家具。

35 **importance** [ɪm`pɔrtəns] (n.) 重要性
We must understand the importance of education.
我們必須了解教育的重要性。

37 **important** [ɪm`pɔrtənt] (a.) 重要的
My family is very important to me.
我的家人對我而言很重要。

37 **impossible** [ɪm`pɑsəbl̩] (a.) 不可能的
It's impossible for me to get high scores.
我不可能考高分。

36 **impress** [ɪm`prɛs] (v.) 給極深的印象，使感動
The young boy's painting impresses me a lot.
這個年輕男孩的畫深深打動了我。

37 **impressive** [ɪm`prɛsɪv] (a.) 予人深刻印象的，感人的
His speech was really impressive.
他的演講真的好感人。

36 **improve** [ɪm`pruv] (v.) 改善
I have to improve my English.
我必須加強我的英文。

32 **in** [ɪn] (prep.) 在…裡面
The gift is wrapped in the box.
禮物被包在盒子裡。

19 **inch** [ɪntʃ] (n.) 英寸
He is six feet five inches tall.
他身高六尺五寸。

36 **include** [ɪn`klud] (v.) 包含
The price includes both room and board.
這個價錢包含食宿。

9 **income** [ˋɪn,kʌm] (n.) 收入
All his income can't cover his expenses.
他入不敷出。

36 **increase** [ɪnˋkris] (v.) 增加
The price of oil has increased a lot over the past few months.
油價過去幾個月，已經漲了不少。

38 **indeed** [ɪnˋdid] (adv.) 真正地，確實
There indeed seems to be something wrong with your health.
你的健康看來真的有問題。

2 **independent** [,ɪndɪˋpɛndənt] (a.) 獨立
Mother is an independent woman.
媽媽是獨立的女性。

36 **indicate** [ˋɪndə,ket] (v.) 指示
The study indicated the population has increased in the past two years.
這項研究顯示，過去兩年間人口數量增加了。

37 **individual** [,ɪndəˋvɪdʒuəl] (a.) 個人的
Everyone has an individual way of dressing.
每個人都有自己的衣著喜好。

17 **indoor** [ˋɪn,dor] (a.) 室內的，戶內的
There is an indoor basketball court in the gym.
體育館裡有一座室內籃球場。

17 **indoors** [ˋɪn,dorz] (adv.) 在室內，在屋裡
We play basketball indoors when it rains.
下雨時，我們在室內打籃球。

37 **industrial** [ɪnˋdʌstrɪəl] (a.) 工業的，產業的
The American economy has changed from an industrial economy to a service economy.
美國經濟已由製造業經濟轉為服務業經濟。

35 **industry** [ˋɪndəstrɪ] (n.) 工業，產業
Dad works in the computer industry.
爸爸從事電腦業。

1 **infant** [ˋɪnfənt] (n.) 嬰兒
The police found the infant alone and wrapped in a blanket.
警方發現嬰兒單獨裹在一條毯子裡。

4 **infect** [ɪnˋfɛkt] (v.) 感染
The wound was infected again.
傷口又感染了。

35 **inferior** [ɪnˋfɪrɪɚ] (a.) 次級的，較劣質的
This type of wood is clearly inferior to that type.
這種木材的品質明顯不如那種。

35 **influence** [ˋɪnflʊəns] (n.) 影響
My English teacher has a large influence on me.
我的英文老師對我的影響很大。

36 **inform** [ɪnˋfɔrm] (v.) 通知，告知
You should inform your teacher ahead of time if you will miss a class.
如果你沒辦法來，應該是要通知老師。

35 **information** [ɪnfɚˋmeʃən] (n.) 資料
I need some information from your parents.
我得跟你父母要一些資料。

10 **ingredient** [inˋgridɪənt] (n.) 成份，原料
The ingredients needed for the recipe were clearly listed.
食譜裡要用的材料都有清楚列出了。

36 **injure** [ˋɪndʒɚ] (v.) 傷害，損害
I injured my back while fixing my roof.
我在修理我家屋頂時傷到背。

35 **injury** [ˋɪndʒərɪ] (n.) 損壞，傷害

My knee still hurts from an injury I got while playing football in college.

我念大學時打美式足球膝蓋受傷，到現在還會痛。

16 **ink** [ɪŋk] (n.) 墨水

The marker is out of ink.

這枝麥克筆沒有墨水了。

17 **inn** [ɪn] (n.)（公路邊或鄉間的）旅館

There are many lovely inns and pubs across the English countryside.

英國鄉間到處都有許多可愛的旅館和酒吧。

37 **inner** [ˋɪnɚ] (a.) 內部的，裡面的

He seldom expresses his inner feelings.

他很少表達內心的感受。

2 **innocent** [ˋɪnəsənt] (a.) 清白的，單純的

The man claimed that he was completely innocent of the crime.

男人聲稱他清清白白。

27 **insect** [ˋɪnsɛkt] (n.) 昆蟲

I zipped up the tent to keep the insects out during the night.

我把帳篷拉鍊拉上，免得昆蟲在夜裡跑進來。

32 **inside** [ˋɪnˋsaɪd] (prep.) 在…裡面

The chocolates are inside the box.

巧克力在盒子裡。

36 **insist** [ɪnˋsɪst] (v.) 堅持

The poor man insisted that he should pay for the meal.

這個貧窮的男人堅持要自己付飯錢。

36 **inspect** [ɪnˋspɛkt] (v.) 檢查，審查

The police inspected the bags of every passenger entering the airport.

每個進入機場的旅客，包包都要接受警方檢查。

A B C D E F G H I J K L M N O P Q R S T U V W X Y Z

24 **inspector** [ɪn`spɛktɚ] (n.) 檢查員，視察員
He is a school inspector.
他是學校督察。

36 **inspire** [ɪn`spaɪr] (v.) 鼓舞
The movie inspired me.
這部電影鼓舞了我。

35 **instance** [`ɪnstəns] (n.) 實例
The attack was the third instance of violence in the area in the last week.
這次攻擊行動是該地區上週第三起暴力事件。

37 **instant** [`ɪnstənt] (a.) 立即的
The manager needs an instant reply.
經理需要立即的答覆。

10 **instant noodles** [`ɪnstənt `nudl̩z] (n.) 泡麵
It's convenient to cook instant noodles.
煮泡麵很方便。

38 **instead** [ɪn`stɛd] (adv.) 反而，卻
Instead of sleeping, I went jogging.
我沒去睡覺，而是去慢跑。

27 **instinct** [`ɪnstɪŋkt] (n.) 本能
All creatures have a natural instinct to survive.
所有生物都有求生本能。

35 **instruction** [ɪn`strʌkʃən] (n.) 用法說明，操作指南
Please read the instructions before taking the medicine.
服用藥物之前，請先閱讀說明。

14 **instrument** [`ɪnstrəmənt] (n.) 樂器
She wishes she could play an instrument.
她真希望自己會彈奏一種樂器。

36 **insult** [ɪn`sʌlt] (v.) 侮辱
What he said insulted me.
他說的話污辱了我。

2 **intelligent** [ɪn`tɛlədʒənt] (a.) 有才智的
Sally is the most intelligent person I know.
莎莉是我認識最聰明的人。

36 **intend** [ɪn`tɛnd] (v.) 打算
He intends to take a trip to Japan.
他打算到日本旅行。

14 **interest** [`ɪntərɪst] (n.) 興趣
James has a strong interest in ancient history.
詹姆士對古代歷史有濃厚興趣。

2 **interested** [`ɪntərɪstɪd] (a.) 感興趣的
She is interested in painting.
她對畫畫感興趣。

37 **interesting** [`ɪnstərɪstɪŋ] (a.) 令人感興趣的
It's an interesting book for the public.
這是一本有趣的書，適合大眾閱讀。

37 **internal** [ɪn`tɜnl̩] (a.) 內在的，固有的
The internal parts of the washing machine are out of order.
這部洗衣機的內部零件壞了。

17 **international** [,ɪntɚ`næʃənl̩] (a.) 國際的
There are many international students studying in California.
許多國際學生在加州讀書。

14 **Internet** [`ɪntɚ,nɛt] (n.) 網際網路
Many people like to surf on the Internet.
許多人喜歡上網瀏覽。

36 **interpret** [ɪn`tɜprɪt] (v.) 解釋
The scientists interpret the event differently.
科學家們對這件事有不同的見解。

36 **interrupt** [͵ɪntə`rʌpt] (v.) 打斷
Don't interrupt when people are talking.
別人說話時別插嘴。

35 **interview** [`ɪntɚ͵vju] (n.) 面試，採訪
My sister has an interview with a computer company today.
我姊姊今天要去電腦公司面試。

32 **into** [`ɪntu] (prep.) 進入到…中
Put your hands into the water.
把雙手放入水中。

36 **introduce** [͵ɪntə`djus] (v.) 介紹，引薦
Let me introduce you to my family.
我來介紹你給我的家人認識。

35 **introduction** [͵ɪntrə`dʌkʃən] (n.) 介紹，正式引見
This film is a short introduction of our new company.
這部影片是我們新公司的簡介。

36 **invade** [ɪn`ved] (v.) 入侵
The enemy invaded the country early this morning.
敵軍在今天清晨入侵本國。

36 **invent** [ɪn`vɛnt] (v.) 發明
He invented a new product.
他發明了一個新產品。

35 **inventor** [ɪn`vɛntɚ] (n.) 發明家，發明者
Edison was the inventor of the light bulb.
愛迪生是發明燈泡的人。

36 **investigate** [ɪn`vɛstə,get] (v.) 調查，研究
The police are investigating the cause of the fire.
警方正在調查起火原因。

35 **invitation** [,ɪnvə`teʃən] (n.) 邀請（函）
I got an invitation to the Christmas party.
我今天收到一封耶誕派對的邀請函。

36 **invite** [ɪn`vaɪt] (v.) 邀請
She invited me to her birthday party.
她邀請我參加她的生日派對。

36 **involve** [`ɪnvɑlv] (v.) 使牽涉
The teenager was involved in a murder.
這名少年捲入一宗謀殺案。

15 **iron** [`aɪɚn] (v.) 熨燙
Can you iron my shirt for me?
你可以幫我燙衣服嗎?

15 **iron** [`aɪɚn] (n.) 熨斗
I used a hot iron to smooth the wrinkles in my shirt.
我用熱熨斗燙平襯衫上的皺摺。

26 **island** [`aɪlənd] (n.) 島嶼
Taiwan is an island.
台灣是一座島嶼。

36 **isolate** [`aɪsə,let] (v.) 隔離
SARS patients were isolated in a special area of the hospital.
SARS病患被隔離在醫院的一個特定區域。

4 **itch** [ɪtʃ] (n.) 癢
I have an itch on my back.
我的背在癢。

35 **item** [ˋaɪtəm] (n.) 項目，品項
Some items are missing here.
這裡有些品項不見了。

27 **ivory** [ˋaɪvərɪ] (n.) 象牙
Piano keys used to be made of ivory.
以前的鋼琴鍵盤是象牙製成。

J

12 **jacket** [ˋdʒækɪt] (n.) 夾克
The jacket is too small to wear.
這件夾克太小穿不下了。

17 **jail** [dʒel] (n.) 監獄，拘留所
The thief ended up in jail.
那個小偷最後被關進監獄。

10 **jam** [dʒæm] (n.) 果醬
I prefer jam to peanut butter.
我喜歡果醬勝於花生醬。

8 **January** [ˋdʒænju,ɛrɪ] (n.) 一月
The students usually have a short break in January.
學生在一月通常有一個短暫的假期。

20 **Japan** [dʒəˋpæn] (n.) 日本
Many tourists visit Japan to see cherry blossoms.
很多觀光客到日本賞櫻花。

21 **Japanese** [,dʒæpəˋniz] (n.) 日本人
The Japanese are island people.
日本人是島國人民。

35 **jar** [dʒɑr] (n.) 罐，瓶
There are jars of honey on the shelf.
在櫃子裡有幾罐蜂蜜。

3 **jaw** [dʒɔ] (n.) 下巴
The girl fell from the tree and hurt her jaw.
小女孩從樹上摔下來，傷到下巴。

14 **jazz** [dʒæz] (n.) 爵士樂
Julian loves to listen to live jazz performances.
朱立安喜歡聽爵士樂現場演奏。

2 **jealous** [`dʒɛləs] (a.) 嫉妒
I am jealous of Doug's new sports car.
我真嫉妒道格的新跑車。

12 **jeans** [dʒinz] (n.) 牛仔褲
Teenagers like to wear jeans.
青少年喜歡穿牛仔褲。

18 **jeep** [dʒip] (n.) 吉普車
Jeeps are not common in the city.
吉普車在城市裡並不常見。

35 **jelly** [`dʒɛlɪ] (n.) 果凍
After the dinner, we had some jelly.
晚餐過後，我們吃了一些果凍。

18 **jet** [dʒɛt] (n.) 噴射機
The jet prepares to take off.
噴射機準備要起飛了。

12 **jewel** [`dʒuəl] (n.) 寶石飾物，首飾
She hid all her jewels in the wall.
她把她所有的首飾藏在牆壁裡。

12 **jewelry** [ˋdʒuəlrɪ] (n.) 珠寶，首飾
The crown is made of jewelry.
這頂皇冠由珠寶打造而成。

24 **job** [dʒɑb] (n.) 工作
What's your father's job?
你父親從事什麼工作？

14 **jogging** [ˋdʒɑgɪŋ] (n.) 慢跑
Jogging is good for your heart.
慢跑對你的心臟有益。

36 **join** [dʒɔɪn] (v.) 參與
May I join your club?
我可以加入你們的社團嗎？

3 **joint** [dʒɔɪnt] (n.) 關節
My joints hurt every morning when I get out of bed.
每天早上起床，我的關節都會痛。

35 **joke** [dʒok] (n.) 玩笑
Jason always likes to make jokes.
傑森總是喜歡開玩笑。

35 **journal** [ˋdʒɝnḷ] (n.) 日記，日誌
The general kept a journal of this battle.
這位將軍為這場戰役逐日寫下紀錄。

24 **journalist** [ˋdʒɝnəlɪst] (n.) 新聞記者
Journalists don't have a fixed working time.
記者的工作時間不固定。

35 **journey** [ˋdʒɝnɪ] (n.) 旅程，行程
I'd like to take a journey through the Sahara desert.
我想穿越撒哈拉沙漠旅行。

35 **joy** [dʒɔɪ] (n.) 喜悅
Molly fills her students with the joy of learning.
茉莉讓她的學生充滿學習樂趣。

37 **joyful** [`dʒɔɪfəl] (a.) 高興的，充滿喜悅的
It was a joyful day when Susie got married to her sweetheart.
蘇希和她所愛的人結婚，當天真是充滿喜悅。

24 **judge** [dʒʌdʒ] (n.) 法官
The judge hasn't ruled on our case yet.
那位法官還未裁決我們的案子。

36 **judge** [dʒʌdʒ] (v.) 判斷，評斷
I don't think that you should judge other people so critically.
我覺得你不應該這麼嚴苛地評斷別人。

10 **juice** [dʒus] (n.) 果汁
I like orange juice.
我喜歡柳丁汁。

8 **July** [dʒu`laɪ] (n.) 七月
The weather is very hot in July.
七月的天氣很熱。

36 **jump** [dʒʌmp] (v.) 跳
Victor jumped off the chair.
維特從椅子上跳下來。

8 **June** [dʒun] (n.) 六月
Emily's birthday is in June.
愛蜜莉的生日在六月。

25 **jungle** [`dʒʌŋg!] (n.) 叢林
The mountaineers got lost in the jungle.
這群登山家在叢林裡迷路了。

16 **junior high school** [ˋdʒunjɚ haɪ skul] (n.) 國中

They've learned English since they were in junior high school.

他們從初中就開始學英語。

35 **junk** [dʒʌŋk] (n.) 廢棄的，垃圾

Hamburgers, fried chicken, and French fries are all junk food.

漢堡、炸雞和薯條都是垃圾食物。

38 **just** [dʒʌst] (adv.) 只是

This is just a fake story.

這只是個虛構的故事。

35 **justice** [ˋdʒʌstɪs] (n.) 正義，公平

Everyone should be treated with justice.

人人都應該受到公平對待。

K

27 **kangaroo** [ˏkæŋgəˋru] (n.) 袋鼠

I saw a kangaroo for the first time ever when I was in Australia.

我這輩子第一次看到袋鼠是在澳洲。

36 **keep** [kip] (v.) 保存

You must keep the receipt.

你一定要把收據留著。

10 **ketchup** [ˋkɛtʃəp] (n.) 番茄醬

Mary likes to put lots of ketchup on hot dogs.

瑪莉喜歡在熱狗上加很多番茄醬。

15 **kettle** [ˋkɛtl̩] (n.) 水壺

I'm boiling some water in the kettle on the stove.

我正在爐子上燒開水。

15 **key** [ki] (n.) 鑰匙
The key doesn't fit the lock.
這把鑰匙不能開這個鎖。

35 **keyboard** [ˋki,bord] (n.) 鍵盤
I bought a new keyboard for my computer last week.
我上週替電腦買了新的鍵盤。

36 **kick** [kɪk] (v.) 踢
Stop kicking the table.
別再踢桌子了。

1 **kid** [kɪd] (n.) 小孩
Mrs. Green has three kids.
格林太太有三個小孩。

3 **kidney** [ˋkɪdnɪ] (n.) 腎臟
Unnecessary medicine hurts the kidneys.
服用非必要的藥會傷害腎臟。

36 **kill** [kɪl] (v.) 殺死
Mother tried to kill the cockroach.
媽媽試圖殺死那隻蟑螂。

19 **kilogram** [ˋkɪlə,græm] (n.) 公斤（縮寫為kg）
I've gained five kilograms since I started working in an office.
我開始坐辦公室之後胖了五公斤。

19 **kilometer** [ˋkɪlə,mitɚ] (n.) 公里（縮寫為km）
It's about 40 kilometers by car from here to Taoyuan.
從這裡開車到桃園有四十公里。

2 **kind** [kaɪnd] (a.) 親切的
My music teacher is very kind to me.
我的音樂老師對我很好。

16 **kindergarten** [ˋkɪndɚ,gɑrtn̩] (n.) 幼稚園
There are 22 students in my son's kindergarten class.
我兒子幼稚園班上有二十二個學生。

1 **king** [kɪŋ] (n.) 國王
King Arthur was a famous fighter.
亞瑟王是有名的戰士。

20 **kingdom** [ˋkɪŋdəm] (n.) 王國
The king rules his kingdom well.
這個國王將王國治理得很好。

36 **kiss** [kɪs] (v.) 親吻
I always give my wife a kiss when I leave the house in the morning.
每天早上出門，我總是會親太太一下。

35 **kit** [kɪt] (n.) 工具箱
We put all the tools in the little kit.
我們將所有工具放進小工具箱。

15 **kitchen** [ˋkɪtʃən] (n.) 廚房
After I cooked, the kitchen was a mess.
我煮完飯後，廚房亂成一團。

14 **kite** [kaɪt] (n.) 風箏
There are many kites in the sky.
空中有很多風箏。

27 **kitten** [ˋkɪtn̩] (n.) 小貓
She had a white kitten.
她曾經養過一隻小白貓。

3 **knee** [ni] (n.) 膝蓋
I hurt my knee when I feel off my bicycle last week.
我上星期騎腳踏車摔倒傷到了膝蓋。

36 **kneel** [nil] (v.) 跪，跪下
He kneeled down to beg for her forgiveness.
他跪下求她原諒。

11 **knife** [naɪf] (n.) 刀
Keep the knife out of the reach of children.
把刀放在孩童拿不到的地方。

35 **knight** [naɪt] (n.) 騎士，武士
The knight rescued the princess in time.
那名騎士及時救了公主。

36 **knit** [nɪt] (v.) 編織
Mother knitted me a sweater.
媽媽幫我織了一件毛衣。

35 **knob** [nɑb] (n.) 球形把手
The little boy is too short to reach the door knob.
這小男孩太矮了搆不到門把。

36 **knock** [nɑk] (v.) 敲打
Always knock on the door before you enter the room.
進房間前都要先敲門。

35 **knot** [nɑt] (n.) 結
He tied a knot in the rope.
他在繩子上打了一個結。

36 **know** [no] (v.) 知道
He doesn't know how to face the difficulty.
他不知道如何面對困難。

16 **knowledge** [ˋnɑlɪdʒ] (n.) 知識
Knowledge is the key to success.
知識是成功之鑰。

3 **knuckle** [ˋnʌkl̩] (n.) （供食用的）蹄、肘，關節
I had a pig's knuckle to celebrate my birthday.
我吃了一個豬腳慶生。

27 **koala** [koˋɑlə] (n.) 無尾熊
Koalas are my favorite animal—they're so cute!
無尾熊是我最喜歡的動物——他們好可愛！

20 **Korea** [koˋriə] (n.) 韓國
The World Cup was held in both Korea and Japan in 2002.
二〇〇二年的世界盃在韓國和日本舉行。

21 **Korean** [koˋriən] (a.) 韓國（人、語）的
Korean dramas have been very popular in Taiwan recently.
韓劇近來在台灣非常受歡迎。

21 **Korean** [koˋriən] (n.) 韓國（人、語）
I like Japanese food, but Korean food is too spicy for my taste.
我喜歡日本食物，韓國食物對我來說太辣了。

L

35 **label** [ˋlebl̩] (n.) 貼紙，標籤
Attach this label to your luggage.
把這張標籤貼在你的行李上。

35 **lace** [les] (n.) 鞋帶，帶子
The boy doesn't know how to tie his laces.
這個小男孩不知道如何綁鞋帶。

36 **lack** [læk] (v.) 缺少
I can not buy it because I lack money.
因為我缺錢，沒辦法買這樣東西。

35 **ladder** [ˋlædɚ] (n.) 梯子
Put the ladder against the wall.
把梯子靠在牆上。

1 **lady** [ˋledɪ] (n.) 小姐
There is a pretty lady on the street.
街上有個漂亮的小姐。

26 **lake** [lek] (n.) 湖
This lake is too wide to swim across.
這個湖太寬了，游不過去的。

27 **lamb** [læm] (n.) 羔羊
Today's special is lamb chops.
本日特餐是小羊排。

15 **lamp** [læmp] (n.) 燈
Turn off the lamp before going to bed.
睡覺前把燈關掉。

26 **land** [lænd] (n.) 陸地
After sailing at sea for days, they finally saw land.
在海中航行多日後，他們終於看到陸地。

35 **landmark** [ˋlænd,mɑrk] (n.) 地標
Taipei 101 is a landmark in Taipei.
台北一〇一在台北是個地標。

35 **landscape** [ˋlænd,skep] (n.) 風景
The landscape in Arizona is especially beautiful in the fall.
亞利桑納州秋天的風景尤其美麗。

25 **landslide** [ˋlænd,slaɪd] (n.) 土石流
The landslide destroyed the bridge and several nearby houses.
土石流摧毀了那座橋和幾棟附近的房屋。

16 **language** [ˋlæŋgwɪdʒ] (n.) 語言
It's difficult to learn a language.
要學會一種語言很困難。

19 **large** [lɑrdʒ] (a.) 大的
I want a large juice.
我要一杯大杯的果汁。

7 **last** [læst] (a.) 最後的
He was the last one to finish the job.
他是最後完成工作的人。

8 **late** [let] (a.) 遲的，晚的
We arrived about 30 minutes late to the party.
我們晚了大約三十分鐘抵達舞會。

8 **lately** [ˋletlɪ] (adv.) 最近
Have you seen this man lately?
你最近有沒有見過這個男人？

8 **later** [ˋletɚ] (adv.) 稍晚的
See you later.
待會見。

8 **latest** [ˋletɪst] (a.) 最新的，最近的
Did you watch the latest movie?
你看過最新上映的那部電影嗎？

37 **latter** [ˋlætɚ] (a.) 後面的
Between Pork & Beed; I prefer the latter.
豬肉和牛肉讓我選，我會選後者。

36 **laugh** [læf] (v.) 笑
I love to watch movies that can make me laugh.
我喜歡看能讓我發笑的電影。

35 **laughter** [ˋlæftɚ] (n.) 笑，笑聲
We all burst into laughter.
我們都笑了出來。

36 **launch** [lɔntʃ] (v.) 發射
The rocket exploded just seconds after launching.
火箭發射幾秒鐘之後就爆炸了。

35 **laundry** [ˋlɔndrɪ] (n.) 洗衣店，洗衣
I do laundry once a week.
我每週洗一次衣服。

16 **law** [lɔ] (n.) 法律
There are many laws in the U.S. to protect people's privacy.
美國有許多保護個人隱私的法律。

35 **lawn** [lɔn] (n.) 草坪，草地
I mow the lawn every Saturday morning.
我每週日早上都會修剪草坪。

24 **lawyer** [ˋlɔjɚ] (n.) 律師
It's important for every business to have a good lawyer.
每一間公司都需要，有個好律師。

36 **lay** [le] (v.) 放，鋪設
Could you lay your books aside and give me a hand?
你可以把書放下，然後過來幫我一下嗎？

2 **lazy** [ˋlezɪ] (a.) 懶惰的
I'm too lazy to do my homework today.
我今天很懶，不想做功課。

36 **lead** [lid] (v.) 帶領
The secretary led me to the restroom.
這祕書帶我到洗手間。

35 **leader** [ˋlidɚ] (n.) 領導者
Oscar is the leader in his class.
奧斯卡是他那一班的班長。

35 **leadership** [ˋlidɚʃɪp] (n.) 領導
The president has great leadership skills.
這個總統有優秀的領導能力。

25 **leaf** [lif] (n.) 葉子
I love watching the leaves turn color in the fall.
我喜歡看葉子在秋天轉變顏色。

36 **leak** [lik] (v.) 漏洞，裂縫
The plumber couldn't stop the pipe from leaking.
這個水管工無法讓水管停止漏水。

36 **leap** [lip] (v.) 跳，跳躍
I tried to grab the frog but it leapt away into the lake.
我想抓那隻青蛙，但牠跳進湖裡了。

16 **learn** [lɝn] (v.) 學習
I'm learning how to do basic computer programming.
我正在學如何寫基本的電腦程式。

19 **least** [list] (adv.) 最少地
I try to save at least 10% of my income every month.
我試著每個月至少把收入的百分之十存起來。

35 **leather** [ˋlɛðɚ] (n.) 皮革製品
The bag is made of leather.
這個背包是由皮革製成。

36 **leave** [liv] (v.) 離開
You can leave first.
你可以先離開。

16 **lecture** [ˋlɛktʃɚ] (n.) 授課
The teacher's lecture was so boring that I fell asleep.
這個老師的課好無聊，我都睡著了。

17 **left** [lɛft] (a.) 左邊
Turn left and you will find the post office.
左轉你就會看到郵局。

3 **leg** [lɛg] (n.) 腿
Models usually have nice long legs.
模特兒經常都有修長的美腿。

37 **legal** [ˋligḷ] (a.) 合法的
She is my legal wife.
她是我的合法妻子。

35 **legend** [ˋlɛdʒənd] (n.) 傳奇
Tiger Woods is still young, but he's become a legend in the game of golf.
老虎伍茲還很年輕，卻已經成為高爾夫球界的傳奇。

35 **leisure** [ˋliʒɚ] (n.) 閒暇，空暇時間
Sean likes to read in his leisure time.
西恩喜歡在閒暇時間閱讀。

10 **lemon** [ˋlɛmən] (n.) 檸檬
Lemons taste sour.
檸檬嚐起來很酸。

9 **lend** [lɛnd] (v.) 把…借給
Could you lend me some money?
你能借我一些錢嗎？

19 **length** [lɛŋθ] (n.) 長度
What's the length of this table?
這張桌子有多長？

36 **lenghten** [ˋlɛŋθən] (v.) 使加長，使延長
Could you lengthen my pants?
你可以把我的褲子放長嗎？

35 **lens** [lɛnz] (n.) 透鏡，鏡片
He wears contact lenses.
他戴隱型眼鏡。

7 **less** [lɛs] (a.) 較少的
The salary is less than what I expected.
薪水比我預期的少。

16 **lesson** [ˋlɛsn̩] (n.) 課
The teacher didn't do a good job explaining this week's lesson.
老師這星期的課講得不好。

36 **let** [lɛt] (v.) 允許，讓
My parents won't let me go out with my friends.
我的父母不讓我跟朋友出去。

16 **letter** [ˋlɛtɚ] (n.) 字母
Four- letter words are not allowed at school.
學校禁止說髒話。

10 **lettuce** [ˋlɛtɪs] (n.) 萵苣
The salad has lettuce, eggs, and tomatoes.
這道沙拉裡有萵苣、蛋和番茄。

35 **level** [ˋlɛvl̩] (n.) 程度，標準
Her levels are not up to standard yet.
她的程度尚未達到標準。

35 **liar** [ˋlaɪɚ] (n.) 說謊的人
I can't be friends with someone who is a liar.
我無法和說謊的人交朋友。

2 **liberal** [ˋlɪbərəl] (a.) 開明的，自由主義的
Young people today seem to have more liberal attitudes about sex.
現在的年輕人對性似乎有比較開放的態度。

35 **liberty** [ˋlɪbɚtɪ] (n.) 自由，自由權
I value liberty far more than wealth.
我重視自由遠勝與財富。

24 **librarian** [laɪˋbrɛrɪən] (n.) 圖書館館長，圖書館員
If you can't find the book you are looking for, you can always ask the librarian.
如果找不到書，你都可以請圖書館員幫忙。

16 **library** [ˋlaɪ,brɛrɪ] (n.) 圖書館
Allison usually studies in the library.
艾莉森經常在圖書館讀書。

35 **license** [ˋlaɪsəns] (n.) 執照
I don't have a driving license.
我沒有駕駛執照。

36 **lick** [lɪk] (v.) 舔
The dog likes to lick the cat.
這隻狗喜歡舔這隻貓咪。

35 **lid** [lɪd] (n.) 蓋子
The boy broke the lid of the expensive teapot.
那個男孩把那只昂貴茶壺的蓋子打破了。

36 **lie** [laɪ] (v.) 躺，位於
My favorite thing to do in the summer is lie on the beach.
我夏天最喜歡躺在沙灘上。

4 **life** [laɪf] (n.) 生命
Tom still hasn't decided what he wants to do with his life.
湯姆還沒決定他這輩子想要做什麼。

18 **lifeboat** [ˋlaɪf,bot] (n.) 救生艇，救生船
The lifeboats are not enough on this ship.
這艘船上的救生艇不夠。

24 **lifeguard** [ˋlaɪf,gɑrd] (n.) 救生員
There should be lifeguards on all the beaches.
每座海灘都應該有救生員。

8 **lifetime** [ˋlaɪf,taɪm] (n.) 一生，終生
The shop owner told me that this watch would last a lifetime.
店老闆告訴我這只錶能用上一輩子。

36 **lift** [lɪft] (v.) 舉起
The suitcase was too heavy for the woman to lift by herself.
這個行李箱太重了，那位女士無法自己抬。

19 **light** [laɪt] (a.) 輕的
He travels with a light backpack.
他背著輕便的背包旅行。

15 **light** [laɪt] (n.) 燈
Please turn the light off.
請關燈。

17 **lighthouse** [ˋlaɪt,haʊs] (n.) 燈塔
The lighthouse guides all the ships in the ocean.
燈塔指引著海中船隻。

25 **lightning** [ˋlaɪtnɪŋ] (n.) 閃電
We ran inside as soon as we saw the flashes of lightning in the sky.
我們一看到空中的閃電就趕緊跑進來。

36 **like** [laɪk] (v.) 喜歡
I like my English teacher.
我喜歡我的英文老師。

37 **likely** [ˋlaɪklɪ] (a.) 可能的
He is likely to be home now.
他現在可能在家。

3 **limb** [lɪm] (n.) 肢，臂，腳
After I got home I stretched out my limbs like a cat and immediately fell asleep.
我一到家就像貓一樣四肢攤開、立刻睡著。

36 **limit** [ˋlɪmɪt] (v.) 限制
I know my own limits.
我知道我自己的極限。

35 **line** [laɪn] (n.) 線
Draw a line between the two pictures.
在兩張圖中間畫一條線。

12 **linen** [ˋlɪnən] (n.) 亞麻布，亞麻紗
Clothes made of linen wrinkle easily.
亞麻布製的衣服很容易皺。

35 **link** [lɪŋk] (v.) 連結
This website links to others.
這個網頁有連結到其他的網頁。

27 **lion** [ˋlaɪən] (n.) 獅子
Last week a zoo worker was killed while feeding a lion.
上週有一位動物園工作人員在餵食獅子時被咬死。

3 **lip** [lɪp] (n.) 嘴唇
Her lips are as soft as cotton.
她的嘴唇像棉花一樣柔軟。

12 **lipstick** [ˋlɪp͵stɪk] (n.) 口紅
Carol likes to wear dark red lipstick when she goes to clubs.
卡蘿上夜店時喜歡塗深色口紅。

10 **liquid** [ˋlɪkwɪd] (n.) 液體
Water, wine and milk are all liquids.
水、酒和牛奶都是液體。

36 **list** [lɪst] (v.) 把…編列成表，列出
Mom listed all the things she needed to buy.
媽媽把她想買的東西列成一張清單。

36 **listen** [ˋlɪsn̩] (v.) 聽從
We have to listen to our parents.
我們必須聽父母的話。

19 **liter** [ˋlitɚ] (n.) 公升
I try to drink at least two liters of water every day.
我儘量每天喝至少兩公升的水。

16 **literature** [ˋlɪtərətʃɚ] (n.) 文學，文學作品
Betty likes to read Chinese literature.
貝蒂喜歡閱讀中國文學作品。

36 **litter** [ˋlɪtɚ] (v.) 丟垃圾
Don't litter in the park.
別在公園裡亂丟垃圾。

19 **little** [ˋlɪtl̩] (a.) 小的
The little girl looks like her mother very much.
這個小女孩長得很像她媽媽。

6 **live** [lɪv] (v.) 活，住
She lives with her grandparents.
她和祖父母住在一起。

37 **lively** [ˋlaɪvlɪ] (a.) 生動的，栩栩如生的
The child drew a lively painting.
這個小孩畫了一幅生動的圖畫。

3 **liver** [ˋlɪvɚ] (n.) 肝臟
Staying up every night is not good for the liver.
每天熬夜對肝臟不好。

15 **living room** [ˋlɪvɪŋ rum] (n.) 客廳
My family always gathers in the living room to watch TV after dinner.
晚餐之後，我們一家人都會聚在客廳裡看電視。

36 **load** [lod] (v.) 裝，裝載
The mule is loaded with goods.
這頭騾子載了貨物。

19 **loaf** [lof] (n.) 一條
Dad buys a loaf of bread every morning in the market.
爸爸每天早上都在市場買一條麵包。

9 **loan** [lon] (n.) 貸款
I applied for a loan from a bank to buy the house.
我向銀行申請貸款買房子。

17 **lobby** [ˋlabɪ] (n.) 大廳
Lots of tourists are waiting in the lobby to check in.
很多觀光客在大廳裡等候辦理住房手續。

10 **lobster** [ˋlabstɚ] (n.) 龍蝦
The restaurant is famous for its delicious lobsters.
這間餐廳以美味龍蝦聞名。

17 **local** [ˋlokl̩] (a.) 當地的，本地的
The firefighter's brave story was reported on the local news.
這個消防隊員的英勇故事被地方新聞報導出來。

36 **lock** [lak] (v.) 鎖
The gatekeeper locked the door after midnight.
過了午夜，管理員就把門鎖起來了。

35 **locker** [ˋlɑkɚ] (n.) 置物櫃
There are lockers at school.
學校裡有置物櫃。

10 **lollipop** [ˋlɑlɪ,pɑp] (n.) 棒棒糖
The little boy licked the lollipop happily.
這個小男孩快樂地舔著棒棒糖。

2 **lonely** [ˋlonlɪ] (a.) 孤獨的
She feels lonely by herself.
她自己一個人覺得孤單。

19 **long** [lɔŋ] (a.) 長的
Carrie has long blond hair.
凱莉留著一頭金色長髮。

36 **look** [luk] (v.) 看
Why are you looking at this picture all the time?
你為什麼一直看著這張照片？

37 **loose** [lus] (a.) 鬆開的，鬆散的
My mother likes to wear loose pants.
我媽媽喜歡穿寬鬆的褲子。

36 **loosen** [ˋlusn̩] (v.) 鬆開，鬆弛
The businessman loosened his tie after the meeting.
會議結束後，這個商人將他的領帶鬆開。

35 **lord** [lɔrd] (n.) 君主，（L大寫）上帝
They treat the boss like a lord.
他們視老闆如國王。

36 **lose** [luz] (v.) 失敗
Nobody wants to lose the game.
沒有人想輸掉這場比賽。

36 **loser** [`luzɚ] (n.) 輸家
The losers will give away world championship trophy.
輸家將會讓出世界冠軍的頭銜。

35 **loss** [lɔs] (n.) 損失
The typhoon didn't lead to any deaths, but it caused tremendous financial loss.
這場颱風未使任何人，但造成極大的財務損失。

37 **loud** [laud] (a.) 吵鬧的
The music is so loud.
音樂好大聲。

35 **loudspeaker** [`laud`spikɚ] (n.) 擴聲器，喇叭
I just had a new pair of loudspeakers installed in my car.
我剛幫我的車子安裝了一對新喇叭。

37 **lousy** [`lauzɪ] (a.) 差勁的
The coffee in that restaurant is very lousy.
這間餐廳的咖啡很難喝。

36 **love** [lʌv] (v.) 愛
I love to ride my bike on Sunday morning.
我喜歡在星期天早晨騎自行車。

2 **lovely** [`lʌvlɪ] (a.) 可愛的
The girl looks lovely in pink.
那女孩穿粉紅色看起來很可愛。

1 **lover** [`lʌvɚ] (n.) 情人
Carrie flew to Paris to meet her lover for Christmas.
凱莉飛到巴黎與情人相會過耶誕節。

19 **low** [lo] (a.) 低矮的
Watch your head—the ceiling is very low here.
小心你的頭——這裡的天花板很低。

37 **lucky** [ˋlʌkɪ] (a.) 幸運的
My grandfather is lucky to still be healthy in his 80s.
我爺爺很幸運，直到八十幾歲都還很健康。

35 **luggage** [ˋlʌgɪdʒ] (n.) 行李
A piece of luggage was left on the bus.
一件行李被遺留在公車上。

35 **lullaby** [ˋlʌlə,baɪ] (n.) 催眠曲，搖籃曲
The mother hums a lullaby for her baby.
這個媽媽哼搖籃曲給她的寶寶聽。

10 **lunch** [lʌntʃ] (n.) 午餐
The Wayne family had lunch together.
韋恩一家人一起吃午餐。

3 **lung** [lʌŋ] (n.) 肺部，肺
My uncle died of lung cancer when he was only 43.
我的伯父才四十三歲就死於肺癌。

M

5 **ma'am** [mæm] (n.)（口）女士
Good morning, ma'am. Anything to drink?
夫人，早安。想喝點什麼嗎？

35 **machine** [məˋʃin] (n.) 機器
The machine is out of order.
那台機器壞了。

2 **mad** [mæd] (a.) 生氣的，瘋的
I am so mad because my girlfriend is always late.
我很生氣因為我女友老是遲到。

16 **magazine** [ˌmægəˋzin] (n.) 雜誌
There are a variety of magazines in the bookstore.
書店裡有各式各樣的雜誌。

37 **magic** [ˋmædʒɪk] (a.) 魔法的，魔術的
My classmate taught me how to do several magic tricks yesterday.
我班上同學昨天教我玩幾招魔術。

37 **magical** [ˋmædʒɪkḷ] (a.) 魔術的，魔法的
The herbs the doctor gave me had a magical effect on my health.
醫生給我的草藥對我的健康有神奇效果。

24 **magician** [məˋdʒɪʃən] (n.) 魔術師
I love trying to figure out how magicians do their tricks.
我很喜歡試著搞懂魔術師如何變魔術。

35 **magnet** [ˋmægnɪt] (n.) 磁鐵，磁石
The note was attached to the refrigerator with a magnet.
這張紙條是用磁鐵附在冰箱上。

24 **maid** [med] (n.) 侍女，女僕
The maid cooked dinner after she mopped the floor.
拖完地之後，女僕把晚餐煮好了。

35 **mail** [mel] (n.) 郵件
I get over 20 pieces of junk mail every day.
我每天收到超過二十封垃圾郵件。

24 **mailman** [ˋmel,mən] (n.) 郵差
The mailman delivers the mail every day.
這名郵差每天送信。

37 **main** [men] (a.) 主要的
What's the main idea of the article?
這篇文章的主要思想為何？

36 **maintain** [men`ten] (v.) 保持，維持
How do you maintain your weight?
你如何維持體重？

16 **major** [`medʒɚ] (v.) 主修
He majored in literature in the university.
他大學主修文學。

37 **major** [`medʒɚ] (a.) 主要的
The major problem with Patrick's health is that he is overweight.
派翠克健康的主要問題是體重過重。

19 **majority** [mə`dʒɔrətɪ] (n.) 多數，過半數
A majority of residents in the area supported the construction of the new school.
本地區居民多數支持新學校的建設。

36 **make** [mek] (v.) 使得，做
Desserts will make you fat.
甜點會讓你發胖。

1 **male** [mel] (n.) 雄性，男性
Males are usually stronger than females.
男性通常比女性強壯。

17 **mall** [mɔl] (n.) 購物中心
The shopping mall attracts lots of people on weekends.
這間購物中心在週末吸引大批人潮。

1 **man** [mæn] (n.) 男人
The man in the white shirt is my father.
那個穿白襯衫的人是我爸爸。

36 **manage** [`mænɪdʒ] (v.) 設法做到，得以完成
He managed to solve all the problems.
他成功解決了所有問題。

37 **manageable** [ˋmænɪdʒəbl̩] (a.) 可控制的
Although the situation got worse, it was still manageable.
雖然情況變糟，但仍然控制得住。

24 **manager** [ˋmænɪdʒɚ] (n.) 經理，負責人
The manager tried his best to encourage those new salespeople.
這位經理盡力鼓勵那些新進業務人員。

21 **Mandarin** [ˋmændərɪn] (n.) 華語
More and more people are learing Mandarin.
越來越多人學習說華語。

10 **mango** [ˋmæŋgo] (n.) 芒果
Mango milkshakes are one of my favorite things to drink in the summer.
芒果奶昔是我夏天最喜歡喝的飲料之一。

35 **mankind** [mænˋkaɪnd] (n.) 人類
Mankind learned how to use tools many thousands of years ago.
人類在好幾千年前學會如何使用工具。

35 **manner** [ˋmænɚ] (n.) 方法，態度
Dr. James has a nice manner when talking with patients.
詹姆士醫師對病患說話時，態度很好。

35 **manners** [ˋmænɚz] (n.) 禮貌，規矩
Parents should teach their children table manners.
父母應該教導孩子餐桌禮儀。

35 **manual** [ˋmænjʊəl] (n.) 手冊
I need to read the manual for this computer before I start to use it.
我開始使用這台電腦前，需要先看說明書。

7 **many** [ˋmɛnɪ] (a.) 很多的
Due to the traffic jam, many students were late today.
因為交通阻塞，許多學生今天遲到了。

16 **map** [mæp] (n.) 地圖
You need either a tour guide or a map.
你需要一個導遊，不然就是一張地圖。

35 **marble** [ˋmɑrbl̩] (n.) 彈珠
We used to play marbles on the ground.
我們以前會在地上玩彈珠。

36 **march** [mɑrtʃ] (v.) 行進，行軍
How far has the army marched since 6 o'clock a.m.?
軍隊從早上六點開始行軍多遠了？

8 **March** [mɑrtʃ] (n.) 三月
Many students have a one-week vacation in March, which is called "spring break."
我的學生在三月有一週的假期，稱做「春假」。

35 **mark** [mɑrk] (n.) 記號
The father made marks on the wall to show how tall his son was.
那位父親在牆上做記號，標出他兒子當時有多高。

16 **marker** [ˋmɑrkɚ] (n.) 麥克筆
We need markers to write on the board.
我們需要幾支麥克筆在板子上寫字。

17 **market** [ˋmɑrkɪt] (n.) 市場
I walked around the flower market for about an hour, but didn't buy anything.
我在花市繞了大約一小時，但什麼也沒買。

6 **marriage** [ˋmærɪdʒ] (n.) 婚姻
He has had three marriages in the past ten years.
他在過去十年來有過三段婚姻。

6 **married** [ˋmærɪd] (a.) 已婚的
Joanna is hoping to get married early next year, but she and her boyfriend haven't set a date yet.
喬安娜希望明年初結婚，但她和男友還沒決定日期。

6 **marry** [ˋmærɪ] (v.) 娶，嫁
Nancy is the girl I want to marry.
南茜是我想娶的女孩。

37 **marvelous** [ˋmɑrvələs] (a.) 令人驚訝的
She has a marvelous gift for languages.
她有驚人的語言天份。

12 **mask** [mæsk] (n.) 面具
She wore a mask to scare her brother.
她戴了一個面具嚇她的弟弟。

1 **mass** [mæs] (n.) 大眾，民眾
Do you think the government is really concerned the interests of the masses?
你認為政府真的關心民眾的利益嗎？

1 **master** [ˋmæstɚ] (n.) 主人，雇主
The dog was often beaten by its master.
這隻狗常被牠的主人打。

15 **mat** [mæt] (n.) 地墊，墊子
Please wipe your feet on the mat before coming in.
進來前請先在地墊上擦腳。

36 **match** [mætʃ] (v.) 相配，適合
The hat doesn't match my shirt.
這頂帽子和我的襯衫不搭。

35 **material** [məˋtɪrɪəl] (n.) 原料
Her dress was made from beautiful material.
她的衣服是漂亮質料所織成的。

16 **math** [mæθ] (n.) 數學
Math is my least favorite subject in school.
數學是我在學校最不喜歡的科目。

16 **mathematical** [ˌmæθəˋmætɪkl̩] (a.) 數學的
John is a mathematical genius.
約翰是數學天才。

35 **matter** [ˋmætɚ] (n.) 事件
It's a matter of life and death.
這件事攸關生死。

37 **mature** [məˋtʃʊr] (a.) 成熟的，穩重的
A mature adult wouldn't do such a thing.
成熟大人並不會做那樣的事。

19 **maximum** [ˋmæksəməm] (n.) 最大量
The maximum speed limit on the freeway is 100 miles an hour.
高速公路上的最高速限為每小時一百英里。

31 **may** [me] (a.) 可能
I may not have the right to approve your leave.
我可能沒有權力准你的假。

8 **May** [me] (n.) 五月
May is my favorite month.
五月是我最愛的月份。

38 **maybe** [ˋmebɪ] (adv.) 也許
Maybe I will come home early today.
我今天也許會早點回家。

22 **mayor** [ˋmeɚ] (n.) 市長，鎮長
Taipei residents recently elected a new mayor.
台北居民最近選出新市長。

25 **meadow** [ˋmɛdo] (n.) 草地，牧草地
Let's take a rest in that beautiful meadow over there.
我們到那片美麗的草地上休息一下。

10 **meal** [mil] (n.) 一餐
We should eat three meals a day.
我們一天應該吃三餐。

36 **mean** [min] (v.) 意指
Nodding your head means you agree on the case.
點頭表示你同意這個案子。

35 **meaning** [ˋminɪŋ] (n.) 意思，意義
Do you know the meaning of this word?
你知道這個字的意思嗎？

37 **meaningful** [ˋminɪŋfəl] (a.) 意味深長的，有意義的
The philosopher's speech was meaningful.
這位哲學家的演講意味深長。

35 **means** [minz] (n.) 手段，方法
Tucker decided he would become rich by any means he could.
塔克決定不擇手段也要致富。

38 **meanwhile** [ˋmin,hwaɪl] (adv.) 同時
John is sleeping; meanwhile, his wife is cooking.
約翰在睡覺，而他老婆在煮飯。

19 **measure** [ˋmɛʒɚ] (v.) 測量
You can use a ruler to measure the length of the table.
你可以用尺測量這張桌子的長度。

10 **meat** [mit] (n.) 肉
Catholics don't eat meat on Fridays.
天主教徒星期五不吃肉。

24 **mechanic** [məˋkænɪk] (n.) 技工
We need a mechanic to fix the refrigerator.
我們需要一個技工來修理冰箱。

35 **medal** [ˋmɛdḷ] (n.) 獎章，紀念章
Lily won a medal for placing 2nd in the race.
莉莉賽跑第二名贏得一片獎牌。

35 **media** [ˋmidɪə] (n.) 傳播媒體
The media claims that it is fair and balanced in its coverage.
該媒體宣稱其報導公正平衡。

37 **medical** [ˋmɛdɪkḷ] (a.) 醫學的，醫術
The army needed more medical supplies to care for the injured soldiers.
軍隊需要更多醫藥補給以照顧傷兵。

4 **medicine** [ˋmɛdəsṇ] (n.) 藥
You have to take your medicine twice a day.
你必須一天服兩次藥。

19 **medium** [ˋmidɪəm] (a.) 適中的
The test was only of medium difficulty.
這個測驗只有中等難度。

36 **meet** [mit] (v.) 遇見，會面
She will meet me in the cafe.
她將在咖啡館跟我碰面。

35 **meeting** [ˋmitɪŋ] (n.) 會議
Don't disturb us in the middle of the meeting.
會議中請不要打擾我們。

10 **melon** [ˋmɛlən] (n.) 瓜
It's refreshing to eat cool melon in the summer.
在夏天吃冰涼的瓜，感覺很清爽。

36 **melt** [mɛlt] (v.) 融化，熔化
The ice cream is melting.
冰淇淋正在溶化。

35 **member** [ˋmɛmbɚ] (n.) 成員
Two members of the famous band are senior high school students.
這個知名樂團的兩名成員是高中生。

35 **membership** [ˋmɛmbɚ,ʃɪp] (n.) 會員身分，全體會員
He applied for membership in the golf club.
他申請成為這家高爾夫俱樂部的會員。

36 **memorize** [ˋmɛmə,raɪz] (v.) 記住，背熟
I had to memorize many poems when I was in elementary school.
我念小學時必須背許多詩。

35 **memory** [ˋmɛmərɪ] (n.) 記憶，回憶
There are a lot of memories in these photos.
這些照片有很多回憶。

36 **mend** [mɛnd] (v.) 改善，改良
The farmer spent several days mending fences after the storm.
暴風雨過後，農人花了好幾天修復籬笆。

17 **men's room** [mɛnz rum] (n.) 男廁
Where's the men's room?
男廁在哪裡？

37 **mental** [ˋmɛntḷ] (a.) 內心的，在腦中進行的
The girl went to see a doctor for her mental illness.
這女孩因為心理疾病去看醫生。

35 **mention** [ˋmɛnʃən] (v.) 提到，說起
Doug didn't mention his new car when I talked to him.
我跟道格說話時，他沒提到他的新車。

10 **menu** [ˋmɛnju] (n.) 菜單
I don't know how to order because the menu is written in French.
我不知道如何點菜，因為菜單是用法文寫的。

35 **merchant** [ˋmɝtʃənt] (n.) 商人
She is a wealthy merchant in the US.
她在美國是一名富有的商人。

35 **mercy** [ˋmɝsɪ] (n.) 慈悲
The father showed no mercy when punishing his son.
那位父親懲罰兒子時毫不留情。

36 **merry** [ˋmɛrɪ] (v.) 歡樂的，愉快的
Merry Christmas to you!
祝你耶誕節快樂！

35 **mess** [mɛs] (n.) 混亂，凌亂的狀態
Your room is a mess.
你的房間一團亂。

35 **message** [ˋmɛsɪdʒ] (n.) 訊息
Please send me a message when you arrive.
當你抵達時請傳簡訊給我。

35 **metal** [ˋmɛtl̩] (n.) 金屬
Would you like your picture frame to be made of wood or metal?
你的相框要用木頭還是金屬材質？

19 **meter** [ˋmitɚ] (n.) 公尺，米
I'm about one point seven meters tall.
我身高大約一米七。

5 **method** [ˋmɛθəd] (n.) 方法
There are many methods of learning English.
學英文的方法有很多種。

35 **microphone** [ˋmaɪkrə,fon] (n.)，麥克風(簡稱mike)
The microphone doesn't work.
這支麥克風壞了。

35 **microscope** [ˋmaɪkrə,skop] (n.) 顯微鏡
You can see bacteria clearly through a microscope.
透過顯微鏡可以清楚看到細菌。

15 **microwave** [ˋmaɪkrə,wev] (n.) 微波爐，微波
The leftovers are in the microwave.
剩飯剩菜在微波爐裡。

17 **middle** [ˋmɪdḷ] (a.) 中間的
The boss left in the middle of the meeting.
老闆開會開到一半就走了。

8 **midnight** [ˋmɪd,naɪt] (n.) 午夜
Cinderella has to leave the palace at midnight.
灰姑娘必須在午夜離開皇宮

31 **might** [maɪt] (aux.)（may的過去式）可能
It might rain tomorrow.
明天可能會下雨。

35 **might** [maɪt] (n.) 力量，威力
The soldier fought back with all his might.
這名士兵傾令力反擊。

37 **mighty** [ˋmaɪtɪ] (a.) 強大的，強而有力的
The boxer gave out the last mighty blow.
這名拳擊手揮出奮力的最後一擊。

19 **mile** [maɪl] (n.) 英里
He lives only miles away from the river.
他住的地方離這條河只有幾哩。

35 **military** [ˋmɪlə,tɛrɪ] (n.) 軍方，軍隊
The U.S. military is much smaller than it was 10 years ago.
相較於十年前，美國的軍力小了許多。

⑩ **milk** [mɪlk] (n.) 牛奶
Milk is good for bones.
牛奶對骨骼有益。

⑩ **milk shake** [mɪlk ʃek] (n.) 奶昔
I have a milk shake at this restaurant almost every week.
我幾乎每星期都到這間餐廳喝一杯奶昔。

㉟ **mill** [mɪl] (n.) 磨坊
Grandpa took his corn to the mill.
爺爺把他的玉米拿去磨坊。

⑦ **million** [ˋmɪljən] (n.) 一百萬
Millions of people are watching the soccer game.
數百萬人正在觀賞這場足球賽。

㉟ **millionaire** [ˏmɪljənˋɛr] (n.) 百萬富翁
I want to be a millionaire.
我想要成為百萬富翁。

㊱ **mind** [maɪnd] (v.) 在意
Do you mind turning off the light?
你介意關燈嗎？

㉙ **mine** [maɪn] (pron.) 我的東西
The wallet is mine.
這個皮夾是我的。

㉔ **miner** [ˋmaɪnɚ] (n.) 礦工
My father worked as a miner ten years ago.
我的父親十年前曾是礦工。

㊲ **minor** [ˋmaɪnɚ] (a.) 次要的
Don't worry; it's a minor problem.
別擔心；那只是小問題。

35 **minority** [maɪ`nɔrətɪ] (n.) 少數的
Only a minority of people voted for him.
只有少數人投票給他。

19 **minus** [`maɪnəs] (prep.) 減去
Five minus three is two.
五減三等於二。

8 **minute** [`mɪnɪt] (n.) 分
There are sixty minutes in an hour.
一小時有六十分鐘。

35 **miracle** [`mɪrəkḷ] (n.) 奇蹟
It's a miracle that she wasn't killed in the car accident.
她沒在車禍中喪生真是奇蹟。

15 **mirror** [`mɪrɚ] (n.) 鏡子
Alice likes to look at herself in the mirror.
愛麗絲喜歡照鏡子。

35 **misery** [`mɪzərɪ] (n.) 痛苦，不幸的
Grandmother has lived in misery since Grandfather passed away.
爺爺過世後奶奶一直活在痛苦當中。

5 **Miss** [mɪs] (n.) 小姐
Miss Bella is still single.
貝拉小姐還是單身。

36 **miss** [mɪs] (v.) 錯失
Johnny never misses the cartoon.
強尼從未錯過這部卡通。

35 **missile** [`mɪsḷ] (n.) 飛彈，導彈
North Korea's military is developing a number of new missiles.
北韓的軍方正在發展數種新飛彈。

A B C D E F G H I J K L M N O P Q R S T U V W X Y Z

37 **missing** [ˋmɪsɪŋ] (a.) 失蹤的
Lila has been missing for three days.
麗拉已經失蹤三天了。

35 **mission** [ˋmɪʃən] (n.) 任務
The soldier completed the mission in time.
這個士兵及時完成任務。

25 **mist** [mɪst] (n.) 薄霧
This mountain is hidden in the mist.
這座山藏在薄霧之中。

35 **mistake** [mɪˋstek] (n.) 錯誤
Don't make the same mistake again.
別再犯同樣的錯誤了。

36 **mix** [mɪks] (v.) 使混合
Ann mixed all the fruits together.
安把所有水果都混在一起了。

35 **mixture** [ˋmɪkstʃɚ] (n.) 混合
The juice is a mixture of vegetables and fruits.
這杯果汁由蔬菜與水果混合而成。

35 **mob** [mɑb] (n.) 犯罪集團
Uncle used to be a member of the mob.
叔叔曾經是犯罪集團的一員。

37 **mobile** [ˋmobɪl] (a.) 可移動的
There are mobile toilets in the park.
公園裡有流動廁所。

24 **model** [ˋmɑdl̩] (n.) 模型，模特兒
The young fashion model doesn't even know how to walk on the runway.
這個年輕模特兒甚至不知該如何在伸展台上走。

37 **modern** [ˋmɑdɚn] (a.) 現代化的，時髦的
This new elementary school is so modern.
這所新小學很現代化。

37 **moist** [mɔɪst] (a.) 溼的，含淚的
The dog's eyes are moist with tears.
這隻狗狗的眼睛含著淚。

35 **moisture** [ˋmɔɪstʃɚ] (n.) 溼氣，水分
The sun will take the moisture out of the clothes.
太陽會把衣服的水分蒸發掉。

8 **moment** [ˋmomənt] (n.) 短暫時刻
He'll be here in a moment.
他馬上就到。

8 **Monday** [ˋmʌnde] (n.) 星期一
We will have a field trip on Monday.
我們星期一有校外教學。

9 **money** [ˋmʌnɪ] (n.) 錢
No matter how much I earn, I feel like I never have enough money.
不論賺多少錢，我總是覺得不夠。

35 **monk** [mʌŋk] (n.) 修道士，憎侶
Many monks live and pray in that temple on the hill.
許多和尚住在山上的那座廟裡修行祈禱。

27 **monkey** [ˋmʌŋkɪ] (n.) 猴子
Monkeys love bananas.
猴子喜歡香蕉。

27 **monster** [ˋmɑnstɚ] (n.) 怪物
Are your afraid of monsters?
你怕怪物嗎？

8 **month** [mʌnθ] (n.) 月
Her family will go to Hong Kong next month.
她們一家人下個月要去香港。

8 **monthly** [ˋmʌnθlɪ] (a.) 每月的
We have a monthly meeting at the end of every month.
我們每個月月底開月會。

35 **mood** [mud] (n.) 心情
She's in a bad mood.
她心情不好。

25 **moon** [mun] (n.) 月亮
We have a full moon tonight.
今晚是滿月。

23 **Moon Festival** [mun ˋfɛstəvḷ] (n.) 中秋節
Moon Festival is usually in September.
中秋節通常在九月。

35 **mop** [mɑp] (n.) 拖把
Mother cleans the floor with a mop.
媽媽用拖把拖地。

37 **moral** [ˋmɔrəl] (a.) 道德的，精神上的
My parents will give me moral support.
我父母會給我精神上的支持。

7 **more** [mɔr] (a.) 更多的
He needs more money.
他需要更多的錢。

8 **morning** [ˋmɔrnɪŋ] (n.) 早晨
We have to wake up early in the morning.
我們必須一大早起床。

27 **mosquito** [mə`skito] (n.) 蚊子
Summer is the season for mosquitoes.
夏天是蚊子出沒的季節。

29 **most** [most] (a.) 最…
Most teachers don't like naughty students.
大部分老師不喜歡頑皮的學生。

17 **motel** [mo`tɛl] (n.) 汽車旅館
They will be staying at the motel tonight.
他們今晚會住在汽車旅館。

6 **mother** [`mʌðɚ] (n.) 母親(口語稱mommy或mom)
Her mother is a nurse.
她媽媽是護士。

35 **motion** [`moʃən] (n.) 移動
The rocking motor of the boat made Amy sick.
船的震動馬達讓艾咪暈船。

18 **motor** [`motɚ] (a.) 汽車的
The twin brothers are both in the motor industry.
這對雙胞胎兄弟都從事汽車業。

18 **motor** [`motɚ] (n.) 馬達,引擎
Your car needs to have a new motor put in it.
你的車需要換新的引擎。

18 **motorcycle** [`motɚ,saɪkl̩] (n.) 摩托車
It's dangerous to ride a motorcycle in a city like Taipei.
在台北這種城市騎機車很危險。

14 **mountain climbing** [`maʊntn̩ `klaɪmɪŋ] (n.) 登山
Let's go mountain climbing on Sunday.
我們星期天去爬山吧。

26 **mountain** [ˋmaʊntn̩] (n.) 山
There are monkeys in the mountains.
山裡有猴子。

27 **mouse** [maʊs] (n.) 老鼠
Most children love Mickey mouse.
大多數小孩都喜歡米老鼠。

3 **mouth** [maʊθ] (n.) 嘴
The dentist asked me to open my mouth very wide.
牙醫要我大大張開嘴巴。

36 **move** [muv] (v.) 移動
Don't move your chair.
別移動你的椅子。

35 **movement** [ˋmuvmənt] (n.) 動作
The dog is lying there without any movement.
這隻狗躺在那裡動也不動。

14 **movie** [ˋmuvɪ] (n.) 電影
I love horror movies.
我愛看恐怖片。

5 **Mr.** [ˋmɪstɚ] (n.) 先生 （mister的簡稱）
Mr. Peterson is Eddy's father.
彼得森先生是艾迪的爸爸。

5 **Mrs.** [ˋmɪsɪz] (n.) 太太
Mrs. Peterson is Eddy's mother.
彼得森太太是艾迪的媽媽。

18 **MRT** [ɛm ɑr ti] (n.) 大眾捷運系統（Mass Rapid Transit的簡稱）
It's convenient to go anywhere by MRT in Taipei.
在台北搭捷運到任何地方都很方便。

5 **Ms.** [mɪz] (a.) 女士
Ms. Smith has lived alone all her life.
史密斯女士一生形影相弔。

35 **MV** [ˋɛmˋvi] (n.) 音樂錄影帶（Music Video的縮寫）
All teenagers love to watch MV.
所有青少年都愛看音樂錄影帶。

7 **much** [mʌtʃ] (a.) 很多
I didn't have much money today.
我今天沒帶多少錢。

35 **mud** [mʌd] (n.) 泥巴
The doorway is full of mud after the rain.
下雨過後，門廊上都是泥巴。

36 **murder** [ˋmɝdɚ] (v., n.) 謀殺
The police are busy with the murder case.
警察正忙著調查這件謀殺案。

3 **muscle** [ˋmʌsl̩] (n.) 肌肉
The bones are covered by muscle.
骨骼被肌肉所包覆。

17 **museum** [mjuˋzɪəm] (n.) 博物館
There are a lot of famoues museums in France.
法國有許多著名的博物館。

10 **mushroom** [ˋmʌʃ,rʊm] (n.) 磨菇
Some mushrooms are poisionous.
有些磨菇是有毒的。

14 **music** [ˋmjuzɪk] (n.) 音樂
Julien loves jazz music.
朱立安喜愛爵士樂。

37 **musical** [ˋmjuzɪkḷ] (a.) 音樂的
Do you want to go to the musical concert tonight?
你今晚想去聽音樂會嗎?

24 **musician** [ˌjuˋzɪʃən] (n.) 音樂家
My sister is determined to be a famous musician.
我姊姊決心要成為出名的音樂家。

31 **must** [mʌst] (aux.) 必須
You must not tell the secret to anyone.
你絕對不可以告訴任何人這個祕密。

29 **myself** [maɪˋsɛlf] (pron.) 我自己
I live by myself.
我一個人住。

37 **mystery** [ˋmɪstərɪ] (n.) 神祕，謎
The death of President Kennedy remains a mystery.
甘迺迪總統的死至今仍是個謎。

N

3 **nail** [nel] (n.) 指甲
We must cut our nails every month.
我們每個月都必須剪指甲。

5 **name** [nem] (n.) 名字
What's her name?
她叫什麼名字？

24 **nanny** [ˋnænɪ] (n.) 保母
My first paid job was a job as a nanny.
我第一份有給職是當保母。

35 **nap** [næp] (n.) 午睡，打盹兒
My grandparents are tired so they are taking a nap.
爺爺奶奶都累了所以他們正在睡午覺。

35 **napkin** [ˋnæpkɪn] (n.) 餐巾（紙）
He folded the napkin into a flower.
他把紙巾摺成一朵花。

19 **narrow** [ˋnæro] (a.) 狹窄的
You shouldn't be so narrow- minded.
你的心胸不該這麼狹小。

20 **nation** [ˋneʃən] (n.) 民族，國家
Cultures are different from nation to nation.
各國文化不盡相同。

20 **national** [ˋnæʃənl̩] (a.) 全國的
He plays baseball for the national team.
他為棒球國家隊效力。

37 **native** [ˋnetɪv] (a.) 祖國的，本國的
They are native speakers of Japanese.
日語是他們的母語。

25 **natural** [ˋnætʃərəl] (a.) 自然的
This is a strange natural scene.
這是一個奇特的自然現象。

25 **nature** [ˋnetʃɚ] (n.) 自然
If man is too selfish, mother nature will be destroyed.
如果人類太自私，大自然將會被摧毀。

2 **naughty** [ˋnɔtɪ] (a.) 頑皮的
Kids from kindergarten are very naughty.
幼稚園的小孩很調皮。

24 **navy** [ˋnevɪ] (n.) 海軍的
My brother works in the navy.
我的哥哥在海軍服務。

19 **near** [nɪr] (a.) 近的
The restaurant is quite near; you can walk there.
這家餐廳很近，你可以走路過去。

19 **nearly** [ˋnɪrlɪ] (adv.) 幾乎
The cat was nearly dead.
這隻貓差一點就死了。

37 **necessary** [ˋnɛsə,sɛrɪ] (a.) 必須的
Oxygen is necessary for us.
氧氣是我們不可或缺的東西。

35 **necessity** [nəˋsɛsətɪ] (n.) 必需品
Water is a necessity for humans.
水是人類的生活必需品。

3 **neck** [nɛk] (n.) 頸部
She wore a scarf around her neck.
她在脖子上圍了一條圍巾。

12 **necklace** [ˋnɛklɪs] (n.) 項鍊
The lady wore a fancy necklace.
那位女士戴著一串華麗的項鍊。

12 **necktie** [ˋnɛk,taɪ] (n.) 領帶
I don't like to wear necktie to work.
我上班不喜歡打領帶。

36 **need** [nid] (v.) 需要
The sneakers need washing.
這雙球鞋需要清洗。

15 **needle** [ˋnidḷ] (n.) 針
The needles in the hospitals should not be used repeatedly.
醫院的針頭不應該重複使用。

37 **negative** [ˋnɛgətɪv] (a.) 否定的，負面的
We must not have negative attitudes toward our parents.
我們對父母親不能有忤逆的態度。

1 **neighbor** [ˋnebɚ] (n.) 鄰居
My neighbors come to see me every weekend.
我的鄰居每個週末都來看我。

1 **neighborhood** [ˋnebɚ,hʊd] (n.) 鄰近地區
We live in the neighborhood of the zoo.
我們就住在動物園附近。

38 **neither** [ˋniðɚ] (conj.) 兩者皆不
Neither one of you will be home early.
你們兩人都不會早到家。

6 **nephew** [ˋnɛfju] (n.) 姪兒，外甥
Her nephew lives in the States.
她的姪兒住在美國。

3 **nerve** [nɝv] (n.) 神經，焦慮
My teacher's staring got on my nerves.
老師盯著我看，讓我很緊張。

2 **nervous** [ˋnɝvəs] (a.) 緊張
Michael was nervous about his wedding.
麥克對他的婚禮很緊張。

15 **nest** [nɛst] (n.) 巢
There are two birds in the nest.
鳥巢裡有兩隻鳥。

35 **network** [ˋnɛt,wɝk] (n.) 網路系統，廣播網
There is something wrong with the network so the Internet isn't working.
網路故障，所以現在無法上網。

38 **never** [ˋnɛvɚ] (adv.) 從不
Never ever accept candies from strangers.
絕對不可以拿陌生人給的糖。

23 **New Year** [ˋnjʊ ˋjɪr] (n.) 新年
We are expecting the coming of New Year.
我們正在期盼新年的到來。

23 **New Year's Eve** [nju jɪrz iv] (n.) 除夕
My brother will come back on New Year's Eve.
我的哥哥會在除夕夜回來。

37 **new** [nju] (a.) 新的
This is my new piano.
這是我的新鋼琴。

35 **news** [njuz] (n.) 新聞
The plane crash became international news.
墜機事件成為國際新聞。

35 **newspaper** [ˋnjuz,pepɚ] (n.) 報紙
I read about the star's suicide in the evening newspaper.
我在晚報上看到那位明星自殺的消息。

32 **next to** [ˋnɛkst tu] 隔壁，旁邊
The fast food restaurant is next to the bus station.
速食店在公車站旁邊。

8 **next** [nɛkst] (a.) 緊接的，居後的
John lives next to school.
約翰住在學校隔壁。

2 **nice** [naɪs] (a.) 美好的
Her grandmother is really nice to everyone.
她祖母對每個人都很好。

2 **nice-looking** [`naɪs`lʊkɪŋ] (a.) 漂亮的，好看的
Uncle Bob is a nice-looking man.
鮑伯叔叔是個英俊的男人。

35 **nickname** [`nɪk,nem] (n.) 別名，小名
Daddy always calls Mother by the nickname"baby."
爸爸總是用暱稱「寶貝」稱呼媽媽。

6 **niece** [nis] (n.) 姪女，外甥女
My niece, Nicole, is five years old now.
我的姪女妮可現在五歲。

8 **night** [naɪt] (n.) 夜
I usually go to the park at night.
我經常晚上去公園。

7 **nine** [naɪn] (n., a.) 九（個的）
Tim has nine dogs.
提姆養了九隻狗。

7 **nineteen** [`naɪn`tin] (n., a.) 十九個（的）
There are nineteen cakes on the table.
桌上有十九塊蛋糕。

7 **nineteenth** [`naɪn`tinθ] (a.) 第十九的
Her new apartment is on the nineteenth floor.
她的新公寓位在十九樓。

7 **ninety** [`naɪntɪ] (n., a.) 九十
Ninety plus ten is one hundred.
九十加十等於一百。

7 **ninth** [naɪnθ] (a.) 第九的
It was the boy's ninth birthday yesterday.
昨天是這男孩的九歲生日。

37 **noble** [ˋnobl̩] (a.) 貴族的，高貴的
I was born in a noble family.
我出生於貴族家庭。

29 **nobody** [ˋno,bɑdɪ] (pron.) 沒有人
When I arrived at the office nobody was there.
我到辦公室的時候，一個人都沒有。

36 **nod** [nɑd] (v.) 點頭
She nodded her head.
她點了點頭。

35 **noise** [nɔɪz] (n.) 噪音
This car makes loud noises.
這部車發出很大的噪音。

37 **noisy** [ˋnɔɪzɪ] (a.) 吵雜的
It's so noisy in the classroom!
教室裡面好吵！

29 **none** [nʌn] (pron.) 沒有任何人（物）
None of students finished their homework.
沒有一個學生有把功課做完。

10 **noodle** [ˋnudl̩] (n.) 麵
We had beef noodles for dinner.
我們晚餐吃牛肉麵。

8 **noon** [nun] (n.) 中午
Students have to take a nap at noon.
學生中午必須睡個午覺。

38 **nor** [nɔr] (conj.) （既不）…也不
Mary didn't do homework; nor did Tony.
瑪莉沒做功課；東尼也沒做。

37 **normal** [ˋnɔrml̩] (a.) 正常的
It's normal for me to come home at five.
對我來說，五點回到家很正常。

17 **north** [nɔrθ] (n.) 北方
This house is facing the north.
這棟房屋面向北方。

17 **northern** [ˋnɔrðən] (a.) 北方的
The northern climate is usually colder than the southern.
北方的氣候通常比南方冷。

3 **nose** [noz] (n.) 鼻子
I have a running nose.
我在流鼻水。

16 **note** [not] (n.) 筆記
Remember to take down some notes for accounting class.
會計課記得抄筆記。

16 **notebook** [ˋnot,bʊk] (n.) 筆記型電腦
I always keep my notebook with me.
我總是隨身攜帶筆記型電腦。

29 **nothing** [ˋnʌθɪŋ] (pron.) 沒什麼
There is nothing to worry about.
沒什麼好擔心的。

36 **notice** [ˋnotɪs] (v.) 注意
I noticed Tammy's new hairstyle.
我注意到泰咪的新髮型。

14 **novel** [`nɑvḷ] (n.) 小說
I like to read novels before going to bed.
我喜歡在睡覺前看小說。

24 **novelist** [`nɑvəlɪst] (n.) 小說家
J.K. Rowling is a famous novelist.
J.K.蘿琳是一位有名的小說家。

8 **November** [no`vɛmbɚ] (n.) 十一月
My birthday is in November.
我的生日在十一月。

8 **now** [naʊ] (adv.) 現在
It's time to go to bed now.
現在該去睡覺了。

7 **number** [`nʌmbɚ] (n.) 電話號碼，數字
I didn't call her because I lost her phone number.
我沒打電話給她，因為我弄丟了她的電話號碼。

24 **nun** [nʌn] (n.) 尼姑，修女
She was raised by a nun.
她由一位尼姑扶養長大。

24 **nurse** [nɝs] (n.) 護士
Nightingale was a great nurse.
南丁格爾是名偉大的護士。

10 **nut** [nʌt] (n.) 堅果
The squirrel stores nuts away for winter.
松鼠為了過冬儲藏堅果。

O

25 **oak** [ok] (n.) 橡樹
This desk is made from real oak.
這張書桌是用橡木實木做的。

36 **obey** [oˋbe] (v.) 服從
We have to obey what the teacher says.
我們必須聽老師的話。

35 **object** [ˋɑbdʒɪkt] (n.) 物體
That is a round object.
那是一個圓形的物體。

36 **observe** [əbˋzɝv] (v.) 觀察
The police observed the man for two hours before arresting him.
警察觀察那個人觀察了兩個小時才逮捕他。

37 **obvious** [ˋɑbvɪəs] (a.) 明顯的
It's quite obvious that they are going on a date.
很明顯的他們正要去約會。

35 **occasion** [əˋkeʒən] (n.) 場合，時機
The party wasn't an occasion for wearing jeans.
這個派對並不是適合穿牛仔褲的場合。

36 **occur** [əˋkɝ] (v.) 發生
It occurs to me that you owe me 500 dollars.
我突然想到你欠我五百元。

26 **ocean** [ˋoʃən] (n.) 海洋
Whales live in the ocean.
鯨生活在海裡。

8 **o'clock** [ə`klɑk] (adv.) 點鐘
It's four o'clock now.
現在時間四點整。

8 **October** [ɑk`tobɚ] (n.) 十月
Halloween is on the 31 October.
萬聖節前夕是十月三十一日。

37 **odd** [ɑd] (a.) 古怪，奇特
She is an odd old lady.
她是一位古怪的老女人。

32 **of** [əv] (prep.)（屬於）…的
The wheels of the car are flat.
車子的輪胎沒有氣了。

32 **off** [ɔf] (adv.) 離開
They took off early today.
他們今天提早離開了。

36 **offer** [`ɔfɚ] (v.) 提供
He offered me a cup of coffee.
他給我一杯咖啡。

17 **office** [`ɔfɪs] (n.) 辦公室
He went to the office early this morning.
他今天早上很早就去辦公室了。

24 **official** [ə`fɪʃəl] (n.) 官員
The officials in the city hall are very efficient.
市政府的官員非常有效率。

19 **often** [`ɔfən] (adv.) 常常
I often sleep till noon on Sundays.
我星期天常睡到中午。

10 **oil** [ɔɪl] (n.) 油
The oil crisis is still unsettled.
石油危機仍未解決。

2 **old** [old] (a.) 老的
My father said he is getting old.
我爸說他越來越老了。

36 **omit** [o`mɪt] (v.) 遺漏，刪除
Omit unnecessary words in your writing.
把文章中不必要的字刪掉。

32 **on** [ɑn] (prep.) 在…上
There are some fruits on the table.
桌上有些水果。

8 **once** [wʌns] (adv.) 一次
They go to the movies once a month.
他們一個月去看一次電影。

7 **one** [wʌn] (a.) 一個的
Only one student could answer the teacher's question.
只有一個學生有辦法回答老師的問題。

29 **oneself** [wʌn`sɛlf] (pron.) 自身
One shouldn't climb the high mountain by oneself.
一個人不應該獨自攀登高山。

10 **onion** [`ʌnjən] (n.) 洋蔥
She flavored her corn soup with a great deal of onion.
她用大量洋蔥給玉米濃湯調味。

7 **only** [`onlɪ] (a.) 唯一的
He is her only child.
他是她唯一的孩子。

32 **onto** [ˋantu] (prep.) 向…之上
My cat jumped onto the computer.
我的貓咪跳上電腦。

36 **open** [ˋopən] (v.) 打開
Please open the door for him.
請幫他開門。

36 **operate** [ˋapə,ret] (v.) 運作
I don't know how to operate this machine.
我不會操作這部機器。

35 **operation** [,apəˋreʃən] (n.) 操作
The operation of this machine is easy to learn.
這部機器的操作方式很容易學。

24 **operator** [ˋapə,retɚ] (n.) 接線生
My sister works as a telephone operator.
我的姊姊是一位電話接線生。

35 **opinion** [əˋpɪnjən] (n.) 觀點
Do you have any opinions on this topic?
你對這個題目有什麼意見嗎?

35 **opportunity** [,apɚˋtjunətɪ] (n.) 機會
Opportunities slip away.
機會稍縱即逝。

32 **opposite** [ˋapəzɪt] (prep.) 對面
She lives opposite the school.
她住在學校對面。

37 **optimistic** [,aptəˋmɪstɪk] (a.) 樂觀的
My parents are optimistic people.
我父母親是樂觀的人。

33 **or** [ɔr] (conj.) 或，否則
Do you want tea or coffee?
你要茶還是咖啡？

37 **oral** [ˋorəl] (a.) 口頭的
We have an oral exam this morning.
我們今天早上有口試。

13 **orange** [ˋɔrɪndʒ] (a.) 橘色的
Dad bought an orange coat for me.
爸爸買了件橘色外套給我。

19 **orange** [ˋɔrɪndʒ] (n.) 柳橙
Grandma bought some oranges from the market.
奶奶從市場買了一些柳橙。

35 **order** [ˋɔrdɚ] (n.) 命令
My boss gave me an order to clean the floor.
我的老闆命令我去清潔地板。

36 **order** [ˋɔrdɚ] (v.) 點菜
I'd like to order something to eat.
我想要點一點東西吃。

37 **ordinary** [ˋɔrdə,nɛrɪ] (a.) 平常的
The famous star looks like an ordinary person.
那知名明星看起來像個平凡人。

24 **organization** [,ɔrgənəˋzeʃən] (n.) 組織
I work in a non-profit organization.
我在一個非營利性組織裡工作。

36 **organize** [ˋɔrgə,naɪz] (v.) 組織
Mother always organizes her free time well.
媽媽總是把她的空閒時間安排得很好。

35 **origin** [ˋɔrədʒɪn] (n.) 起源
He has a great family whose origins can be traced back to 18th century.
他有個不凡的家族，起源可追溯到十八世紀。

37 **original** [əˋrɪdʒənl̩] (a.) 原始
The original price of the house was too high.
這房子的原價太高。

35 **orphan** [ˋɔrfən] (n.) 孤兒
I became an orphan at the age of four.
我四歲時成為孤兒。

29 **other** [ˋʌðɚ] (a.) 其他的
There is no other way to settle the quarrel.
沒有其他方式可以解決紛爭了。

31 **ought to** [ɔt tu] (aux.) 應當
You ought to study hard before the exam.
考試前應該認真念書。

7 **our** [aʊr] (pron.) 我們的
Our children are all in college already.
我們的小孩都已經上大學了。

29 **ours** [aʊrz] (pron.) 我們的（東西）
It is not your money; it is ours.
這不是你的錢，是我們的。

29 **ourselves** [ˌaʊrˋsɛlvz] (pron.) 我們自己
Since living away from home, we have to take of ourselver.
既然不住家裡，我們就必須自己照顧自己。

38 **out of** [aʊt əv] (phr.) 自…離開
Don't put your head out of the window.
不要把頭伸出車外。

❸❽ **out** [aʊt] (adv.) 出外
He went out today.
他今天出去了。

❸❼ **outdoor** [ˋaʊt,dor] (a.) 戶外的
I like to play outdoor sports.
我喜歡從事戶外運動。

❸❽ **outdoors** [ˋaʊt,dorz] (adv.) 在戶外
They played outdoors until the sun set.
他們在戶外一直玩到太陽下山。

❸❼ **outer** [ˋaʊtɚ] (a.) 在外的，外面的
The outer door of the apartment isn't locked.
公寓外面的那扇門沒有鎖。

❸❺ **outline** [ˋaʊt,laɪn] (n.) 外型，輪廓
Uncle Kenny isn't satisfied with the outline of the car.
肯尼叔叔對車子的外型不滿意。

❸❷ **outside** [ˋaʊtˋsaɪd] (prep.) 在…外
Dad will wait outside.
爸爸會在外面等。

❶❺ **oven** [ˋʌvən] (n.) 烤箱
We don't have a oven to make pizza.
我們沒有烤箱可以做比薩。

❸❷ **over** [ˋovɚ] (prep.) 在…上面
The dark clouds floated over the mountain.
山頂上烏雲密布。

❶❷ **overcoat** [ˋovɚ,kot] (n.) 外套，大衣
It's very cold outside; put on your overcoat.
外面很冷，把外套穿上。

18 **overpass** [͵ovɚ`pæs] (n.) 天橋

Walking through the overpass is safer than walking across the road.

走天橋比橫越馬路安全。

37 **overseas** [`ovɚ`siz] (a.) 國外的

They are overseas now.

他們目前人在國外。

2 **over-weight** [`ovɚ͵wet] (a.) 過重的

I am overweight and I need a diet.

我太重了，需要節食。

36 **owe** [o] (v.) 欠，應該給…

I owe you an apology.

我應該向你道歉。

37 **own** [on] (a.) 自己的

I want to have my own house some day.

我希望有朝一日能擁有屬於自己的房子。

24 **owner** [`onɚ] (n.) 擁有者

Tina is the owner of the music shop.

蒂娜是那家唱片行的老闆。

35 **ownership** [`onɚ͵ʃɪp] (n.) 所有權

The ownership of the property belongs to that old man.

這片地產的所有權屬於那個老人。

27 **ox** [ɑks] (n.) 牛，複數為oxen [`ɑksən]

Oxen don't produce milk.

公牛不生產牛乳。

P

8 **p.m.** [ˋpi ˋɛm] (abbr.) 下午

I usually go home at 7 p.m.

我通常晚上七點回家。

19 **pack** [pæk] (n.) 包

The beggar went in to the shop and bought a pack of cigaretts.

那個乞丐到商店裡買了包香菸。

35 **pack** [pæk] (v.) 打包，包裝

How long will you take to pack your luggage?

你打包行李要花多少時間？

35 **package** [ˋpækɪdʒ] (n.) 包裹

Would you like to guess what's inside the package?

你要不要猜猜看包裹裡是什麼東西啊？

19 **page** [pedʒ] (n.) 頁

How many pages are there in this book?

這本書有多少頁？

19 **pail** [pel] (n.) 桶

Dad fetched a pail of purple paint back home.

爸爸提了一桶紫色油漆回家。

4 **pain** [pen] (n.) 疼痛

I had a sharp pain in my left knee while running.

我跑步的時候左膝覺得刺痛。

4 **painful** [ˋpenfəl] (a.) 痛的

It looked so painful when he hurt his arm.

他手臂受傷，看起來很痛苦。

36 **paint** [pent] (v.) 油漆，上顏色
We painted our wall green.
我們把牆壁漆成綠色。

24 **painter** [ˋpentɚ] (n.) 畫家
She wants to be a painter.
她想要當畫家。

16 **painting** [ˋpentɪŋ] (n.) 畫作
An oil paintint is hung on the wall.
牆上掛了一幅油畫。

19 **pair** [pɛr] (n.) 一對
I am getting fat, and I think I need a pair of new jeans.
我變胖了，我想我需要一條新的牛仔褲。

12 **pajamas** [pəˋdʒæməz] (n.) 睡衣
I don't get used to sleeping in pajamas.
我不習慣穿睡衣睡覺。

1 **pal** [pæl] (n.) 朋友，同伴
We became good pals after a year in the school.
同窗一年後，我們結為好友。

15 **palace** [ˋpælɪs] (n.) 皇宮
He lives in the palace on a small island.
他住在一座小島上的皇宮。

13 **pale** [pel] (a.) 蒼白
Her skin is so pale white.
她的皮膚好蒼白。

15 **pan** [pæn] (n.) 平底鍋
It's not convenient to stir-fry rice in a pan.
用平底鍋炒飯並不方便。

10 **pancake** [ˋpæn,kek] (n.) 煎薄餅
Blueberry pancakes are my favorite breakfast!
藍莓薄餅是我最愛吃的早餐！

27 **panda** [ˋpændə] (n.) 貓熊
Pandas are from China.
貓熊產於中國。

36 **panic** [ˋpænɪk] (v.) 恐慌
Do not panic when there is an earthquake.
遇到地震時別恐慌。

12 **pants** [pænts] (n.) 褲子，長褲
He is wearing a colorful pants today.
他今天穿了一條五顏六色的長褲。

10 **papaya** [pəˋpɑjə] (n.) 木瓜
Papayas are usually grown in the tropical zone.
木瓜是熱帶常見的作物。

16 **paper** [ˋpepɚ] (n.) 紙
The detective wrote down the number on a piece of paper.
偵探把號碼寫在一張紙上。

35 **parade** [pəˋred] (n.) 閱兵，慶祝遊行
There will be a parade on New Year's Day.
元旦那天會有慶祝遊行。

17 **paradise** [ˋpærə,daɪz] (n.) 天堂
This place is like a paradise.
這個地方簡直是天堂。

35 **parcel** [ˋpɑrsl̩] (n.) 包裹
The mailman is at the door—are you expecting a parcel?
郵差在門口——你在等包裹送來嗎？

36 **pardon** [ˋpardṇ] (v.) 原諒
Pardon me for not writing to you as soon as possible.
原諒我沒能盡早寫信給你。

6 **parent** [ˋpɛrənt] (n.) 父親，母親
I love my parents.
我愛我的父母。

36 **park** [park] (v.) 停車
We can't park our car here.
我們不能在這裡停車。

17 **parking lot** [ˋparkɪŋ lat] (n.) 停車場
Do you know where the nearest parking lot is around here?
你知道這附近最近的停車場在哪裡嗎？

27 **parrot** [ˋpærət] (n.) 鸚鵡
My parrot isn't very smart--he can only say three words.
我的鸚鵡不太聰明——他只會說三個字。

29 **part** [part] (n.) 部分
He is going to take part in the play.
他將參與這齣劇的演出。

36 **participate** [parˋtɪsə,pet] (v.) 參與
I am going to participate in the speech contest.
我將要參加演講比賽。

37 **particular** [pəˋtɪkjələ] (a.) 特定的，獨特的
Harry wants a particular type of cellphone.
哈利想要某種特定款式的行動電話。

1 **partner** [ˋpartnə] (n.) 夥伴
He is my father's business partner.
他是我爸爸的生意夥伴。

17 **party** [ˋpɑrtɪ] (n.) 舞會，社交聚會
My parents will throw a birthday party for me this year.
我父母今年將會為我舉辦生日派對。

36 **pass** [pæs] (v.) 傳遞
Please pass the salt and pepper.
請把鹽和胡椒遞過來。

17 **passage** [ˋpæsɪdʒ] (n.) 走廊
The supermarket is in the end of the passage.
超級市場在這條走道的盡頭。

18 **passenger** [ˋpæsəndʒɚ] (n.) 乘客
After the emergency landing, all the passengers are safe and sound.
緊急迫降後，所有乘客都安然無恙。

35 **passion** [ˋpæʃən] (n.) 熱情
Mother has a great passion for painting.
媽媽非常熱愛畫畫。

35 **passport** [ˋpæs,pɔrt] (n.) 護照
He has ten passports from ten different countries.
他有十個國家的護照。

35 **password** [ˋpæs,wɜd] (n.) 密碼
The password is a ten-digit number.
這組密碼是十個數字的號碼。

8 **past** [pæst] (n.) 過去
He wasn't around for the past five years.
過去五年他人不在這裡。

36 **paste** [pest] (v.) 黏貼
Paste your drawings in the book, please.
請將你的畫貼在書本上。

18 **path** [pæθ] (n.) 路徑
There is a little path leading to the riverside.
有一條小徑通往河邊。

35 **patience** [`peʃəns] (n.) 耐心
Taking care of old people needs great patience.
照顧老人需要很大的耐心。

1 **patient** [`peʃənt] (n.) 病患
When the fire broke out, patients in the hospital all ran out.
火災發生時，醫院裡所有病患都跑出來了。

2 **patient** [`peʃənt] (a.) 有耐心的
Miss Lin is a patient teacher.
林小姐是位有耐心的老師。

35 **pattern** [`pætən] (n.) 圖案
It's said that the huge patterns in the corn field were made by aliens.
據說玉米田裡的巨大圖案是外星人做的。

36 **pause** [pɔz] (n.) 暫停
She continued her speech after a brief pause.
她稍作暫停便繼續她的演講。

17 **pavement** [`pevmənt] (n.) 人行道
The pavement is covered with snow.
人行道被雪覆蓋。

27 **paw** [pɔ] (n.) 爪子
The cat got injured paws.
那貓的爪子受傷了。

9 **pay** [pe] (v.) 付費
Can you pay back my money?
你能還我錢嗎？

16 **PE** [ˋpi ˋi] (n.) 體育課
I don't like PE class at school, especially swimming class.
我不喜歡上體育課，尤其是游泳課。

10 **pea** [pi] (n.) 豌豆
Peas are my favorite kind of vegetable.
豌豆是我最喜歡的一種蔬菜。

35 **peace** [pis] (n.) 平靜，和平
I told my little brother to leave me in peace.
我叫弟弟別來打擾我。

37 **peaceful** [ˋpisfəl] (a.) 和平的，寧靜的
My girlfriend and I enjoyed a peaceful evening at home last night.
我和女友昨晚在家享受寧靜的夜晚。

10 **peach** [pitʃ] (n.) 桃子
Peaches are more expensive than apples.
桃子比蘋果還貴。

35 **peak** [pik] (a.) 高峰的
July and August are the peak season for travelling.
七、八月是旅遊的旺季。

10 **pear** [pɛr] (n.) 梨
She bought a bag of pears.
她買了一袋梨子。

35 **pearl** [pɜl] (n.) 珍珠
The model is wearing a necklace made of pearls.
這模特兒戴著珍珠做的項鍊。

36 **peel** [pil] (v.) 削
You have to peel off the potato skin before you cook it.
煮馬鈴薯之前要削皮。

36 **peep** [pip] (v.) 偷窺
Don't peep through the keyhole.
別從鑰匙孔裡偷窺。

16 **pen** [pɛn] (n.) 筆，鋼筆
I need a pen to write with.
我需要一支筆來寫字。

16 **pencil box** [ˋpɛnsḷ bɑks] (n.) 鉛筆盒
There are no pencils in the pencil box.
這個鉛筆盒裡沒有鉛筆。

16 **pencil case** [ˋpɛnsḷ kes] (n.) 鉛筆盒
He puts his allowance in the pencil case.
他把零用錢放在鉛筆盒裡。

16 **pencil** [ˋpɛnsḷ] (n.) 鉛筆
The girl sharpens her pencils every day.
這個女孩每天削鉛筆。

9 **penny** [ˋpɛnɪ] (n.) 一分錢
My mother keeps a jar for pennies in the kitchen.
我媽媽在廚房放了一個罐子的一分錢硬幣。

1 **people** [ˋpipḷ] (n.) 人
There are five people in my family.
我家裡有五個人。

10 **pepper** [ˋpɛpɚ] (n.) 胡椒
I like to put pepper in my noodle soup.
我喜歡在湯麵裡加胡椒。

37 **perfect** [ˋpɝfɪkt] (a.) 完美的
Sarah says that she has found her perfect match.
莎拉說她已經找到她的完美伴侶。

36 **perform** [pɚ`fɔrm] (v.) 表演

Phil performed well in the play.

菲爾在話劇中表演得很好。

35 **performance** [pɚ`fɔrməns] (n.) 演出

The performance begins at six tonight.

表演在今天晚上六點開始。

8 **perhaps** [pɚ`hæps] (adv.) 或許

Perhaps I should buy him a pizza instead of a hamburger.

或許我該買個比薩給他，而不是漢堡。

35 **period** [`pɪrɪəd] (n.) 時期

The photo was taken during exciting period of life.

這張照片是在她人生最精彩的階段拍的。

35 **permission** [pɚ`mɪʃən] (n.) 准可

I got permission to be home after twelve tonight.

我今晚獲准過十二點後回家。

36 **permit** [pɚ`mɪt] (v.) 允許

She was not permitted to enter the country.

她不被允許進入這國家。

1 **person** [`pɝsn̩] (n.) 人

Who was the person next to you?

你身旁那個人是誰？

37 **personal** [`pɝsənl̩] (a.) 私人的

John doesn't like being asked too many personal questions.

約翰不喜歡被問到太多私人問題。

2 **personality** [,pɝsə`nælətɪ] (n.) 個性

My brother has a strong personality.

我哥哥很有個性。

36 **persuade** [pə`swed] (v.) 說服
Dad persuaded Mom to buy a new car.
爸爸說服媽媽買部新車。

35 **pest** [pɛst] (n.) 討厭的人
What a pest!
這人真討厭！

27 **pet** [pɛt] (n.) 寵物
Cats are cool but independent pets.
貓是冷淡而獨立的寵物。

35 **photo** [`foto] (n.) 照片
That is our family photo on the wall.
牆上那張是我們的全家福照片。

35 **photograph** [`fotə,græf] (n.) 照片
He took so many photographs on my wedding day.
我結婚那天他拍了好多照片。

24 **photographer** [fə`tɑgrəfɚ] (n.) 攝影師
The famous photographer will have an exhibition.
那位有名的攝影師將舉辦展覽。

16 **physics** [`fɪzɪks] (n.) 物理學
Physics is not an easy subject.
物理不是一門簡單的學科。

14 **piano** [pɪ`æno] (n.) 鋼琴
She has been learning playing the piano for a long time.
她學鋼琴學了很長一段時間。

36 **pick** [pɪk] (v.) 揀選
Mother picked a necktie as a birthday gift for father.
媽媽替爸爸挑了條領帶當生日禮物。

10 **pickle** [ˋpɪkḷ] (n.) 酸黃瓜
I love pickles on my hot dog.
我最喜歡熱狗加酸黃瓜。

14 **picnic** [ˋpɪknɪk] (n.) 野餐
We go on a picnic every Sunday.
我們每個星期天都去野餐。

16 **picture** [ˋpɪktʃɚ] (n.) 圖畫，照片
She doesn't like to have her picture taken.
她不喜歡拍照。

10 **pie** [paɪ] (n.) 派，餡餅
The apple pie is too hot to eat.
這蘋果派太燙了還不能吃。

19 **piece** [pis] (n.) 一片，一小塊
Could you give me a piece of cake?
你能給我一片蛋糕嗎？

27 **pig** [pɪg] (n.) 豬
Pigs are kept in the pen.
豬養在豬圈裡。

27 **pigeon** [ˋpɪdʒən] (n.) 鴿子
There are a lot of pigeons in the park.
公園裡有很多鴿子。

35 **pile** [paɪl] (n.) 堆
Please throw these piles of newspapers away.
請把這幾堆報紙丟掉。

35 **pill** [pɪl] (n.) 藥丸
Mother relies on sleeping pills every night.
媽媽每晚都靠安眠藥入睡。

15 **pillow** [ˋpɪlo] (n.) 枕頭

The pillow is so hard that I can't sleep well.

這枕頭太硬了，我睡不好。

24 **pilot** [ˋpaɪlət] (n.) 飛行員

Jay always wants to be a pilot.

傑一直想成為一位飛行員。

35 **pin** [pɪn] (n.) 別針

Kitty has so many cartoon pins.

凱蒂有好多卡通別針。

25 **pine** [paɪn] (n.) 松樹

The squirrels jump up and down on the pine trees.

松鼠在松樹上蹦蹦跳跳。

10 **pineapple** [ˋpaɪn,æpl̩] (n.) 鳳梨

This pineapple doesn't taste nice.

這顆鳳梨不好吃。

13 **pink** [pɪŋk] (a.) 粉紅色的

Pink doesn't match with black.

粉紅色和黑色不搭。

19 **pint** [pɪnt] (n.) 品脫

Can you bring me a pint of milk?

你可以幫我買一品脫牛奶嗎?

35 **pipe** [paɪp] (n.) 管子

The pipe at the bathroom is leaking.

浴室的水管在漏水。

35 **pit** [pɪt] (n.) 凹處

There is a huge pit in the road.

路上有一個大凹洞。

35 **pity** [ˋpɪtɪ] (n.) 憐憫
Scrooge shows no pity to the poor.
史庫齊對窮人毫無憐憫之心。

10 **pizza** [ˋpitsə] (n.) 比薩
I often have pizza on weekends.
我週末常吃比薩。

17 **place** [ples] (n.) 地方
This is a quiet place.
這裡是個安靜的地方。

26 **plain** [plen] (n.) 平原，原野
After you pass the small hill, you will see a green plain.
越過小山丘之後，就可以看到一片綠野。

35 **plan** [plæn] (n.) 計劃
Do you have any plan for your summer vacation?
暑假有任何計畫嗎？

36 **planet** [ˋplænɪt] (n.) 行星，星球
The planets move around the sun.
行星繞著太陽運行。

35 **plant** [plænt] (v., n.) 植物，種植
Grandma likes to plant flowers and vegetables in the backyard.
奶奶喜歡在後院種花和蔬菜。

37 **plastic** [ˋplæstɪk] (a.) 塑膠的，整形的
Stores can't provide customers with plastic bags now.
商店現在不可以提供塑膠袋給顧客。

17 **plate** [plet] (n.) 碟子，盤子
I need a little plate of soy-bean sauce to go with my fish.
我需要一小碟醬油沾魚肉。

18 **platform** [ˋplæt,fɔrm] (n.) 月台
I don't know which platform I should go.
我不知道該去哪個月台。

14 **play** [ple] (v.) 玩，打球，玩樂器
Do not play your drums at midnight.
不要在深夜打鼓。

24 **player** [ˋpleɚ] (n.) 選手
Ken wants to be a famous soccer player.
肯想要成為一位出名的足球選手。

16 **playground** [ˋple,graʊnd] (n.)（學校的）運動場，操場
During the break, students all play on the playground.
下課休息時間，學生都在操場玩。

37 **pleasant** [ˋplɛzənt] (a.) 令人愉快的
We had a pleasant evening at the party.
我們在宴會上度過愉快的夜晚。

36 **please** [pliz] (v.) 請
Please fill the water for me.
請幫我把水裝滿。

37 **pleased** [plizd] (a.) 愉悦的
I was pleased to see my cousins after five years.
真高興在五年後和我的堂兄弟相會。

35 **pleasure** [ˋplɛʒɚ] (n.) 愉快
It is my pleasure to help you.
能為您服務是我的榮幸。

35 **plenty** [ˋplɛntɪ] (n.) 豐富，充足
There is plenty of food for us for five months.
食物很充足，夠我們維持五個月。

35 **plug** [plʌg] (n.) 插頭
The electric plugs in Europe are different than in Taiwan.
歐洲使用的電插頭和台灣不同。

10 **plum** [plʌm] (n.) 梅子
This wine is made of plums.
這是梅子釀的酒。

24 **plumber** [`plʌmɚ] (n.) 水管工
The bathroom isn't working; we need a plumber.
浴室壞了，需要叫水電工。

19 **plus** [plʌs] (prep.) 加上
Eight plus two is ten.
八加二等於十。

12 **pocket** [`pɑkɪt] (n.) 口袋
I have a handful of candy in my pocket.
我口袋裡有一把糖果。

16 **poem** [`poɪm] (n.) 詩
Chinese poems are so beautiful.
中國詩好美啊。

24 **poet** [`poɪt] (n.) 詩人
The king was also known as a poet.
那位國王也是有名的詩人。

37 **poetic** [po`ɛtɪk] (a.) 詩意的
I am impressed with his poetic paintings.
他充滿詩意的畫作讓我印象深刻。

19 **point** [pɔɪnt] (n.) 點，分數
We got fifty points.
我們得到五十分。

35 **poison** [ˋpɔɪzn̩] (n.) 毒藥，毒物
Some cosmetics contain poisons.
有些化妝品含有毒性。

37 **poisonous** [ˋpɔɪzənəs] (a.) 有毒的
Some Chinese medicine is poisonous.
有些中藥有毒。

26 **pole** [pol] (n.) 極地區域
It's freezing in the South Pole.
南極非常寒冷。

24 **police officer** [ˋpəlɪs ˋɔfɪsɚ] (n.) 警員，警官
The police officer arrested the speeding driver.
那警察逮捕了那個超速的司機。

17 **police station** [pəˋlis ˋsteʃən] (n.) 警察局
We went to the police station to report the bike theft.
我們去警局報腳踏車失竊。

24 **policeman** [pəˋlismən] (n.) 警察
His father is a policeman.
他的爸爸是警察。

35 **policy** [ˋpɑləsɪ] (n.) 政策
Many people are unhappy about the government's policies.
很多人對政府的政策不滿意。

2 **polite** [pəˋlaɪt] (a.) 禮貌的
We have to be polite to other people.
我們必須對人有禮貌。

37 **political** [pəˋlɪtɪkl̩] (a.) 政治的
Sometimes educational issues are also political issues.
教育議題有時也是政治議題。

24 **politician** [,palə`tɪʃən] (n.) 從政者
Politicians are always busy during the election time.
選舉期間，政治人物總是非常忙碌。

16 **politics** [`palətɪks] (n.) 政治（學）
My brother wants to study politics.
我哥哥想研究政治學。

35 **poll** [pol] (n.) 民意調查
The public opinion poll shows that most are against wars.
民意調查顯示多數人反對戰爭。

36 **pollute** [pə`lut] (v.) 污染
Garbage pollutes our environment.
垃圾會污染環境。

35 **pollution** [pə`luʃən] (n.) 污染
Water pollution is getting serious in the countryside.
水污染在鄉村地區日益嚴重。

26 **pond** [pand] (n.) 池塘
There are leaves in the pond.
池塘裡有葉子。

27 **pony** [`ponɪ] (n.) 小馬
The little girl wants a pony for her birthday.
小女孩想要一匹小馬當作生日禮物。

17 **pool** [pul] (n.) 池子
This is a huge swimming pool!
這游泳池可真大啊！

2 **poor** [pʊr] (a.) 貧窮的
She gave the poor old man some money.
她給那個老人一些錢。

A B C D E F G H I J K L M N O P Q R S T U V W X Y Z

36 **pop** [pɑp] (v.) 突然出現

A clown popped out of the present when I opened it.

我打開禮物時，一個小丑突然跳了出來。

10 **popcorn** [ˋpɑp,kɔrn] (n.) 爆米花

I love eating popcorn at the movies.

我看電影的時候喜歡吃爆米花。

37 **popular** [ˋpɑpjələ˞] (a.) 受歡迎的

The mayor is very popular with his people.

這位市長很受人民歡迎。

35 **population** [,pɑpjəˋleʃən] (n.) 人口

The population of this country rose by 5%.

這個國家的人口成長了百分之五。

35 **porcelain** [ˋpɔrslɪn] (n.) 瓷器

There is an antique porcelain store around this area.

這附近有一家古董瓷器店。

10 **pork** [pɔrk] (n.) 豬肉

I am never tired of pork chop lunch box.

豬排便當我永遠都吃不膩。

19 **portion** [ˋporʃən] (n.) 份量，部分

The king left only a small portion of money to his daughter.

國王只留了一小部分的錢給他的女兒。

35 **portrait** [ˋportret] (n.) 肖像

She drew herself a portrait.

她畫了一幅自畫像。

17 **position** [pəˋzɪʃən] (n.) 位置

Can you show me the correct position of the police station?

可以告訴我警察局的正確位置嗎?

37 **positive** [ˋpɑzətɪv] (a.) 肯定的，正面的
I'm always positive about my life.
我對人生始終抱持正面的態度。

37 **possible** [ˋpɑsəbḷ] (a.) 可能的
Is it possible for you to come at five?
你有可能五點鐘來嗎?

17 **post office** [post ˋɔfɪs] (n.) 郵局
You can also save money in the post office.
你也可以在郵局存錢。

35 **postage** [ˋpostɪdʒ] (n.) 郵資
The overseas postage is expensive.
寄到國外的郵資很貴。

35 **postcard** [ˋpost,kɑrd] (n.) 明信片
I always send postcards back home when traveling.
旅行時我都會寄明信片回家。

35 **poster** [ˋpostɚ] (n.) 海報
The movie theater hangs a lot of huge posters on the wall.
這間電影院在牆上掛了許多大型海報。

36 **postpone** [postˋpon] (v.) 延期
The meeting must be postponed to next week.
會議必須延到下星期舉行。

15 **pot** [pɑt] (n.) 鍋，罐，壺
Vicky made a pot of tea.
維琪泡了一壺茶。

10 **potato** [pəˋteto] (n.) 馬鈴薯
The poor family only had potatoes for dinner.
那戶窮人家晚餐只吃了馬鈴薯。

14 **pottery** [ˋpɑtərɪ] (n.) 陶藝
Pottery is one of my hobbies.
陶藝是我的嗜好之一。

19 **pound** [paʊnd] (n.) 英鎊
He weighs 90 pounds.
他有九十磅重。

36 **pour** [por] (v.) 倒，灌入
The waitress poured me some free coffee.
那名女服務生幫我倒了些免費的咖啡。

35 **poverty** [ˋpɑvɚtɪ] (n.) 貧窮
She lives in poverty.
她的生活很貧窮。

35 **powder** [ˋpaʊdɚ] (n.) 粉末
The pills are ground into powder.
那些藥丸被磨成粉末。

35 **power** [ˋpaʊɚ] (n.) 權力
She doesn't have the power over you.
她沒有權力管你。

37 **powerful** [ˋpaʊɚfəl] (a.) 有力量的
The president of the U.S. is the most powerful president in the world.
美國總統是全球最有權力的總統。

37 **practical** [ˋpræktɪkl̩] (a.) 實際的
Please be practical in your research.
你的研究請實際一點。

16 **practice** [ˋpræktɪs] (v.) 練習
He practices the piano every day.
他每天練習彈鋼琴。

35 **praise** [prez] (n.) 讚美
Mike had lots of praise for the work that Jonna had done.
麥可對喬娜的工作成果讚不絕口。

36 **pray** [pre] (v.) 祈禱
He prays to God every day.
他每天向上帝祈禱。

35 **prayer** [ˋpreɚ] (n.) 祈禱文
We say our prayers every night before we go to bed.
我們每晚睡前都唸祈禱文。

37 **precious** [ˋprɛʃəs] (a.) 寶貴的
Life is presious.
生命是寶貴的。

36 **prefer** [prɪˋfɝ] (v.) 更喜歡
I prefer to study in the library.
我比較喜歡在圖書館念書。

35 **preparation** [ˌprɛpəˋreʃən] (n.) 準備
We need a lot of preparation before the family gathers.
我們必須在家人聚集之前，做好許多準備工作。

36 **prepare** [prɪˋpɛr] (v.) 準備
It will take about six weeks to prepare for the seminar.
準備研討會大約要花六週的時間。

35 **present** [ˋprɛzənt] (n.) 禮物
My parents put many presents under the Christmas tree.
我父母親在耶誕樹下放好多禮物。

36 **present** [prɪˋzɛnt] (v.) 呈現，提交
The lawyer presented the judge with lots of evidence.
律師向法官出示多項證據。

24 **president** [ˋprɛzədənt] (n.) 總統
She's the first female president.
她是第一位女總統。

36 **press** [prɛs] (v.) 按
If you need water, just press the button.
如果你需要水，就按那個按鈕。

35 **pressure** [ˋprɛʃɚ] (n.) 壓力
He is under a lot of pressure now.
他現在壓力很大。

36 **pretend** [prɪˋtɛnd] (v.) 假裝
She pretends to be busy in the office.
她在辦公室裡裝忙。

2 **pretty** [ˋprɪtɪ] (a.) 漂亮的
Gina's mother is a pretty woman.
吉娜的媽媽是個美女。

36 **prevent** [prɪˋvɛnt] (v.) 預防
You have to prevent the children from getting sick.
你要預防孩子生病。

37 **previous** [ˋprivɪəs] (a.) 先前的
The previous owner of this house must be a female.
這房子先前的主人一定是女性。

9 **price** [praɪs] (n.) 價格
The price of the MP3 is nine hundred dollars.
這個MP3隨身聽的價格是九百元。

24 **priest** [prist] (n.) 教士，神父
I go to my priest when I feel lost.
當我感到迷惘時，就去找我的神父。

1 **prince** [prɪns] (n.) 王子

The prince finally won the girl's heart.

王子終於贏得女孩的芳心。

24 **princess** [ˋprɪnsɪs] (n.) 公主

The princess married a normal farmer.

公主嫁給一位平凡的農夫。

24 **principal** [ˋprɪnsəpl̩] (n.) 校長

He's a principal in a high school.

他是一位中學校長。

35 **principle** [ˋprɪnsəpl̩] (n.) 原則，原理

Time traveling is an idea that is acceptable in principle.

時光旅行是在原理上可以接受的概念。

36 **print** [prɪnt] (v.) 印

This picture is printed out by the printer.

這張照片是用印表機印出來的。

35 **printer** [ˋprɪntɚ] (n.) 印表機

The ink is more expensive than the cheap printer.

墨水比便宜的印表機還貴。

17 **prison** [ˋprɪzn̩] (n.) 監獄

They were in prison for five years.

他們坐了五年的牢。

1 **prisoner** [ˋprɪzənɚ] (n.) 囚犯

The prisoners should wear uniforms here.

囚犯在這裡必須穿制服。

37 **private** [ˋpraɪvɪt] (a.) 私人的

This is her mother's private office.

這是他媽媽的私人辦公室。

35 **prize** [praɪz] (n.) 獎品

The first prize for the winner is a car.

頭獎是一部汽車。

37 **probable** [ˋprɑbəbḷ] (a.) 很有可能的

It is highly probable that it will snow today.

今天很有可能會下雪。

35 **problem** [ˋprɑbləm] (n.) 問題

I'm having problems getting along with my coworkers.

我和同事相處有問題。

36 **proceed** [prəˋsid] (v.) 繼續進行

You may proceed with your speech.

你可以繼續你的演講了。

35 **process** [ˋprɑsɛs] (n.) 過程，步驟

Do you know the process of making cakes?

妳知道做蛋糕的步驟嗎?

36 **produce** [prəˋdjus] (v.) 生產，製造

The factory produces shoes.

這間工廠製造鞋子。

35 **product** [ˋprɑdəkt] (n.) 產品

The new product can't meet the demand of the market.

新產品無法滿足市場需求。

35 **production** [prəˋdʌkʃən] (n.) 製作

The production of this movie cost almost two millions dollars.

這部電影的製作費用將近兩百萬元。

37 **productive** [prəˋdʌktɪv] (a.) 具有生產力的

She's a productive writer.

她是一位多產的作家。

24 **profession** [prə`fɛʃən] (n.) 職業
He chooses teaching as his lifetime profession.
他選擇教書為終身職業。

24 **professional** [prə`fɛʃənl̩] (a.) 職業的
She is a professional dancer.
她是一位職業舞者。

24 **professor** [prə`fɛsɚ] (n.) 教授
She was a professor of English literature.
她以前是英國文學教授。

35 **profit** [`prɑfɪt] (n.) 利潤，利益
Selling ice-cream brings her a lot of profit.
賣冰淇淋為她帶來很多利潤。

37 **profitable** [prə`fɪtəbl̩] (a.) 有利潤的
Rasing cattle can be profitable.
養牛有可觀利潤。

35 **program** [`progræm] (n.) 節目
I never watch sports programs on TV.
我從不看電視的運動節目。

35 **progress** [`prɑgrɛs] (n.) 前進，進步
We made slow progress towards the mountain peak.
我們緩緩往山頂前進。

35 **project** [`prədʒkt] (n.) 企畫，方案
I handed in two English projects today.
我今天交了兩份英文作業。

37 **prominent** [`prɑmənənt] (a.) 突出的，顯眼的
The man is prominent in the crowd.
那位男士在人群裡顯得很突出。

36 **promise** [ˋprɑmɪs] (v.) 承諾

She promised not to cry again.

她答應不會再哭了。

37 **promising** [ˋprɑmɪsɪŋ] (a.) 大有可為的

You have a promising future.

你的未來大有可為。

36 **promote** [prəˋmot] (v.) 晉升

He will be promoted to the sixth grade soon.

他很快就要升上六年級了。

35 **promotion** [prəˋmoʃən] (n.) 提升

Congratulations on your new promotion!

恭喜你剛剛升官！

16 **pronounce** [prəˋnaʊns] (v.) 發…音

Do you know how to pronounce this word?

你知道這個字如何發音嗎？

16 **pronunciation** [prə,nʌnsɪˋeʃən] (n.) 發音

My English pronunciation isn't perfect.

我的英語發音不是很完美。

35 **proof** [pruf] (n.) 證據

She provide the proof on this research.

她為這項研究提供一個證據。

37 **proper** [ˋprɑpɚ] (a.) 適合的

I wondered whether it would be proper to knock on his door.

我不知道該不該敲他的門。

35 **property** [ˋprɑpɚtɪ] (n.) 資產

That house is my mother's only property.

那棟房子是我媽媽唯一的資產。

35 **proposal** [prə`pozḷ] (n.) 建議，提案
This is a new proposal for the new project.
這是為那項新計畫提出的新提案。

36 **propose** [prə`poz] (v.) 提議
Justin proposed to have a farewell party during the meeting.
賈斯汀在會議中提議舉辦告別派對。

36 **protect** [prə`tɛkt] (v.) 保護
The witness was protected by the police officer.
目擊者受到警察的保護。

35 **protection** [prə`tɛkʃən] (n.) 保護
People who ride motorbikes should wear helmets for protections.
為安全起見，機車騎士應戴安全帽。

37 **protective** [prə`tɛktɪv] (a.) 防護，保護
Her mother is too protective of her children.
她的媽媽太過保護她的孩子。

35 **protest** [prə`tɛst] (n.) 抗議
There was a strong protest to the new anti-smoking laws.
有一場反對新反菸法的強烈抗議。

2 **proud** [praʊd] (a.) 自豪的，驕傲的
My parents are proud of me.
我雙親對我感到驕傲。

36 **prove** [pruv] (v.) 證實
You need to prove that you are innocent.
你必須證明你是無辜的。

35 **proverb** [`prɑvɝb] (n.) 諺語，俗語
"Time is money" is a proverb.
「時間就是金錢」是一句諺語。

36 **provide** [prə`vaɪd] (v.) 提供

The school provides free lunch.

這所學校供應免費午餐。

24 **psychologist** [saɪ`kɑlədʒɪst] (n.) 心理學家

I'm so frustrated these days that I have to go to a psychologist.

我最近深感挫折，得去看心理醫師。

35 **psychology** [saɪ`kɑlədʒɪ] (n.) 心理學

Daddy has finally obtained his psychology degree.

爸爸終於獲得心理學學位。

17 **pub** [pʌb] (n.) 酒吧

She held her birthday party at a pub.

她在一間酒吧舉辦她的生日派對。

37 **public** [`pʌblɪk] (a.) 公眾的，公共的

I got this book from a public library.

我本書是向公立圖書館借來的。

35 **publication** [,pʌblɪ`keʃən] (n.) 出版

This magzine has been ceased publication.

這本雜誌已經停止出版了。

35 **publicity** [pʌb`lɪsətɪ] (n.) 名聲

Movie stars paticipate in a lot of activities to gain publicity.

電影明星參加很多活動來打知名度。

36 **publish** [`pʌblɪʃ] (v.) 出版，發行

My article was published in the evening newpapers.

我的文章刊在晚報上。

24 **publisher** [`pʌblɪʃɚ] (n.) 出版者，出版社

They are the top magazine publisher in England.

他們是英國頂尖的雜誌出版社。

36 **pull** [pʊl] (v.) 拉
She pulled the door open.
她把門拉開。

36 **pump** [pʌmp] (v.) 打水，汲水
We use this machine to pump water from our basement.
我們用這種機器把水從地下室抽出來。

10 **pumpkin** [ˋpʌmpkɪn] (n.) 南瓜
Jack-o'-lantern is made of a pumpkin.
感恩節燈籠是用南瓜做的。

36 **punch** [pʌntʃ] (v.) 用拳猛擊
He was so angry that he punched a hole on the door.
他氣到用拳頭把門打出一個洞。

36 **punish** [ˋpʌnɪʃ] (v.) 懲罰
My English teacher never punishes students.
我的英文老師從不處罰學生。

27 **puppy** [ˋpʌpɪ] (n.) 小狗
I had a small puppy when I was ten.
我十歲時養過一隻小狗。

36 **purchase** [ˋpɝtʃəs] (v.) 購買
We need to purchase the movie tickets from the counter.
我們必須在櫃檯購買電影票。

37 **pure** [pjʊr] (a.) 純粹的
This bowl is made from pure gold.
這只碗是純金打造的。

13 **purple** [ˋpɝpl̩] (a.) 紫色的
Grapes are purple.
葡萄是紫色的。

35 **purpose** [ˋpɝpəs] (n.) 目的
I know you didn't do it on purpose.
我知道你不是故意這樣做。

12 **purse** [pɝs] (n.) 錢包
She lost her purse.
她的錢包不見了。

36 **pursue** [pɚˋsu] (v.) 進行，從事
She has set her goals on pursuing her studies overseas.
她下定決心要去國外進修。

35 **pursuit** [pɚˋsut] (n.) 追求，尋求
His pursuit of fortune makes him greedier.
他對財富的追求使他更加貪婪。

36 **push** [pʊʃ] (v.) 推
Don't push in the hallway.
不要在走廊上推擠。

36 **put** [pʊt] (v.) 放
She put the fresh milk in the freezer.
她把新鮮的牛奶放進冰箱。

14 **puzzle** [ˋpʌzḷ] (n.) 拼圖
It takes time to put pieces of puzzles together.
把一片片拼圖拼起來需要時間。

36 **puzzle** [ˋpʌzḷ] (v.) 使困惑
The mystery puzzles me for a long time.
這個謎題讓我百思不得其解。

Q

36 **quake** [kwek] (v.) 震動，顫抖

The young boy was quaking in fear after being yelled at by his teacher.

老師對小男孩大吼大叫，害他怕得發抖。

35 **quality** [ˋkwɑlətɪ] (n.) 品質

The quality of this computer is not very good.

這部電腦的品質不是很好。

35 **quarrel** [ˋkwɔrəl] (n.) 爭吵

Mother has never had a quarrel with anyone.

媽媽從沒跟誰吵過架。

8 **quarter** [ˋkwɔrtɚ] (n.) 四分之一，一刻鐘

It's a quarter to eight.

現在是七點四十五分。

1 **queen** [kwin] (n.) 皇后，女王

Queen Elizabeth is the Queen of England.

伊麗莎白女王是英國女皇。

37 **queer** [kwɪr] (a.) 古怪，奇怪

The queer situation made me confused.

這古怪的情況讓我感到很困惑。

16 **question** [ˋkwɛstʃən] (n.) 疑問

Do you have any questions?

你有任何疑問嗎?

37 **quick** [kwɪk] (a.) 快速的

She is quick at learning Chinese.

她學中文學得很快。

A B C D E F G H I J K L M N O P Q R S T U V W X Y Z

37 **quiet** [ˋkwaɪət] (a.) 安靜的

It's very quiet at night where I live.

我住的地方夜裡很寧靜。

35 **quilt** [kwɪlt] (n.) 被子

Mother put a quilt next to the baby.

媽媽在寶寶旁邊放了一件被子。

38 **quite** [kwaɪt] (adv.) 相當地

The movie is quite funny.

那部電影很好笑。

16 **quiz** [kwɪz] (n.) 小考

We had quizzess every morning.

我們以前每天早上都有小考。

36 **quote** [kwot] (v.) 引用

The lecturer quoted some lines from the movie.

演講者引用了一些電影裡的對白。

R

27 **rabbit** [ˋræbɪt] (n.) 兔子

Rabbits has long ears.

兔子有長耳朵。

14 **race** [res] (n.) 種族，賽跑

There are countless races in the world.

世界上有許許多多的種族。

37 **racial** [ˋræʃəl] (a.) 人種的

Many countries are still dealing with racial problems.

很多國家仍有種族問題。

35 **radar** [ˋredɑr] (n.) 雷達
He has a radar in his car.
他車上有裝雷達。

15 **radio** [ˋredɪ,o] (n.) 收音機，無線電設備
At work, she likes to listen to the Internet radio.
她喜歡邊工作邊聽網路廣播。

35 **rag** [ræg] (n.) 抹布，碎布
We used some rages to wipe up the oil on the ground.
我們用一些抹布把地上的油擦起來。

35 **rage** [redʒ] (v.) 狂怒，肆虐
The typhoon is raging.
颱風正在肆虐。

18 **railroad** [ˋrel,rod] (n.) 鐵道
I love sitting near the railroad and watching the trains go by.
我喜歡坐在鐵道附近看火車經過。

18 **railway** [ˋrel,we] (n.) 鐵路
Taipei railway station is a landmark in Taipei.
台北火車站是台北的一個地標。

25 **rain** [ren] (n.) 雨
We had heavy rain last night.
昨天晚上下大雨。

25 **rainbow** [ˋren,bo] (n.) 彩虹
There are seven colors in a rainbow.
彩虹有七種顏色。

12 **raincoat** [ˋren,kot] (n.) 雨衣
I look stupid in that funny raincoat.
我穿那件怪雨衣看起來很笨。

25 **rainy** [ˋrenɪ] (a.) 下雨的
She likes rainy days.
她喜歡雨天。

36 **raise** [rez] (v.) 舉起
You can raise your hand if you have any questions.
有問題請舉手。

10 **raisin** [ˋrezn̩] (n.) 葡萄乾
Grandmother put some raisins in the cake.
奶奶在蛋糕裡放了一些葡萄乾。

35 **range** [rendʒ] (n.) 範圍
This missile has a range of over 100 kilometers.
這種飛彈的射程超過一百公里。

35 **rank** [ræŋk] (n.) 等級，身份
You can tell the rank of a general by the number of stars on his uniform.
從軍服上的星星數量，可以分辨將軍的階級。

37 **rapid** [ˋræpɪd] (a.) 迅速的
Grandma had a rapid recovery after her sickness.
奶奶的病很快就痊癒了。

37 **rare** [rɛr] (a.) 半生的
My mother doesn't like her steak rare.
我媽媽不喜歡五分熟的牛排。

27 **rat** [ræt] (n.) 鼠
Rats are the most terrible animals.
老鼠是最恐怖的動物。

35 **rate** [ret] (n.) 比率
The unemployment rate has increased for the past two years.
過去兩年的失業率上升了。

38 **rather** [ˋræðɚ] (adv.) 寧願
Dad would rather play golf than go shopping with mom.
爸爸寧願打高爾夫球也不陪媽逛街。

37 **raw** [rɔ] (a.) 生的，未煮過
I can't eat raw beef.
生牛肉我無法下嚥。

25 **ray** [re] (n.) 光線，射線
Rays of morning light came streaming through the windows at 6 a.m.
早上六點，一道道晨光透過窗子射進來。

35 **razor** [ˋrezɚ] (n.) 剃刀，刮鬍刀
That is a sharp razor.
那是一把鋭利的剃刀。

36 **reach** [ritʃ] (v.) 抵達
We have reached the top of the mountain.
我們已經抵達山頂。

36 **react** [rɪˋækt] (v.) 做出反應
How did he react to the news?
他對這新聞有什麼反應?

35 **reaction** [rɪˋækʃən] (n.) 反應
Her reaction was unpredictable.
她的反應出人意料。

16 **read** [rid] (v.) 閱讀
Father reads newspapers every day.
爸爸每天看報。

37 **ready** [ˋrɛdɪ] (a.) 準備好的
Dinner is ready.
晚飯準備好了。

37 **real** [ril] (a.) 真實的
It is a real story.
這是個真實的故事。

36 **realize** [rɪə,laɪz] (v.) 明白
Mandy finally realized how to solve the problem.
曼蒂終於明白這題目該怎麼解了。

38 **really** [`rɪəlɪ] (adv.) 真的
Did you really win the prize?
你真的得獎了嗎?

35 **reason** [`rizn̩] (n.) 理由
What's the reason for your absence?
你缺席的理由是什麼?

36 **reason** [`rizn̩] (v.) 理論
That old man is so crazy; you can't reason with him.
那個老人瘋了,你無法跟他講道理。

2 **reasonable** [`rizənəbl̩] (a.) 講道理的
My parents were always reasonable.
我的父母過去一直都很明理。

35 **receipt** [rɪ`sit] (n.) 收據
You must keep your receipt for at least three months.
你至少要保留收據三個月。

36 **receive** [rɪ`siv] (v.) 收到
I received a lot of presents from my classmates.
我收到很多同學給我的禮物。

35 **receiver** [rɪ`sivɚ] (n.) 收件人
Who is the receiver of this letter?
這封信的收件人是誰?

8 **recent** [ˋrisənt] (a.) 最近的
Recent studies show that 70% of people don't have dinner at home.
最近的研究顯示有七成的人不在家吃晚餐。

8 **recently** [ˋrisəntlɪ] (adv.) 近來
How have you been recently?
你近來如何?

36 **recognize** [ˋrɛkəg,naɪz] (v.) 識別
She couldn't recognize me after two years.
兩年不見，她認不出我了。

16 **record** [ˋrɛkɚd] (n.) 紀錄
The swimmer set a new world record at the Olympics.
這名游泳選手在奧運會刷下新世界紀錄。

16 **record** [rɪˋkɔrd] (v.) 記錄
The scholar recorded what he could find in the library.
那學者記下他在圖書館找到的資料。

35 **recorder** [rɪˋkɔrdɚ] (n.) 錄音器
There's a recorder on the phone.
這部電話有裝錄音器。

36 **recover** [rɪˋkʌvɚ] (v.) 恢復
She was sick a few days ago, but she has recovered now.
她前幾天生病，不過已經復原了。

19 **rectangle** [ˋrɛk,tæŋgḷ] (n.) 矩形，長方形
A rectangle has four sides.
矩形有四個邊。

36 **recycle** [rɪˋsaɪkḷ] (v.) 回收
Plastic bottles can be recycled.
塑膠瓶可以回收。

13 **red** [rɛd] (n.) 紅色
Red usually stands for emergency.
紅色通常代表緊急。

36 **reduce** [rɪˋdjus] (v.) 縮短
Our five day-holiday has been reduced to two days.
我們五天的假期已經被減為兩天。

15 **refrigerator** [rɪˋfrɪdʒə,retɚ] (n.) 冰箱
The new refrigerator doesn't work at all.
這台新冰箱根本就不能用。

36 **refuse** [rɪˋfjuz] (v.) 拒絕，不肯
Andy refused to go to school.
安迪不肯去上學。

36 **regard** [rɪˋgɑrd] (v.) 認為
He is regarded as the best teacher in the school.
大家都認為他是學校裡最棒的老師。

17 **region** [ˋridʒən] (n.) 地區
Which region of the United States are you living in?
你住在美國哪一個地區？

17 **regional** [ˋridʒənl̩] (a.) 地區的
A regional downpour will take place this afternoon.
今天下午將有局部性豪雨。

36 **regret** [rɪˋgrɛt] (v.) 後悔，遺憾
I regret that I can't come to your party this weekend.
我很遺憾這個週末沒辦法參加你的派對。

37 **regular** [ˋrɛgjəlɚ] (a.) 正常的，固定的
Her dad doesn't have a regular job.
他的爸爸沒有固定的工作。

36 **reject** [rɪ`dʒɛkt] (v.) 拒絕
She was rejected by Jimmy.
她被吉米拒絕了。

36 **relate** [rɪ`let] (v.) 有關，涉及
This matter is not related to you.
這件事跟你無關。

6 **relative** [`rɛlətɪv] (n.) 親戚
There are many relatives in my family.
我家有好多親戚。

36 **relax** [rɪ`læks] (v.) 輕鬆
He should feel more relaxed after his exams.
他考完試應該會覺得比較輕鬆了。

36 **release** [rɪ`lis] (v.) 釋放
The thief will be released from prision soon.
這小偷很快就會從牢裡放出來。

37 **reliable** [rɪ`laɪəbl̩] (a.) 可靠的
The employee isn't reliable.
那個員工並不可靠。

35 **relief** [rɪ`lif] (n.) 緩和，寬心
Much to my relief, I didn't fail my math test.
我大大鬆了一口氣，我的數學考試沒有當掉。

35 **religion** [rɪ`lɪdʒən] (n.) 宗教
She doesn't believe in any religions.
她沒有任何宗教信仰。

37 **religious** [rɪ`lɪdʒəs] (a.) 虔誠的
Grandma is a religious person.
奶奶是個虔誠的教徒。

36 **rely** [rɪ`laɪ] (v.) 依靠，信賴
You can always rely on me .
你永遠都可以信賴我。

36 **remain** [rɪ`men] (v.) 剩下
There are only two students remaining in the class.
教室裡只剩下兩位學生。

36 **remember** [rɪ`mɛmbɚ] (v.) 記得
He still remembers the day he got his bicycle.
他仍然記得他拿到腳踏車的那一天。

36 **remind** [rɪ`maɪnd] (v.) 提醒
The picture reminds me of my dead mother.
這張照片讓我想起死去的媽媽。

35 **remote** [rɪ`mot] (n.) 遙控器
Mother couldn't find the TV remote.
媽媽找不到電視遙控器。

36 **remove** [rɪ`muv] (v.) 移走
Please remove your car from my parking spot.
你的車停在我的停車位上，請把它開走。

36 **renew** [rɪ`njʊ] (v.) 更新
These broken chairs must be renewed.
這些壞掉的椅子必須換新的。

36 **rent** [rɛnt] (v.) 租
I rented a room in a big city.
我在大城市裡租了一間房間。

36 **repair** [rɪ`pɛr] (v.) 修理
The floor should be repaired soon.
地板應該要趕快修理。

16 **repeat** [rɪ`pit] (v.) 重複
Please repeat after me.
請跟著我複誦。

36 **replace** [rɪ`ples] (v.) 取代
The workers were replaced with robots.
工人被機器人給取代了。

36 **reply** [rɪ`plaɪ] (v.) 回答
Ben did not reply to the question.
班沒有回答問題。

35 **report** [rɪ`port] (v.) 報告
This is my study report for lung cancer.
這是我的肺癌研究報告。

24 **reporter** [rɪ`portɚ] (n.) 記者
He is a reporter for *Washington Post*.
他是《華盛頓郵報》的記者。

36 **represent** [,rɛprɪ`zɛnt] (v.) 代表
I represent my school in this swimming contest.
我代表學校參加這次游泳比賽。

35 **representative** [rɛprɪ`zentətɪv] (n.) 代表人，典型
She has been voted in as the chairman of the students' committee.
她被選為學生委員會的主席。

36 **request** [rɪ`kwɛst] (v.) 請求
Could I request that you wait outside for a minute?
可以請你在外面稍等一下嗎？

35 **request** [rɪ`kwɛst] (n.) 請求
This is his last request before he leaves.
這是他離開前最後一個請求。

36 **require** [rɪ`kwaɪr] (v.) 需要
You are required to bring two pencils with you to the test.
參加考試請務必攜帶兩枝鉛筆。

36 **reserve** [rɪ`zɝv] (v.) 儲備，保存
The restaurant will reserve ten seats for us.
餐廳會為我們保留十個座位。

36 **resist** [rɪ`zɪst] (v.) 抗拒
I can't resist her offer to go to Paris.
我無法拒絕她邀請我到巴黎的提議。

35 **resource** [rɪ`sors] (n.) 資源
Africa is rich in natural resources like oil, coal and diamonds.
非洲擁有豐富的自然資源，如石油、煤及鑽石。

36 **respect** [rɪ`spɛkt] (v.) 尊敬
I respect my teachers.
我尊敬我的老師們。

36 **respond** [rɪ`spɑnd] (v.) 回答，回應
I don't know how to respond to his reaction.
對於他的反應，我不知該如何回應。

35 **response** [rɪ`spɑns] (n.) 回答，答覆
Mother made no response to Dad's question.
媽媽沒有回答爸爸的問題。

35 **responsibility** [rɪ,pɑnsə`bɪlətɪ] (n.) 責任
Daddy has the responsibility of taking care of our family.
爸爸擔起了照顧我們全家的責任。

37 **responsible** [rɪ`spɑnsəbl̩] (a.) 負責的
I'm responsible for my own actions.
我會為我自己的行為負責。

36 **rest** [rɛst] (v.) 休息
Dad had a long day; he needs to rest.
爸爸今天很累，他需要休息。

17 **restaurant** [`rɛstərənt] (n.) 餐廳
There is a nice French restaurant around the corner.
附近有一家不錯的法國餐廳。

36 **restrict** [rɪ`strɪkt] (v.) 限制
Travel to Iraq has been restricted due to the war there.
由於當地發生戰爭，前往伊拉克旅遊受到限制。

17 **restroom** [`rɛst,rum] (n.) 化妝室
The restrooms in the parks are usually in a mess.
公園裡的廁所通常髒亂不堪。

35 **result** [rɪ`zʌlt] (n.) 結果
Grandpa's health check results were fine.
祖父的健康檢查結果正常。

36 **return** [rɪ`tɜn] (v.) 歸還
That book needs to be returned on Saturday.
那本書必須要在星期六歸還。

36 **reveal** [rɪ`vil] (v.) 展現
She has revealed her ambition to become successful.
她展現出一定要成功的雄心壯志。

16 **review** [rɪ`vjʊ] (v.) 複習
I need to review my notes before tomorrow's test.
我必須在明天考試前複習我的筆記。

36 **revise** [rɪ`vaɪz] (v.) 修訂
The text book was revised last year.
這本教科書去年修訂過。

35 **ribbon** [ˋrɪbən] (n.) 蝴蝶結
The girl tied her hair with a pink ribbon.
小女孩用粉紅色蝴蝶結綁頭髮。

10 **rice** [raɪs] (n.) 米飯
Rice is served with most meals in Thailand.
在泰國，米飯會搭配各種肉類。

2 **rich** [rɪtʃ] (a.) 富有的
Everyone wants to be rich!
每個人都想致富！

36 **rid** [rɪd] (v.) 使擺脫
Matt is trying to get rid of his little brother.
麥特正在想辦法擺脫他弟弟。

35 **riddle** [ˋrɪdl̩] (n.) 謎語
What's the answer to this riddle?
這個謎語的解答是什麼？

18 **ride** [raɪd] (v.) 騎
He can ride a horse.
他會騎馬。

37 **right** [raɪt] (a.) 正確的
Can you give me a right answer?
你可以給我正確的答案嗎？

12 **ring** [rɪŋ] (n.) 戒指
Women love diamond rings.
女人都愛鑽戒。

37 **ripe** [raɪp] (a.) 成熟的，適合食用
The peaches are ripe.
這些桃子熟了。

36 **rise** [raɪz] (v.) 上升
The temperature rose ten degrees within two days.
溫度在兩天內上升了十度。

35 **risk** [rɪsk] (n.) 風險
I try to avoid risk when I invest my money.
我投資時都會試著避開風險。

35 **risk** [rɪsk] (v.) 冒險
The firefighter risked his life to save others.
那位消防隊員冒生命危險拯救他人。

26 **river** [ˋrɪvɚ] (n.) 河流
There are crabs and fish in the river.
河裡有螃蟹和魚。

15 **road** [rod] (n.) 道路
The post office is on the second road.
郵局在第二條路上。

36 **roar** [ror] (v.) 大聲喊叫
My boss roared with anger.
我的老闆氣得大叫。

36 **roast** [rost] (v.) 烤，烘烤
Mother roasted some beef for dinner.
媽媽烤了一些牛肉做晚餐。

36 **rob** [rɑb] (v.) 搶劫
He was robbed last weekend.
他上週末被搶了。

35 **robber** [ˋrɑbɚ] (n.) 搶劫者，強盜
The police officer shot at the robber.
警察朝搶匪開槍。

35 **robbery** [ˋrɑbərɪ] (n.) 搶劫案
There were two bank robberies at the same time in the morning.
上午同一時間發現兩起銀行搶案。

35 **robe** [rob] (n.) 睡袍
I like to wear a robe after I finish showering.
我洗完澡後喜歡穿上睡袍。

35 **robot** [ˋrobət] (n.) 機器人
Most boys like robot toys.
男生大多喜歡玩具機器人。

25 **rock** [rɑk] (n.) 岩石
Many rocks fell off the cliff after the earthquake.
地震後許多岩石從懸崖落下。

35 **rocket** [ˋrɑkɪt] (n.) 火箭
He made a small rocket for his science project.
他為造了一座小火箭。

35 **role** [rol] (n.) 角色
Everyone has his own role to paly.
每個人都有自己該扮演好的角色。

36 **roll** [rol] (v.) 滾動，轉動
The tire was so flat that it couldn't be rolled.
輪胎沒氣，癟到轉都轉不動了。

14 **rollerblades** [ˋrolɚ,bled] (n.) 直排輪鞋
He got his first rollerblades when he was ten.
他十歲時拿到第一雙直排輪鞋。

14 **roller-skate** [ˋsolɚ,sket] (v.) 四輪溜冰
My little sister can roller-skate very well.
我妹妹溜輪鞋溜得很好。

37 **romantic** [rə`mætɪk] (a.) 浪漫的
She likes to watch romantic movies.
她喜歡看愛情電影。

15 **roof** [ruf] (n.) 屋頂
The roof is leaking.
屋頂在漏水。

15 **room** [rum] (n.) 房間
We don't have spare rooms for guests.
我們沒有多餘的房間給客人。

35 **root** [rut] (n.) 根，地下莖
Some roots of plants can be eaten.
有些植物的根可以吃。

35 **rope** [rop] (n.) 繩子
The children are playing jumping rope.
孩子們正在跳繩。

35 **rose** [roz] (n.) 玫瑰
This flower shop has blue roses.
這間花店有藍色的玫瑰花。

36 **rot** [rɑt] (v.) 腐爛，腐敗
The meat will rot under the sun.
肉經過曬會腐爛。

37 **rotten** [`rɑtn̩] (a.) 腐爛
The meat is rotten.
這肉已經壞掉了。

37 **rough** [rʌf] (a.) 粗糙
The surface of her face is rough.
她的臉皮膚很粗糙。

19 **round** [raʊnd] (a.) 圓形的
The earth is round.
地球是圓的。

35 **routine** [rʊ`tin] (n.) 例行公事
Making phone calls is one of the routines of her day.
打電話是她每天的例行公事之一。

35 **row** [ro] (n.) 排，列
Can you hear me in the back row?
你在後排聽得見我說話嗎？

37 **royal** [`rɔɪəl] (a.) 皇室的
Michelle was born into a royal family.
米雪兒誕生於皇室家族。

36 **rub** [rʌb] (v.) 摩擦
He rubbed his hands to keep warm.
他摩擦雙手保持溫暖。

35 **rubber** [`rʌbɚ] (n.) 橡膠
Do you have some rubber bands?
你有橡皮筋嗎?

2 **rude** [rud] (a.) 粗魯的，無禮的
It's rude to talk when you are eating.
邊吃東西邊講話很沒禮貌。

35 **rug** [rʌg] (n.) 小地毯，毛皮地毯
There is a pink rug by the doorway.
玄關有一個粉紅色的小地毯。

36 **ruin** [`ruɪn] (v.) 毀壞
The house was ruined by the earthquake.
房子被地震摧毀了。

35 **rule** [rul] (n.) 規則
Students must obey classroom rules.
學生必須遵守教室規則。

16 **ruler** [ˋrulɚ] (n.) 統治者，尺
The ruler should be considerate to his people.
統治者必須體恤人民。

35 **rumor** [ˋrumɚ] (n.) 謠言
Don't start rumors.
不要製造謠言。

36 **run** [rʌn] (v.) 跑
She ran to catch the bus.
她跑著趕搭巴士。

36 **rush** [rʌʃ] (v.) 倉促行動
Mother rushed to work.
媽媽趕著去上班。

20 **Russia** [ˋrʌʃə] (n.) 俄羅斯
One of my classmate was born in Russia.
我有一個同學在俄羅斯出生。

21 **Russian** [ˋrʌʃən] (n., a.) 俄國人（的）
Russian women are tall and beautiful.
俄國女人又高又漂亮。

36 **rust** [rʌst] (v.) 鏽
Iron rusts easily.
鐵容易生鏽。

37 **rusty** [ˋrʌstɪ] (a.) 荒廢的
My German is a bit rusty.
我的德語有點荒廢了。

S

35 **sack** [sæk] (n.) 袋，（俚）床
I want to hit the sack.
我要去睡覺了。

2 **sad** [sæd] (a.) 悲傷
She feels sad because her grandmother passed away.
因為奶奶過世了，她覺得很難過。

37 **safe** [sef] (a.) 安全的
Is it safe for you to go home by yourself?
你一個人回家安全嗎?

35 **safety** [ˋseftɪ] (n.) 安全
For safety, please put the baby in the back seat.
安全起見，請把嬰兒置於後座。

18 **sail** [sel] (v.) 航行
He can sail a boat.
他會開船。

24 **sailor** [ˋselɚ] (n.) 水手，船員
Sailors can travel around.
水手可以到處旅行。

35 **sake** [sek] (n.) 利益
Howard did it for his own sake.
霍爾這麼做是為了自己的利益。

10 **salad** [ˋsæləd] (n.) 沙拉
She always has salad for lunch.
她午餐總是吃沙拉。

35 **salary** [ˋsælərɪ] (n.) 薪水
You work for your salary.
你為薪水而工作。

35 **sale** [sel] (n.) 販售
Are there any drinks for sale?
有賣飲料嗎?

24 **salesman** [ˋselzmən] (n.) 推銷員
The salesman is promoting the products for the store.
推銷員正在為店家推銷產品。

10 **salt** [sɔlt] (n.) 鹽
Could you pass the salt, please.
麻煩鹽巴遞過來，謝謝。

37 **same** [sem] (a.) 相同的
We are wearing the same clothes.
我們穿一樣的衣服。

35 **sample** [ˋsæmpḷ] (n.) 樣本
These are the free samples for the new cosmetics.
這些是新化妝品的免費試用品。

25 **sand** [sænd] (n.) 沙
Let's build a sand castle on the beach.
來去沙灘上築沙堡吧。

10 **sandwich** [ˋsændwɪtʃ] (n.) 三明治
I don't like the tomato in sandwiches.
我不喜歡三明治夾番茄。

37 **satisfactory** [ˌsætɪsˋfæktərɪ] (a.) 令人滿意的
She gave a satisfactory answer.
她給了一個令人滿意的答案。

36 **satisfy** [ˋsætɪs,faɪ] (v.) 使滿意
My teacher wasn't satisfied with my homework.
我的老師對我的作業不滿意。

8 **Saturday** [ˋsætɚ,de] (n.) 星期六
People usually don't work on Saturdays.
星期六人們通常不工作。

11 **saucer** [ˋsɔsɚ] (n.) 淺碟
You can put soy sauce in your saucer.
你可以把醬油倒在淺碟子裡。

35 **sausage** [ˋsɔsɪdʒ] (n.) 香腸
Sausage goes well with garlic.
大蒜跟香腸很配。

36 **save** [sev] (v.) 拯救，儲蓄
I have already saved over a million NT for my retirement.
我已經為存了一百萬台幣的退休金了。

35 **saving** [ˋsevɪŋ] (n.) 節儉，節省
My parents always taught me the value of saving.
我的父母一直教我節儉的重要。

16 **say** [se] (v.) 說
It is too late to say sorry now.
現在說抱歉太遲了。

19 **scale** [skel] (n.) 刻度
This ruler has one scale in centimeters and another in millimeters.
這把尺有公分及公釐的刻度。

37 **scarce** [skɛrs] (a.) 缺乏
Fresh water was scarce after the typhoon.
颱風過後缺乏乾淨的水。

35 **scarecrow** [ˋskɛr,kro] (n.) 稻草人
The scarecrows will frighten birds away from the field.
稻草人會把田裡的鳥嚇跑。

2 **scared** [skɛrd] (a.) 驚恐的
Ryan was so scared of snakes.
萊恩很怕蛇。

12 **scarf** [skɑrf] (n.) 圍巾
Mom knitted a scarf for me this winter.
媽媽今年冬天織了一條圍巾給我。

37 **scary** [ˋskɛrɪ] (a.) 恐怖的
Children say the clowns look scary because of their make-up.
小朋友說那些小丑的妝看起來好恐怖。

36 **scatter** [ˋskætɚ] (v.) 灑，散布
The toys were scattered all over the floor.
玩具散落一地。

35 **scene** [sin] (n.) 地點，背景，現場
This scene seems so familiar.
這場景看起來很熟悉。

35 **scenery** [ˋsinərɪ] (n.) 風景
This is the most beautiful scenery I've ever seen!
這是我見過最漂亮的風景了！

35 **schedule** [ˋskɛdʒul] (n.) 清單，目錄
Do you have the schedule for tonight's TV programs?
你有今晚的電視節目表嗎?

24 **scholar** [ˋskɑlɚ] (n.) 學者
He's a scholar of business management.
他是一位商業管理學者。

35 **scholarship** [ˋskɑlɚ,ʃɪp] (n.) 獎學金
I obtained a scholarship for this semester.
我這學期獲得獎學金。

16 **science** [ˋsaɪəns] (n.) 科學
The computer is one of the wonders of modern science.
電腦是現代科學的奇蹟之一。

37 **scientific** [,saɪənˋtɪfɪk] (a.) 科學的
The detective employed scientific methods to solve the case.
那名偵探運用科學方法破案。

24 **scientist** [ˋsaɪəntɪst] (n.) 科學家
Many Jewish scientists were killed during the World War II.
二次大戰期間，許多猶太科學家被殺。

35 **scoop** [skup] (n.) 一勺
Can I have two scoops of chocolate ice cream?
請給我兩球巧克力冰淇淋好嗎？

18 **scooter** [ˋskutɚ] (n.) 機車
Scooters are no good for long-distance traveling.
機車不適合長途旅行。

16 **score** [skor] (n.) 分數
What is your score on the test?
你這次考試成績如何？

35 **scout** [skaʊt] (n.) 搜索
The firefighter had a scout around to see if there were any more survivors.
消防員四處搜索，看看是否還有人生還。

36 **scream** [skrim] (v.) 尖叫
My brother couldn't find his toys so he screamed loudly.
我的弟弟因為找不到玩具而放聲尖叫。

35 **screen** [skrin] (n.) 螢幕，銀幕
Movie theaters have huge screens.
電影院有很大的銀幕。

35 **screw** [skru] (n.) 螺絲釘
Please tighten up the loose screw.
請把鬆掉的螺絲釘鎖緊。

36 **scrub** [skrʌb] (v.) 用力擦洗，揉
Mother scrubs the floor slowly.
媽媽慢慢擦地板。

26 **sea** [si] (n.) 海洋
Someday people will live under the sea.
總有一天，人類會住在海底。

10 **seafood** [ˋsi,fud] (n.) 海鮮
I am allergic to seafood.
我對海鮮過敏。

36 **seal** [sil] (v.) 密閉，蓋章
The envelope is sealed with a stamp.
這信封是用郵票封起來的。

36 **search** [sɝtʃ] (v.) 搜尋
They searched every place for the lost child.
他們到處尋找走失的小孩。

8 **season** [ˋsizn̩] (n.) 季節
There are four seasons in a year.
一年有四季。

35 **seat** [sit] (n.) 座位
This seat has been taken.
這個位子已經有人坐了。

7 **second** [ˋsɛkənd] (a.) 第二的
Her house is on the second floor.
他家在二樓。

8 **second** [ˋsɛkənd] (n.) 一秒鐘
There are sixty seconds in a minute.
一分鐘有六十秒。

37 **secondary** [ˋsɛkən,dɛrɪ] (a.) 第二的
Most secondary schools are in towns.
大部份中學都位於市區。

35 **secret** [ˋsɪkrɪt] (n.) 祕密
The secret is only between us.
這個祕密不能透露給第三者知情。

24 **secretary** [ˋsɛkrə,tɛrɪ] (n.) 祕書
My secretary is busy with the files.
我的祕書正忙著整理檔案。

35 **section** [ˋsɛkʃən] (n.) 段落
Some sections of the story are sacry.
這個故事有些段落還蠻嚇人的。

35 **security** [sɪˋkjʊrətɪ] (n.) 安全，保全措施
There are some holes in your home's security.
府上的保全措施有一些漏洞。

36 **see** [si] (v.) 看見
I saw your mother today.
我今天看到你的媽媽。

35 **seed** [sid] (n.) 種子
Sow the seeds during spring.
在春天播種。

36 **seek** [sik] (v.) 搜索
The police officers are seeking the killer.
這些警察正在搜索殺人犯。

36 **seem** [sim] (v.) 好像
You seem very tired now.
你好像很累的樣子。

16 **seesaw** [ˋsi,sɔ] (n.) 蹺蹺板
You can play on the seesaw after school.
放學後你可以玩蹺蹺板。

36 **seize** [siz] (v.) 抓住
We seized the opportunity to go abroad.
我們把握機會出國。

38 **seldom** [ˋsɛldəm] (adv.) 不常
I seldom go hiking.
我很少去健行。

36 **select** [səˋlɛkt] (v.) 選擇
They selected a class leader.
他們選出一個班長。

2 **selfish** [ˋsɛlfɪʃ] (a.) 自私的
Joey is selfish; he doesn't share his toys.
喬伊很自私，不肯和別人分享他的玩具。

36 **sell** [sɛl] (v.) 賣
He sells fruits on the street.
他在街上賣水果。

16 **semester** [səˋmɛstɚ] (n.) 學期
There are two semesters in a year.
一年有兩個學期。

36 **send** [sɛnd] (v.) 發送，寄
I sent her a birthday card.
我寄了一張生日卡片給她。

16 **senior high school** [ˋsinjɚ haɪ skul] (n.) 高中
Senior high school students have a lot of pressure.
高中生的壓力很大。

35 **sense** [sɛns] (n.) 理智，道理
It doesn't make sense.
這一點道理也沒有。

2 **sensible** [ˋsɛnsəbl̩] (a.) 意識到的，察覺到的
He is sensible of his error.
他察覺到他犯的錯誤了。

37 **sensitive** [ˋsɛnsətɪv] (a.) 敏感的，易受傷的
She is so sensitive to his words.
他說的話讓她受傷害。

35 **sentence** [ˋsɛntəns] (n.) 句子
The teacher asked me to write down a long sentence.
老師要我寫一個長句。

36 **separate** [ˋsɛpə,ret] (v.) 分開
Try to separate the naughty kids in different places.
想辦法把頑皮的孩子分散開來。

8 **September** [sɛpˋtɛmbɚ] (n.) 九月
Schools usually open in September.
學校通常在九月開學。

37 **serious** [ˋsirɪəs] (a.) 嚴重的
His illness is getting more serious.
他的病情越來越嚴重了。

24 **servant** [`sɜvənt] (n.) 佣人
They have two servants in their house.
他們家有兩個僕人。

36 **serve** [sɜv] (v.) 服務
The waiters serve well in this restaurant.
這間餐廳的侍者服務很好。

35 **service** [`sɜvɪs] (n.) 服務
They have the best service at the restaurant.
這家餐廳有最好的服務。

35 **set** [sɛt] (v.) 一套
Dad bought a set of books.
爸爸買了一套書。

7 **seven** [`sɛvn̩] (n.) 七
My lucky number is seven.
我的幸運號碼是七。

7 **seventeen** [,sɛvən`tin] (n.) 十七
Please open to page seventeen.
請翻開第十七頁。

7 **seventeenth** [,sɛvən`tinθ] (a.) 第十七的
The seventeenth page of the book is missing.
這本書的第十七頁不見了。

7 **seventh** [`sɛvənθ] (a.) 第七的
Saturday is the seventh day of the week.
星期六是一星期的第七天。

7 **seventy** [`sɛvəntɪ] (n.) 七十
Annie's father is seventy years old already.
安妮的爸爸已經七十歲了。

7 **several** [ˋsɛvərəl] (a.) 幾個
Only several students stay to study in the classroom.
只有幾個學生留在教室念書。

36 **sew** [so] (v.) 縫，縫製
Mother sewed my shirt for me last night.
媽媽昨晚幫我縫上衣。

35 **sex** [sɛks] (n.) 性別
What sex is the baby?
這個小嬰兒是男生女生啊？

37 **sexual** [ˋsɛkʃuəl] (a.) 性的，兩性的
It's never appropriate for teachers to have sexual relations with their students.
老師和學生發生性關係絕對是不恰當的。

37 **sexy** [ˋsɛksɪ] (a.) 性感，迷人的
The lady is very sexy in her miniskirt.
那位女士穿迷你裙真性感。

35 **shade** [ʃed] (n.) 蔭暗
It's so hot today so students are sitting under the shade of the tree.
今天很熱，所以學生都坐在樹蔭下。

35 **shadow** [ˋʃædo] (n.) 影子，陰暗的地方
There's a strange man hiding in the shadows.
有個奇怪的人躲在陰暗處。

37 **shady** [ˋʃedɪ] (a.) 成蔭
The old man walks under the shady trees.
這老人走在成蔭的樹下。

36 **shake** [ʃek] (v.) 搖動
Shake it before you drink it.
飲用前請搖一搖。

31 **shall** [ʃæl] (aux.) 應當，將
We shall finish cooking by six o'clock.
我們應在六點前把飯煮好。

35 **shallow** [ˋʃælo] (a.) 淺的
The river is quite shallow.
這條河相當淺。

35 **shame** [ʃem] (v.) 羞恥
Her behavior brings shame her whole family.
她的行為讓全家人感到羞恥。

35 **shampoo** [ʃæmˋpu] (n.) 洗髮精
I use different shampoos every day.
我每天用不一樣的洗髮精。

19 **shape** [ʃep] (n.) 形狀
The shape of the cloud is like a dog.
那片雲的形狀像隻狗。

36 **share** [ʃɛr] (v.) 分享
May I share this cake with you?
我可以和你分享這個蛋糕嗎?

27 **shark** [ʃɑrk] (n.) 鯊魚
Some Chinese people eat shark fins.
有些中國人吃魚翅。

37 **sharp** [ʃɑrp] (a.) 銳利的
The chef's knife was very sharp.
那個廚師的刀子很利。

36 **shave** [ʃev] (v.) 刮
Dad shaves three times a week.
爸爸一星期刮三次鬍子。

A B C D E F G H I J K L M N O P Q R S T U V W X Y Z

35 **sheep** [ʃip] (n.) 羊，綿羊
Sheep produces wool.
綿羊產羊毛。

16 **sheet** [ʃit] (n.)（紙等的）一張，床單
The student wrote the answers on a sheet of paper.
學生把答案寫在一張紙上。

15 **shelf** [ʃɛlf] (n.)（書櫥等的）架子
The book shelf is not stable.
那書架不是很穩。

24 **shepherd** [ˋʃɛpɚd] (n.) 牧羊人
The shephered gathered in the sheep.
牧羊人將羊趕成一群。

36 **shine** [ʃaɪn] (v.) 照耀，閃耀
The smile shines on her face.
她笑得燦爛。

35 **sunshine** [ˋsʌn͵ʃaɪn] (n.) 陽光
The sunshine blinds my eyes.
陽光讓我張不開眼。

37 **shiny** [ˋʃaɪnɪ] (a.) 發光的，閃亮的
The stars are so shiny in the sky at night.
夜空裡的星星好閃亮。

18 **ship** [ʃɪp] (n.) 船
We fish on a ship in the sea.
我們坐船出海捕漁。

12 **shirt** [ʃɝt] (n.) 襯衫
He is ironing his shirt.
他正在燙他的襯衫。

35 **shock** [ʃak] (n.) 震驚
I was in shock when she told me the breaking news.
她告訴我這重大新聞時，我嚇呆了。

12 **shoes** [ʃuz] (n.) 鞋子
This pair of shoes is not comfortable.
這雙新鞋穿起來不舒服。

36 **shoot** [ʃut] (v.) 發射
The police officer shot at him.
警察對他開槍。

24 **shopkeeper** [ˋʃap,kipɚ] (n.) 店主
Daniel is the shopkeeper of a pet shop.
丹尼爾是一家寵物店的老闆。

35 **shore** [ʃor] (n.) 岸
She picked some shells along the sea shore.
她沿著海邊撿了些貝殼。

2 **short** [ʃɔrt] (a.) 短的，矮的
No one is as short as Jean in her class.
珍是班上最矮的。

36 **shorten** [ˋʃɔrtn̩] (v.) 縮短，減少
This new freeway shortens the trip.
新的高速公路縮短了行程。

38 **shortly** [ˋʃɔrtlɪ] (adv.) 立刻，不久
I'm going to Germany shortly.
我過不久要去德國。

12 **shorts** [ʃorts] (n.) 短褲
It's impolite to wear shorts to a party.
穿短褲參加宴會是不禮貌的。

35 **shot** [ʃɑt] (n.) 投，射
The police officer shot at the criminal twice.
警察朝罪犯開槍兩次。

31 **should** [ʃʊd] (aux.) 應該
You should have told me that.
你應該要告訴我那件事的。

3 **shoulder** [ˋʃoldɚ] (n.) 肩膀
He has broad shoulders.
他有寬大的肩膀。

36 **shout** [ʃaʊt] (v.) 大叫
Mother shouted at me.
媽媽對我大叫。

35 **shovel** [ˋʃʌvl̩] (n.) 鏟子
Grandfather always works with a shovel.
爺爺總是拿著鏟子工作。

35 **show** [ʃo] (n.) 表演
The puppet show attracts lots of children.
那個木偶秀吸引許多小孩。

36 **show** [ʃo] (v.) 告知，指出
Please show me the way.
請告訴我該怎麼走。

25 **shower** [ˋʃaʊɚ] (n.) 淋浴，陣雨
I need a hot shower afte the basketball game.
打完籃球我需要洗個熱水澡。

10 **shrimp** [ʃrɪmp] (n.) 蝦
The restaurant is famous for its grilled shrimp.
這家餐廳以烤蝦聞名。

36 **shrink** [ʃrɪŋk] (v.) 收縮，縮短

My shirt shrinked after mom washed it.

我的襯衫被媽媽洗過之後縮水了。

36 **shut** [ʃʌt] (v.) 關上

The door will be shut at five o'clock.

門將於五點關閉。

2 **shy** [ʃaɪ] (a.) 害羞的

The girl was so shy that she didn't say a word.

那個女孩好害羞，一句話都沒說。

4 **sick** [sɪk] (a.) 生病的

He was sick this morning, so he didn't go to school.

他今天早上生病了，所以沒去上學。

35 **side** [saɪd] (n.) 邊

This is a double-sided mirror.

這是一面雙面鏡。

18 **sidewalk** [ˋsaɪd,wɔk] (n.) 人行道

Don't park your motorcycle on the sidewalk.

不要把機車停在人行道上。

36 **sigh** [saɪ] (v.) 嘆息，嘆氣

I heard him sigh after he saw the sales report.

我聽到他看了業績之後在嘆氣。

35 **sight** [saɪt] (n.) 視覺

The boy lost his sight when he was born.

這小男生一出生就失明了。

36 **sign** [saɪn] (n.) 符號，標誌

There is a non-smoking sign on the door.

門上有一個禁菸標誌。

35 **signal** [ˋsɪgnl̩] (n.) 信號，暗號
Give me a signal when you are ready.
準備好就跟我打個手勢。

37 **significant** [sɪgˋnɪfəkənt] (a.) 有意義的
It's significant to all the the people in the office all lost jobs.
這對所有曾經參與工作的死者意義重大。

35 **silence** [ˋsaɪləns] (n.) 寂靜
The speaker raised his hands and asked for silence.
主講者舉手請大家安靜。

37 **silent** [ˋsaɪlənt] (a.) 沈默的
The teacher kept silent for a moment.
老師沉默了一會兒。

2 **silly** [ˋsɪlɪ] (a.) 傻的
That silly boy didn't know how to express his feelings.
那個傻男孩不知如何表達他的情感。

12 **silver** [ˋsɪlvɚ] (n.) 銀
Gold is much more valuable than silver.
金比銀有價值得多。

37 **similar** [ˋsɪmələ̄] (a.) 相似的
The two pictures look similar.
這兩張照片看起來很相似。

35 **similarity** [ˌsɪməˋlærətɪ] (n.) 類似
The similarity between the two writers is obvious.
這兩位作家的相似處非常明顯。

37 **simple** [ˋsɪmpl̩] (a.) 簡易的
It's simple to make the cake.
做蛋糕很容易。

38 **simply** [`sɪmplɪ] (adv.) 簡單地，只要
Simply fill in the questionnaire and you will win the money.
只要填這問卷就可以獲得獎金。

35 **sin** [sɪn] (n.) 罪孽
It's a sin to lie.
說謊是種罪。

32 **since** [sɪns] (adv.) 自從
I have lived there since I was a child.
我從小時候就住在那裡了。

2 **sincere** [sɪn`sɪr] (a.) 真心的
Please accept my sincere apology.
請接受我誠心的道歉。

35 **sincerity** [sɪn`sɛrətɪ] (n.) 真誠
Everyone can feel his sincerity.
每個人都能感受到他的真誠。

36 **sing** [sɪŋ] (v.) 唱歌
He's good at singing!
他很會唱歌！

24 **singer** [`sɪŋɚ] (n.) 歌唱家，歌手
She is a pop music singer.
她是一位流行歌手。

37 **single** [`sɪŋg!] (a.) 單一的
Melind is from a single-parent family.
瑪琳達來自單親家庭。

15 **sink** [sɪŋk] (n.) 水槽
The sink is full of dirty dishes.
水槽裡堆滿髒碗盤。

35 **sip** [sɪp] (n.) 一小口
May I have a sip of your coffee?
我可以喝一小口你的咖啡嗎？

5 **sir** [sɝ] (n.) 先生
How may I help you, sir?
先生，有什麼我能幫忙的嗎？

6 **sister** [ˋsɪstɚ] (n.) 姐妹
She has two sisters.
她有兩個姊妹。

36 **sit** [sɪt] (v.) 坐
Everybody sits down quietly.
大家都安靜坐下。

35 **situation** [ˏsɪtʃʊˋeʃən] (n.) 處境
She is in a difficult situation now.
她正處於困境。

7 **six** [sɪks] (a.) 六個
There are six chairs over there.
那裡有六張椅子。

7 **sixteen** [ˋsɪksˋtin] (a.) 十六個
There are sixteen students in the class.
班上有十六個學生。

7 **sixteenth** [ˋsɪksˋtinθ] (a.) 第十六的
The restaurant is on Sixteenth Street.
那家餐廳位於第十六街上。

7 **sixth** [sɪksθ] (a.) 第六的
He has to pay rent on the sixth day of each month.
他得在每月六號繳房租。

7 **sixty** [ˋsɪkstɪ] (n.) 六十
Her grandpa is sixty years old.
她祖父現在六十歲。

19 **size** [saɪz] (n.) 尺寸
This is not my shoe size.
這不是我的鞋子尺寸。

14 **skate** [sket] (v.) 溜冰
Can you show me how to ice skate?
你能示範給我看要怎麼溜冰嗎?

14 **ski** [ski] (n.) 滑雪，滑雪板
I wish I could have my own skis.
真希望我能擁有自己的滑雪板。

14 **skiing** [ˋskiɪŋ] (n.) 滑雪
My younger brother loves skiing.
我弟弟很愛滑雪。

35 **skill** [skɪl] (n.) 技術
Computer skills are getting more and more important nowadays.
今天，運用電腦的技能越來越重要了。

37 **skillful** [ˋskɪlfəl] (a.) 技巧的
He is a skillful mechanic.
他是一位技術純熟的技師。

3 **skin** [skin] (n.) 皮膚
I take care of my skin by applying some lotion.
我擦乳液保養皮膚。

2 **skinny** [ˋskɪnɪ] (a.) 皮包骨的
Harry is a skinny boy.
哈利是個瘦巴巴的男孩。

36 **skip** [skɪp] (v.) 略過，漏掉
The teacher skipped me when she took the register.
老師點名時沒點到我。

12 **skirt** [skɝt] (n.) 裙子
The weather is too cold for her to wear a skirt.
天氣太冷了，她辦法穿裙子。

25 **sky** [skaɪ] (n.) 天空
The sky is blue.
天空是藍的。

35 **skyscraper** [ˋskaɪ,skrepɚ] (n.) 摩天樓
We can see the skyscrapers in the center of the city.
在市中心可以看到很多摩天樓。

35 **slave** [slev] (n.) 奴隸
Grandma worked as hard as slave before.
奶奶以前像奴隸般辛苦工作。

36 **sleep** [slip] (v.) 睡覺
I sleep at ten every day.
我每天十點睡覺。

37 **sleepy** [ˋslipɪ] (a.) 想睡的
My cats are always sleepy.
我的貓咪總是想睡覺。

12 **sleeve** [sliv] (n.) 袖子
Roll up your sleeves before you start drawing.
畫畫前先把袖子捲起來。

2 **slender** [ˋslɛndɚ] (a.) 苗條的
Many girls prefer slender figures.
許多女孩偏好苗條的身材。

35 **slice** [slaɪs] (n.) 切片，片
I want a slice of pizza.
我想要一片比薩。

16 **slide** [slaɪd] (n.) 滑梯
The children are playing on the slides.
孩子們在玩溜滑梯。

2 **slim** [slim] (a.) 苗條的
She was very slim when I last saw her.
我最後一次看到她時，她很瘦。

36 **slip** [slɪp] (v.) 失足
Grandma slipped on the bathroom floor.
奶奶在浴室地板跌滑倒。

12 **slippers** [ˋslɪpɚz] (n.) 拖鞋
Don't wear slippers to the party.
別穿拖鞋參加宴會。

37 **slippery** [ˋslɪpərɪ] (a.) 滑的
The floor is very slippery.
地板非常滑。

35 **slope** [slop] (n.) 坡，斜面
The slope is very steep.
這個坡很陡。

18 **slow** [slo] (a.) 緩慢的
The bike is slower than the motorbike.
腳踏車比機車慢。

19 **small** [smɔl] (a.) 小的
The world is becoming smaller and smaller.
世界變得越來越小了。

2 **smart** [smɑrt] (a.) 聰明伶俐的
We have a smart boy in our class.
我們班上有個聰明的男孩。

36 **smell** [smɛl] (v.) 聞到
The dog smells the dog food.
這隻狗聞到狗食的味道。

35 **smile** [smaɪl] (n.) 微笑
The little girl has a beautiful smile.
這小女孩有美麗的笑容。

36 **smoke** [smok] (v.) 抽菸
Dad smokes every day.
爸爸每天抽菸。

37 **smooth** [smuð] (a.) 平滑的
The cloth is so smooth.
這布料好光滑啊。

10 **snack** [snæk] (n.) 點心
Kids love to have snacks before dinner.
小孩子愛在晚餐前吃零食。

27 **snail** [snel] (n.) 蝸牛
There are snails all over on the riverbank.
河岸上到處都是蝸牛。

27 **snake** [snek] (n.) 蛇
Grandpa found a snake in the house.
祖父在屋裡發現一條蛇。

36 **snap** [snæp] (v.) 拉斷
The branch snapped because of the heavy snow.
因為積雪太重，樹枝被壓斷了。

⓬ **sneakers** [ˋsnikɚz] (n.) 運動鞋
The sneakers need washing.
這雙球鞋該洗了。

❷ **sneaky** [ˋsnikɪ] (a.) 鬼鬼祟祟的
The student was so sneaky that he read comics in the back of the class.
那學生鬼鬼祟祟在教室後面看漫畫。

㊱ **sneeze** [sniz] (v.) 打噴嚏
Father sneezed all the time.
爸爸一直在打噴嚏。

㉕ **snow** [sno] (n.) 雪
It snows in the U.S. every year.
美國每年都下雪。

㉕ **snowman** [ˋsno,mæn] (n.) 雪人
It's a huge snowman.
這是一個巨大的雪人。

㉕ **snowy** [snoɪ] (a.) 下雪的
She puts on her boots on the snowy days.
她在下雪天會穿靴子。

㊳ **so** [so] (adv.) 非常
He came to my party so late.
他好晚才到我的派對來。

⓯ **soap** [sop] (n.) 肥皂
There is a bar of soap in the bathroom.
浴室裡有一塊香皂。

㊱ **sob** [sɑb] (v.) 啜泣
The girl sobbed alone in the dark.
那個女孩獨自在黑暗中啜泣。

14 **soccer** [ˋsɑkɚ] (n.) 足球
We watched the soccer game all night.
我們看足球賽看了整晚。

37 **social** [ˋsoʃəl] (a.) 社會的
The social problems are getting more and more complicated.
社會問題越來越複雜。

16 **social science** [ˋsoʃəl ˋsaɪəns] (n.) 社會科學
Social science is not popular at school.
社會科學在學校並不熱門。

35 **society** [səˋsaɪətɪ] (n.) 社會
I want to live in France for a year so I can learn about French society.
我想在法國住一年，以了解法國社會。

12 **socks** [sɑks] (n.) 襪子
Your socks are so smelly.
你的襪子好臭。

10 **soda** [ˋsodə] (n.) 蘇打，汽水
Many people like soda drinks.
許多人喜歡喝蘇打飲料。

15 **sofa** [ˋsofə] (n.) 沙發
There are comfortable sofas in this coffee shop.
這間咖啡廳有舒服的沙發。

10 **soft drink** [sɔft drɪŋk] (n.) 不含酒精的飲料
I always have soft drinks.
我都喝不含酒精的飲料。

37 **soft** [sɔft] (a.) 柔軟的
Her hair feels so soft.
她的頭髮摸起來好柔軟。

14 **softball** [ˋsɔft,bɔl] (n.) 壘球
Lots of girls play softball instead of baseball.
很多女孩打壘球不打棒球。

35 **software** [ˋsɔft,wɛr] (n.) 軟體
He is a software designer.
他是軟體設計師。

25 **solar** [ˋsolɚ] (a.) 太陽能的，日光
The fan is powered by solar energy.
這電扇是太陽能發電。

24 **soldier** [ˋsoldʒɚ] (n.) 士兵
We need soldiers to protect our country.
我們需要士兵保家衛國。

37 **solid** [ˋsɑlɪd] (a.) 堅固
These boxes are solid.
這些箱子很堅固。

35 **solution** [səˋluʃən] (n.) 解決方式
There is no solution to the problem.
這個問題沒辦法解決。

36 **solve** [sɑlv] (v.) 解決
She doesn't know how to solve this problem.
她不知道如何解決這個問題。

7 **some** [sʌm] (a.) 一些
I need some dog food to feed my dog.
我需要一些狗食來餵我的狗。

29 **somebody** [ˋsʌm,bɑdɪ] (n.) 某人
Somebody stole my bike.
有人偷了我的腳踏車。

38 **someday** [ˋsʌm,de] (adv.) 有朝一日
Someday, I will see you again.
總有一天，我會再見到你。

38 **somehow** [ˋsʌm,haʊ] (adv.) 不知怎麼了
Somehow, my dad is afraid of my mom.
不知怎麼地，我爸就是怕我媽。

29 **someone** [ˋsʌm,wʌn] (pron.) 某人
I need someone that I can talk to.
我需要有個人可以聊天。

29 **something** [ˋsʌm,θɪŋ] (pron.) 某事
I have something to ask you.
我有事情要問你。

38 **sometime** [ˋsʌm,taɪm] (adv.) 在某一時候
I met her sometime last year.
我去年遇見過她。

38 **sometimes** [ˋsʌm,taɪmz] (adv.) 有時候
We sometimes go to the restaurant.
我們有時候會上館子。

38 **somewhat** [ˋsʌm,hwɑt] (adv.) 有點，稍微
The news was somewhat of a surprise.
這新聞有點令人驚訝。

38 **somewhere** [ˋsʌm,hwɛr] (adv.) 在某處
You must have put your money somewhere here.
你一定是把錢放在這兒的哪裡了。

6 **son** [sʌn] (n.) 兒子
Michael has three sons and a daughter.
麥可有三個兒子和一個女兒。

14 **song** [sɔŋ] (n.) 歌
You can learn English by singing English songs.
你可以唱英文歌來學英文。

8 **soon** [sun] (adv.) 很快地
Come back home as soon as possible.
趕快回家吧。

16 **sophomore** [ˋsɑfə,mor] (n.) 二年級
She is a sophomore in the university.
她是大學二年級生。

4 **sore throat** [ˋsor,θrot] (n.) 喉嚨痛
My sore throat is killing me.
我喉嚨痛死了。

37 **sore** [sor] (a.) 疼痛
I have a sore throat.
我的喉嚨痛。

36 **sorrow** [ˋsɑro] (n.) 悲傷
Grandfather felt sorrow at the death of Grandmother.
爺爺為奶奶過世感到悲傷。

37 **sorrowful** [ˋsɑrofəl] (a.) 悲傷的，傷心的
The dog was giving them sorrowful looks.
狗狗哀傷的看著他們。

37 **sorry** [ˋsɔrɪ] (a.) 感到難過的
I feel so sorry for you.
我真替你感到難過。

36 **sort** [sɔrt] (v.) 分類
The librarian sorts books by their numbers.
圖書館員按照號碼將書分類。

3 **soul** [sol] (n.) 心靈，靈魂
Many people say music is good for the soul.
很多人認為音樂對心靈有益。

36 **sound** [saʊnd] (v.) 聽起來
That idea sounds nice.
那點子聽起來不錯。

10 **soup** [sup] (n.) 湯
Dad likes hot chicken soup.
爸爸喜歡喝熱雞湯。

10 **sour** [saʊr] (a.) 酸的
Lemons are sour.
檸檬是酸的。

35 **source** [sors] (n.) 來源
You can go to the library for reference sources.
你可以到圖書館找參考資料。

17 **south** [saʊθ] (n.) 南方
The warm breeze is coming from the south.
溫暖的微風南方吹來。

17 **southern** [`sʌðɚn] (a.) 南方的
The baseball player comes from the southern part of the island.
這名棒球選手來自這個島的南部。

35 **souvenir** [`suvə,nɪr] (n.) 紀念品
We spent two days on buying some souvenirs.
我們花了兩天的時間買紀念品。

10 **soy sauce** [sɔɪ sɔs] (n.) 醬油
Soy sauce is made from soybeans.
醬油是大豆製成。

35 **space** [spes] (n.) 空間，空地
There is a huge space in the middle of the school.
學校中央有很大的空地。

35 **spade** [sped] (n.) 鏟子
The farmer was digging the bamboo shoots with a little spade.
農夫用小鏟子挖竹筍。

10 **spaghetti** [spəˋgɛtɪ] (n.) 義大利麵
I love spaghetti with white sauce.
我喜歡加奶油白醬的義大利麵。

36 **spare** [spɛr] (v.) 騰出
Could you spare me some time?
你可以為我騰出一些時間嗎？

35 **spark** [spɑrk] (n.) 火花，火星
A little spark kindles a great fire.
星星之火，可以燎原。

27 **sparrow** [ˋspæro] (n.) 麻雀
The sparrows are flying over the rice fields.
一群麻雀飛越稻田。

16 **speak** [spik] (v.) 說話
May I speak to your parents?
我可以跟你爸媽談一談嗎？

35 **speaker** [ˋspikɚ] (n.) 擴音器，喇叭
The speaker doesn't work.
喇叭壞了。

35 **spear** [spɪr] (n.) 矛，魚叉
They use spears to catch the fish.
他們用魚叉捕魚。

37 **special** [ˋspɛʃəl] (a.) 特別的
He is a special friend to me.
對我來說，他是很特別的朋友。

37 **specific** [spɪˋsɪfɪk] (a.) 特定的
Do I need any specific equipment to go mountain climbing?
登山需要特定的裝備嗎？

35 **speech** [spitʃ] (n.) 演講
It's time for the principal to make a speech.
現在是校長演講的時間。

35 **speed** [spid] (n.) 速度
The maximum speed for this car is 300 km per hour.
這輛車最高時速三百公里。

16 **spell** [spɛl] (v.) 拼字
Can you spell this word?
你會拼這個字嗎？

16 **spelling** [ˋspɛlɪŋ] (n.) 拼寫
We will have a spelling contest tomorrow.
我們明天有一場拼字比賽。

9 **spend** [spɛnd] (v.) 花費
I spent 1000 dollars on that camera.
我花了一千美元買那台相機。

35 **spice** [spaɪs] (n.) 香料
Curry powder is made from different spices.
咖哩粉是用多種香料製成。

37 **spicy** [ˋspaɪsɪ] (a.) 辛辣的
This dish is very spicy.
這道菜很辣。

27 **spider** [ˋspaɪdɚ] (n.) 蜘蛛
Spiders have eight legs.
蜘蛛有八隻腳。

36 **spill** [spɪl] (v.) 溢出，流出
Who spilt the milk on the floor?
是誰把牛奶灑在地上的？

35 **spin** [spɪn] (v.) 旋轉
The neon light is spinning on the wall.
霓虹燈在牆上旋轉。

35 **spirit** [ˋspɪrɪt] (n.) 精神，志氣
The student's great spirit lasted till the end of the game.
到比賽結束為止，那名學生始終鬥志高昂。

37 **spiritual** [ˋspɪrɪtʃuəl] (a.) 精神上，心靈上
Richard is a very spiritual person, and he prays every night
理查是很重視精神生活的人，每天晚上都會禱告。

36 **spit** [spɪt] (v.) 吐
Spit your gum out before you go into the MRT station.
進入捷運站之前要把口香糖吐掉。

35 **spite** [spaɪt] (n.) 怨恨，惡意
I was full of spite towards Mike for the trouble he caused me.
我恨死麥可了，他給我惹了一堆麻煩。

36 **splash** [splæʃ] (v.) 濺，濕
Mother accidently splashed coffee on her shirt.
媽媽不小心把咖啡灑到上衣上。

37 **splendid** [ˋsplɛndɪd] (a.) 輝煌的
The school basketball team has won another splendid victory.
籃球校隊又贏得一次輝煌的勝利。

36 **split** [splɪt] (v.) 劈開，切開
Grandpa split the wood into pieces.
爺爺將木頭劈成一小塊一小塊。

36 **spoil** [spɔɪl] (v.) 寵愛，溺愛
You will spoil your children if you give them everything they ask for.
對孩子有求必應會把他們寵壞。

11 **spoon** [spun] (n.) 湯匙
The spoons and forks are laid out on the table neatly.
湯匙和叉子整齊地擺在桌上。

14 **sport** [spɔrt] (n.) 運動
Soccer is an exciting sport to watch.
足球是一種觀賞起來很刺激的運動。

14 **sportsman** [`sportsmən] (n.) 運動家
He was born to be a sportsman.
他是天生的運動家。

14 **sportsmanship** [`sportsmən,ʃɪp] (n.) 運動家精神
He is an athlete with sportsmanship.
他是具有運動家精神的運動員。

35 **spot** [spɑt] (n.) 斑點
This dog has spots all over him.
這隻小狗全身都是斑點。

36 **sprain** [spren] (v.) 扭傷
I sprained my ankle yesterday.
我昨天扭傷腳踝。

36 **spray** [spre] (v.) 噴液，噴灑
He sprayed paint all over the factory wall.
他在工廠的牆上噴滿油漆。

36 **spread** [sprɛd] (v.) 散播
The terrible rumor was spreaded all over the country.
這個可怕的謠言傳遍了整個國家。

8 **spring** [sprɪŋ] (n.) 春季
Spring is the season of blossoms.
春天是花開的季節。

36 **sprinkle** [ˋsprɪŋkl̩] (v.) 點綴
This cake is sprinkled with brown sugar.
這個蛋糕上點綴了很多赤砂糖。

35 **spy** [spaɪ] (n.) 間諜
The spy was caught and put in the jail without any trial.
那名間諜被逮捕後，未經審判就被關入監獄。

19 **square** [skwɛr] (n.) 正方形
The parade formed a perfect square.
遊行隊伍構成一個正方形。

36 **squeeze** [skwiz] (v.) 擠，壓，榨
Mother squeezed some orange juice.
媽媽榨了一些柳橙汁。

36 **stab** [stæb] (v.) 刺，刺入
A woman was stabbed to death at home yeserday afternoon.
昨天下午，一名婦女在家被刺身亡。

37 **stable** [ˋstebl̩] (a.) 可信賴的，穩重的
He is a man of stable character.
他是穩重的男人。

17 **stadium** [ˋstedɪəm] (n.) 體育場
The stadium was packed with people for the soccer game.
體育場擠滿了來看足球比賽的人。

35 **staff** [stæf] (n.) 職員，（全體）工作人員
This is the tea room for the school staff.
這是學校職員的茶水間。

35 **stage** [stedʒ] (n.) 舞台
The students decorated the stage with balloons and ribbons.
學生用氣球和緞帶布置舞台。

35 **stairs** [stɛrz] (n.) 樓梯
The old lady goes up the stairs to the fifth floor.
那個老太太爬樓梯上五樓。

37 **stale** [stel] (a.) 不新鮮的，厭倦的
The cheese is getting stale.
那起司不新鮮了。

14 **stamp** [stæmp] (n.) 郵票
Children like to collect stamps.
小孩喜歡集郵。

36 **stand** [stænd] (v.) 站立
Will you stand up now?
你現在可以站起來嗎？

35 **standard** [ˋstændɚd] (n.) 標準
Teachers have high standards for exams.
老師對考試成績的標準很高。

25 **star** [stɑr] (n.) 星星
There are so many stars in the sky.
天空有好多星星。

36 **stare** [stɛr] (v.) 盯，凝視
Do not stare at him directly.
別直接盯著他瞧。

36 **start** [stɑrt] (v.) 開始
The first semester starts from September.
第一學期從九月開始。

36 **starve** [stɑrv] (v.) 餓死，非常餓
Many people starved to death in Ethiopia.
衣索比亞有很多人餓死。

35 **state** [stet] (n.) 狀態
The president declared a state of emergency after the attack.
總統在攻擊事件之後，宣布進入緊急狀態。

17 **stationery store** [ˋsteʃə,nɛrɪ stor] (n.) 文具店
You can buy paper at the stationary stores.
在文具行可以買到紙張。

35 **statue** [ˋstætʃʊ] (n.) 雕像
The Statue of Liberty is famous in New York.
紐約的自由女神像很出名。

36 **stay** [ste] (v.) 停留
We will stay in the city for two days.
我們將在城裡停留兩天。

37 **steady** [ˋstɛdɪ] (a.) 平穩的，堅定的
I'm a steady employee.
我是穩定的雇員。

10 **steak** [stek] (n.) 牛排
We had steak for dinner.
我們晚餐吃牛排。

36 **steal** [stil] (v.) 偷，竊取
Piracy is stealing.
盜版就是偷竊。

35 **steam** [stim] (n.) 蒸氣
Steam is coming out from the bathroom.
蒸氣從浴室裡冒出來。

37 **steep** [stip] (a.) 陡峭的，驟升 / 降的
Dad had a steep rise in his salary.
爸爸獲得到大幅加薪。

35 **stem** [stɛm] (n.)（工具）柄，把手
The stem of this knife is made from gold.
這把刀的柄是黃金做的。

35 **step** [stɛp] (n.) 腳步，步驟
You have to finish the project step by step.
你必須按照步驟完成這個案子。

6 **stepchild** [ˋstɛp,tʃaɪld] (n.) 配偶前夫 / 妻所生的孩子
He is my stepchild.
他是我的繼子。

6 **stepfather** [ˋstɛp,fɑðɚ] (n.) 繼父
Bryan is my stepfather.
布萊恩是我的繼父。

6 **stepmother** [ˋstɛp,mʌðɚ] (n.) 繼母
Claire is my new stepmother.
克萊兒是我新的繼母。

35 **stereo** [ˋstɛrɪo] (n.) 立體聲效果
This movie is being broadcast in stereo.
這部電影用立體聲播放。

35 **stick** [stɪk] (n.) 棒，棍
The old man needs to walk with a stick.
那老人需要拄著枴杖走路。

37 **sticky** [ˋstɪkɪ] (a.) 黏
Little Jeff's hands are so sticky after he finished his candy.
小傑夫吃完糖，手黏兮兮的。

37 **stiff** [stɪf] (a.) 僵硬的
I felt stiff after sitting down too long.
我坐太久了，感到很僵硬。

38 **still** [stɪl] (adv.) 仍然
Tony was still hungry after having dinner.
湯尼吃完晚餐仍然很餓。

36 **sting** [stɪŋ] (v.) 刺，螫，叮
A bee stung me on my back.
一隻蜜蜂叮了我的背。

2 **stingy** [ˋstɪŋdʒɪ] (a.) 小氣的，吝嗇的
My parents tried to save money without being stingy.
我爸媽設法在不小氣的情況下省吃儉用。

36 **stir** [stɝ] (v.) 攪動
Mother stirred the eggs with the flour.
媽媽把雞蛋和麵粉攪拌在一起。

36 **stitch** [stɪtʃ] (v.) 縫，繡
The doctor stitched the cut on my leg.
醫生縫合了我腳上的傷口。

12 **stockings** [ˋstɑkɪŋz] (n.) 長襪
She likes different colors of stockings.
她喜歡各種顏色的長襪。

3 **stomach** [ˋstʌmək] (n.) 胃
She had too much food so her stomach isn't well now.
她吃太多了，現在胃不舒服。

4 **stomachache** [ˋstʌmək,ek] (n.) 胃痛
She has a stomachache now.
她在鬧胃痛。

25 **stone** [ston] (n.) 石頭
Do not throw stones into the well.
不要丟石頭到井裡。

15 **stool** [stul] (n.) 凳子，腳凳
Grandmother bought four stools from the mall.
奶奶從大賣場買了四張小凳子。

8 **stop watch** [stɑp wɑtʃ] (n.) 碼錶
The coach lost his stop watch.
那個教練把了他的碼錶弄丟了。

36 **stop** [stɑp] (v.) 中斷，阻止
The heavy rain stopped the baseball game.
大雨中斷了這場棒球比賽。

25 **storm** [stɔrm] (n.) 暴風雨
There will be a storm coming soon.
暴風雨快要來了。

25 **stormy** [ˋstɔrmɪ] (a.) 風強雨大的
The stormy weather damaged all the roads.
狂風暴雨大把道路破壞殆盡。

16 **story** [ˋstɔrɪ] (n.) 故事
The novel is a true story.
這部小說是真實故事。

15 **stove** [stov] (n.) 爐子
My mom made some coffee on the stove.
我媽媽用爐子煮了些咖啡。

19 **straight** [stret] (a.) 筆直的
She had straight hair.
她有一頭直髮。

37 **strange** [strendʒ] (a.) 奇怪的
It's so strange that I failed my exam.
我考試竟然會不及格，真是奇怪。

1 **stranger** [ˋstrendʒɚ] (n.) 陌生人
Never talk to strangers.
別和陌生人說話。

35 **strategy** [ˋstrætədʒɪ] (n.) 策略，計謀，對策
Our baseball coach is trying to tell us about the new strategy.
我們的棒球教練試著教我們新戰術。

11 **straw** [strɔ] (n.) 吸管
I need a straw to drink my soda.
我要一根吸管來喝汽水。

10 **strawberry** [ˋstrɔ,bɛrɪ] (n.) 草莓
Strawberries taste so good..
草莓好好吃。

26 **stream** [strim] (n.) 溪流
The stream runs through the mountains.
這條小溪流過群山重嶺間。

15 **street** [strit] (n.) 街道
We live on the same street.
我們住在同一條街上。

35 **strength** [strɛŋθ] (n.) 力量，力氣
Lifting weights can help build strength.
舉重有助於增大力氣。

36 **strengthen** [ˋstrɛŋθən] (v.) 加強
We need to strengthen this wall in case there is a flood.
我們需要補強這面牆，以防洪水。

35 **stress** [strɛs] (n.) 壓力
The young man can't deal with stress.
那個年輕人不會排解壓力。

36 **strike** [straɪk] (v.) 打擊
She was struck by lightning.
她被閃電擊中。

36 **strip** [strɪp] (v.) 剝，剝去，剝光
My brother stripped off his clothes and jumped into the pool.
我哥哥脫光衣服跳進池子。

36 **strive** [straɪv] (v.) 努力，奮鬥
Buying a huge house is the goal I'm striving toward.
買間大房子是我努力奮鬥的目標。

4 **strong** [strɔŋ] (a.) 強壯的
My father never got sick; he's very strong.
我爸爸從不生病，他很強壯。

35 **structure** [ˋstrʌktʃɚ] (n.) 結構，構造
This building is 200 years old, but its structure is still sound solid.
這棟建築有兩百年的歷史，但結構還很堅固。

36 **struggle** [ˋstrʌgḷ] (v.) 奮鬥，爭扎
The poor animal struggles to stand up.
這隻可憐的動物掙扎著想站起來。

2 **stubborn** [ˋstʌbɚn] (a.) 倔強的，頑固的
He is a stubborn old man.
他是頑固的老頭子。

(16) **student** [ˋstjudənt] (n.) 學生
Students often study late into the night.
學生常苦讀到深夜。

(17) **studio** [ˋstjudɪ,o] (n.) 攝影棚，影音製作公司
He works for a movie studio.
他在電影製片公司上班。

(15) **study** [ˋstʌdɪ] (v.) 學習
He has studied English for years.
他學英文已經學了很多年了。

(36) **stuff** [stʌf] (v.) 把…裝滿，把…塞進
The doll is stuffed with cotton.
這個洋娃娃塞滿了棉花。

(2) **stupid** [ˋstjupɪd] (a.) 蠢笨的
Kitty made a stupid mistake on her English test.
考英文時，凱蒂犯了一個愚蠢的錯誤。

(35) **style** [staɪl] (n.) 風格，作風
I don't like the style of his writing.
我不喜歡他的寫作風格。

(16) **subject** [ˋsʌbdʒɪkt] (n.) 主題，科目
I had to take twenty subjects in college.
讀大學時，我必須修二十門課。

(35) **submarine** [ˋsʌbmə,rin] (n.) 潛艇
The submarine never came up again.
那艘潛水艇此後再也沒有浮上來過。

(35) **substance** [ˋsʌbstəns] (n.) 物質
The water contains some substance that is poisionous.
這水裡含有一些有毒物質。

17 **suburb** [ˋsʌbɝb] (n.) 郊區
My family lives in a suburb.
我們家住在郊區。

18 **subway** [ˋsʌb,we] (n.) 地下鐵
The subway is fast, clean, and comfortable.
地鐵迅速、乾淨又舒服。

36 **succeed** [səkˋsid] (v.) 成功
We don't always succeed at once.
我們不見得馬上就能成功。

35 **success** [səkˋsɛs] (n.) 成功
The performance was a great success.
這場表演非常成功。

2 **successful** [səkˋsɛsfəl] (a.) 成功的
Tom is a very successful businessman.
湯姆是非常成功的商人。

37 **such** [sʌtʃ] (a.) 如此
I've not heard from you for such a long time.
好久沒你的消息了。

36 **suck** [sʌk] (v.) 吸，吮，啜
The baby sucks the baby food with a straw.
嬰兒用吸管吸嬰兒食品。

37 **sudden** [ˋsʌdn̩] (a.) 突然的
There is a sudden curve on the road.
路上有個急轉彎。

38 **suddenly** [ˋsʌdənlɪ] (adv.) 突然地
My dog suddenly jumped up.
我的狗突然跳了起來。

36 **suffer** [ˋsʌfɚ] (v.) 受苦，患病
He is suffering from a headache.
他頭痛，很不舒服。

37 **sufficient** [səˋfɪʃənt] (a.) 足夠的，充分的
The food is sufficient for a month.
這裡的食物夠吃一個月。

10 **sugar** [ˋʃʊgɚ] (n.) 糖
Sugar is made from sugar canes.
糖是甘蔗製成的。

36 **suggest** [səˋdʒɛst] (v.) 建議
Mother suggested that I take the business course.
媽媽建議我修商業課程。

35 **suicide** [ˋsuə,saɪd] (n.) 自殺，自殺行為
Suicide cannot solve problems.
自殺解決不了問題。

12 **suit** [sut] (n.) 套裝，西裝
He is wearing a black suit.
他穿了一套黑色西裝。

37 **suitable** [ˋsutəbl̩] (a.) 適當的，合適的
It's not suitable to wear jeans at this restaurant.
這間餐廳不合適穿牛仔褲。

9 **sum** [sʌm] (n.) 金額，一筆
You owe me a large sum of money.
你欠我一大筆錢。

36 **summarize** [ˋsʌmə,raɪz] (v.) 作總結，作概括
The teacher asked me to summarize the speech.
老師要我為演講做個總結。

35 **summary** [ˋsʌmərɪ] (n.) 摘要，總結
I made a summary of the speech.
我為這場演說整理出一份摘要。

8 **summer** [ˋsʌmɚ] (n.) 夏天
We are going on a vacation in summer.
我們夏天要去度假。

35 **summit** [ˋsʌmɪt] (n.) 頂峰，絕頂
Many people climbed to the mountain summit to see the sunrise.
許多人爬到山頂看日出。

25 **sun** [sʌn] (n.) 太陽
All creatures cannot live without the sun.
不是所有生物都能在沒有陽光下生存。

8 **Sunday** [ˋsʌnde] (n.) 星期天
My family goes to church on Sundays.
我們家星期日都上教堂。

25 **sunny** [ˋsʌnɪ] (a.) 陽光充足的
It is a sunny day today.
今天是晴天。

37 **super** [ˋsupɚ] (a.) 超級的
My dad can make hamburgers that are super tasty.
我爸爸會做超好吃的漢堡。

37 **superior** [səˋpɪrɪɚ] (a.) 較高的，上級的
This desk is made of superior quality wood.
這張書桌是用較高級的木頭製成。

17 **supermarket** [ˋsupɚ,mɑrkɪt] (n.) 超級市場
The supermarket provides me with everything I want.
我想買什麼，超級市場都有。

⑩ **supper** [ˋsʌpɚ] (n.) 晚餐
Mom always makes supper for us.
媽媽總是為我們做晚餐。

㊱ **supply** [səˋplaɪ] (v.) 提供
This pipe supplies water to the whole community.
這條水管供水給整個社區。

㊱ **support** [səˋport] (v.) 支持
Will you support me?
你會支持我嗎？

㊱ **suppose** [səˋpoz] (v.) 猜想，以為
I suppose that he doesn't know the situation.
我想他並不了解情況。

㊲ **sure** [ʃur] (a.) 確定的
I'm sure dad will be home on time.
我確定爸爸會準時到家。

⑭ **surf** [sɝf] (v.) 滑水，上網搜索資料
People loves to surf at the beach in summer.
夏天人們喜歡去海邊衝浪。

㉟ **surface** [ˋsɝfɪs] (n.) 表面
The surface of the floor is too slippery.
地板表面太滑了。

㊱ **surprise** [səˋpraɪz] (n.) 驚訝，驚喜
What a surprise!
真令人驚訝！

㊲ **surprised** [səˋpraɪzd] (a.) 驚訝的
She was so surprised to see me.
她看到我覺得很驚訝。

36 **surrender** [sə`rɛndɚ] (v.) 投降，自首
After resisting for hours, the soldier surrendered.
經過幾小時的反抗，士兵投降了。

36 **surround** [sə`raʊnd] (v.) 圍，圍繞
The castle was surrounded by a river.
這座城堡被一條河環繞。

35 **surroundings** [sə`raʊndɪŋz] (n.) 環境，周圍的事物
I am not quite familiar with the surroundings.
我對這個環境還不太了解。

36 **survey** [sɚ`ve] (v.) 考察，審視
The researcher surveyed all the documents.
研究員審查了所有文件。

35 **survival** [sɚ`vaɪvl̩] (n.) 倖存，殘存
"The survival of the fittest" is the theory of Darwin.
「適者生存」是達爾文的理論。

36 **survive** [sɚ`vaɪv] (v.) 生存
People need to learn how to survive on their own.
大家應該學習如何自力更生。

35 **survivor** [sɚ`vaɪvɚ] (n.) 倖存者，生還者，殘存物
There is only one survivor in the car accident.
這場車禍只有一人生還。

35 **suspect** [sə`spɛkt] (n.) 嫌疑犯，可疑分子
The suspect ran away after the investigation.
嫌疑犯接受調查之後逃走了。

35 **suspicion** [sə`spɪʃən] (n.) 懷疑，疑心
Don't bear any suspicion; he is innocent.
別懷疑，他是無辜的。

37 **suspicious** [sə`spɪʃəs] (a.) 猜疑的，疑心的
I am suspicious that someone is following me.
我懷疑有人在跟蹤我。

27 **swallow** [`swɑlo] (n.) 燕子
Swallows like to build the nest under the roof.
燕子喜歡在屋頂下築巢。

36 **swallow** [`swɑlo] (v.) 嚥下，吞
He swallowed the pills with difficulty.
他好不容易才把藥丸吞下去。

35 **swan** [swɑn] (n.) 天鵝
Swans sail on the lake gracefully.
天鵝在湖面優雅地浮游。

36 **swear** [swɛr] (v.) 發誓，宣誓
John swore he didn't steal the money.
約翰發誓錢不是他偷的。

35 **sweat** [swɛt] (n.) 汗，汗水
After jogging an hour, the man was coverd with sweat.
慢跑了一小時之後，男人渾身是汗。

12 **sweater** [`swɛtɚ] (n.) 毛衣
I need heavy sweaters in winter.
我在冬天需要穿厚毛衣。

36 **sweep** [swip] (v.) 掃
Grandma sweeps the floor every day.
奶奶每天掃地。

10 **sweet** [swit] (a.) 甜的
This pineapple is very sweet.
這顆鳳梨很甜。

36 **swell** [swɛl] (v.) 腫起，腫脹
Joseph's left foot began to swell after being hit by the bike.
喬瑟夫的左腳被腳踏車撞之後腫起來了。

37 **swift** [swɪft] (a.) 即時的，迅速的
A swift wave came and took away the boat.
一道突如其來的海浪將那艘船捲走了。

14 **swimming** [ˋswɪmɪŋ] (n.) 游泳
Let's go swimming.
我們去游泳吧。

12 **swimsuit** [ˋswim,sut] (n.)（女）泳裝
The swimsuit doesn't fit.
這件泳裝不合身。

35 **swing** [swɪŋ] (n.) 鞦韆
There is a swing in my garden.
我的花園裡有一座鞦韆。

36 **switch** [swɪtʃ] (v.) 切換，打開 / 關掉
Could you switch off the light?
你可以把燈關掉嗎？

35 **sword** [sord] (n.) 劍，刀
Not very many people use swords as weapons anymore.
不太有人拿劍當武器了。

35 **symbol** [ˋsɪmbḷ] (n.) 符號
The symbol on the wall is difficult to understand.
牆上的符號很難懂。

35 **sympathy** [ˋsɪmpəθɪ] (n.) 同情，同理心
He has no sympathy for the poor boy.
他一點都不同情這個可憐的男孩。

35 **symphony** [`sɪmfənɪ] (n.) 交響樂團，交響曲
The famous symphony will play Mozart tonight.
這個著名的交響樂團今晚將演奏莫札特的樂曲。

35 **system** [`sɪstəm] (n.) 系統
This computer system keeps crashing and no one knows how to fix it
電腦系統一直當機，沒有人知道怎麼修理。

T

25 **table** [`tebḷ] (n.) 桌子
There are thirty tables in this classroom.
這間教室裡有三十張桌子。

14 **table tennis** [`tebḷ `tɛnɪs] (n.) 桌球
My brother is good at table tennis.
我哥哥很會打桌球。

35 **tablet** [`tæblɪt] (n.) 藥片
The doctor told me to take two tablets after meals.
醫生告訴我三餐飯後吃兩顆藥。

36 **tack** [tæk] (v.) 釘（圖釘）
Could you tack the notice on the board?
你可以將公告釘到板子上嗎？

35 **tag** [tæg] (n.) 牌子，標籤
There is no tag on the luggage.
這件行李上沒有任何標籤。

27 **tail** [tel] (n.) 尾巴
The dog ran around in circles, chasing its own tail.
那隻狗兜著圈子追自己的尾巴。

24 **tailor** [ˋtelɚ] (n.) 裁縫師
My dress was made by a French tailor.
這女人的洋裝是一位法國裁縫師做的。

27 **Taiwanese** [ˌtaɪwɑˋniz] (n.) 台灣人
Taiwanese are hard-working people.
台灣人工作勤奮。

36 **take** [tek] (v.) 拿，取
She took the wrong luggage.
她拿錯行李了。

35 **talent** [ˋtælənt] (n.) 天才
My talent for languages showed at an early age.
我很小就展露語言天份。

16 **talk** [tɔk] (v.) 講話
Linda is a quiet girl; she doesn't talk much.
琳達是個安靜的女孩，並不多話。

2 **talkative** [ˋtɔkətɪv] (a.) 多話的
Alvin is a lively and talkative boy.
艾文是個活潑健談的男孩。

2 **tall** [tɔl] (a.) 高的
My daddy is handsome and tall.
我爸又帥又高。

2 **tame** [tem] (a.) 溫順的，馴服的
The circus elephant is tame.
馬戲團的大象很溫順。

10 **tangerine** [ˋtændʒəˌrin] (n.) 橘子
Tangerines contain a lot of vitamin C.
橘子含有豐富維他命C。

18 **tank** [tæŋk] (n.) 坦克車
The soliders fired a missle at the tank.
士兵向那輛坦克車發射一枚飛彈。

30 **tap** [tæp] (v.) 輕拍，輕叩
Everyone was tapping their feet to the music.
大家都隨著音樂用腳打拍子。

15 **tape** [tep] (n.) 膠帶
We need some tapes to tighten up the chair.
我們得用膠帶把那張椅子弄牢固些。

15 **tape recorder** [tep rɪˋkɔrdɚ] (n.) 錄音機
There are some old tape recorders in our audio center.
視聽中心裡有幾部老舊的錄音機。

35 **target** [ˋtɑrgɪt] (n.) 目標
My target is to have my own art exhibition.
我的目標是開一場藝術個展。

35 **task** [tæsk] (n.) 任務，工作
Baby-sitting is a difficult task for me.
當保母對我來説是件困難的工作。

36 **taste** [test] (v.) 嚐
The cake tastes very sweet.
這蛋糕嚐起來非常甜。

9 **tax** [tæks] (n.) 税，税金
We all need to pay taxes.
我們都需要納税。

18 **taxi** [ˋtæksɪ] (n.) 計程車
We took a taxi to our hotel after we got off the plane.
我們下飛機後，搭計程車到旅館。

10 **tea** [ti] (n.) 茶，茶葉
Would you like a cup of tea?
要來一杯茶嗎？

16 **teach** [titʃ] (v.) 教
My sister teaches in the kindergarten.
我的姊姊在教幼稚園。

16 **teacher** [ˋtitʃɚ] (n.) 老師
My dad is an English teacher at our school.
我爸爸是本校的英文教師。

14 **team** [tim] (n.) 隊
John'd like to join the soccer team in the school.
約翰想要參加足球校隊。

15 **teapot** [ˋti,pɑt] (n.) 茶壺
That is an antique teapot.
那是一個古董茶壺。

35 **tear** [tɪr] (n.) 眼淚
My mother had tears in her eyes when I left for college.
我離家去上大學時，媽媽熱淚盈眶。

36 **tease** [tiz] (v.) 戲弄，逗弄
Don't tease these kids.
別捉弄這些小孩子。

37 **technical** [ˋtɛknɪkl̩] (a.) 專門的，技術性的
The spaceship can't be launched due to some technical problems.
某些技術問題導致太空船無法發射。

35 **technician** [tɛkˋnɪʃən] (n.) 技術人員，技師
We need a special technician to solve the mechanical fault.
我們需要專門技術人員來解決機械問題。

35 **technique** [tɛk`nɪk] (n.) 技巧，技術
You need to learn some writing techniques to improve your writing.
你要學一些寫作技巧來增進作文能力。

35 **technology** [tɛk`nɑlədʒɪ] (n.) 科技，技術
Technology advanced greatly in the 20th Century.
二十世紀的科技進步迅速。

1 **teenager** [`tin,edʒɚ] (n.) 青少年
Teenagers like pop music.
青少年喜歡流行音樂。

35 **telegram** [`tɛlə,græm] (n.) 電報
Telegrams are not popular nowadays.
電報已經沒那麼普通了。

35 **telegram** [`tɛlə,græm] (n.) 向…發電報，用電報發送
Not many people send telegrams these days--email is much more popular.
現在很少人在用電報了，電子郵件比較普遍。

15 **telephone** [`tɛlə,fon] (n.) 電話
He asked that pretty girl for her telephone number.
他跟那漂亮女孩要了電話號碼。

35 **telescope** [`tɛlə,skop] (n.) 望遠鏡
We need a telescope to see star constellation.
我們需要望遠鏡看星星。

15 **television** [`tɛlə,vɪʒən] (n.) 電視機
My little brother always sits in front of the television.
我弟弟老是坐在電視機前。

36 **tell** [tɛl] (v.) 說
Did you tell your mother that you are coming tonight?
你有告訴你媽今晚要來這裡嗎？

35 **temper** [ˋtɛmpɚ] (n.) 情緒，性情
The old man cannot control his bad temper.
那個老人控制不了他的壞脾氣。

25 **temperature** [ˋtɛmprətʃɚ] (n.) 溫度，氣溫
The temperature is getting higher and higher every year.
氣溫正在逐年升高。

17 **temple** [ˋtɛmpl̩] (n.) 寺廟
This Buddhist temple is huge.
這座佛寺規模宏大。

37 **temporary** [ˋtɛmpə,rɛrɪ] (a.) 臨時的，暫時的
I have a temporary job as a salesperson.
我暫時從事業務員的工作。

7 **ten** [tɛn] (a.) 十
The witch has ten cats.
那個女巫養了十隻貓。

36 **tend** [tɛnd] (v.) 走向，趨向
The child tends to lie.
這孩子很愛說謊。

2 **tender** [ˋtɛndɚ] (a.) 溫柔的，體貼的
The babysitter is very tender to the children.
這位保母對孩子非常溫柔。

14 **tennis** [ˋtɛnɪs] (n.) 網球
Tennis is one of my favorite sports.
網球是我最喜愛的運動之一。

35 **tension** [ˋtɛnʃən] (n.) 神經緊繃，緊張狀況
The nervous tension almost drove him crazy.
神經緊繃的情況讓他幾近瘋狂。

14 **tent** [tɛnt] (n.) 帳篷
My parents bought a large tent for me.
我的父母親買了一個大帳篷給我。

7 **tenth** [tɛnθ] (a.) 第十的
He's the tenth son in his family.
他是家裡的第十個兒子。

16 **term** [tɝm] (n.) 學期
We usually have a parents' meeting at the end of the term.
我們經常在學期結束時舉辦家長會。

37 **terrible** [ˋtɛrəbl̩] (a.) 可怕的，糟糕的
It was a terrible movie.
那是一部很糟糕的電影。

37 **terrific** [təˋrɪfɪk] (a.) 很棒的
I had a terrific summer in the U.S.
我在美國過了一個很棒的夏天。

36 **terrify** [ˋtɛrə,faɪ] (v.) 使害怕，使恐怖
The scary movie terrified the children.
這部恐怖電影把小朋友嚇壞了。

17 **territory** [ˋtɛrə,torɪ] (n.) 領土，版圖，領地
The soldiers fought for the lost territory.
士兵為失去的領土而戰。

35 **terror** [ˋtɛrɚ] (n.) 恐怖，驚駭
I am in terror of the mean dog which bit me once.
我很怕那隻咬過我的惡犬。

16 **test** [tɛst] (n.) 測驗，考試
I didn't do well on the English test today.
我今天的英文考試考砸了。

A B C D E F G H I J K L M N O P Q R S T U V W X Y Z

16 **text** [tɛkst] (n.) 課文，文字
The text of the article is blurred.
這篇文章的字跡模糊不清。

16 **textbook** [`tɛkst,bʊk] (n.) 教科書
Patty forgot to bring her English textbook today.
佩蒂今天忘了帶英文課本。

32 **than** [ðæn] (conj.) 比
He is taller than you.
他比你高。

36 **thank** [θæŋk] (v.) 感謝
Thank you for your gift.
謝謝你的禮物。

37 **thankful** [`θæŋkfəl] (a.) 感謝的，感激的
Be thankful to those who help you.
對幫助你的人要心存感激。

23 **Thanksgiving** [,θæŋks`gɪvɪŋ] (n.) 感恩節
We always have turkey on Thanksgiving Day.
感恩節總要吃火雞。

35 **theme** [θim] (n.) 主題，主題思想
The theme of his thesis is about political issues.
他的論文題目與政治議題相關。

29 **themselves** [ðɛm`sɛlvz] (pron.) 他/她/它們自己
I told them they should visit Los Angeles for themselves.
我早跟他們說過要親自去一趟洛杉磯。

38 **then** [ðen] (adv.) 然後，接下來
She had dinner and then went to take a shower.
她吃完晚餐，接著去洗澡。

35 **theory** [ˋθiərɪ] (n.) 理論，學理
The scientist's theory doesn't work at all.
科學家的理論完全不成立。

17 **there** [ðɛr] (adv.) 在那裡
The airport is over there.
飛機場在那邊。

33 **therefore** [ˋðɛr,for] (adv.) 因此
She isn't home yet; therefore she couldn't come to the party.
她到現在還沒回家，因此無法前來參加宴會。

37 **thick** [θɪk] (a.) 厚的
How thick is this cutting board?
這個砧板有多厚？

35 **thief** [θif] (n.) 小偷
The thief was trying to climb into the house.
那個小偷想要爬進屋裡。

2 **thin** [θɪn] (a.) 薄的，細瘦的
How did you get so thin !
你怎麼變這麼瘦 !

35 **thing** [θɪŋ] (n.) 事，物
Don't forget to bring your things to school.
別忘了帶你的東西到學校。

36 **think** [θɪŋk] (v.) 想，認為
What do you think of this place?
你認為這地方怎麼樣？

7 **third** [θɝd] (a.) 第三的
Jay is her third cousin.
傑是她的第三個表弟。

85 **thirst** [θɝst] (n.) 渴望
His thirst for knowledge drove him to study diligently.
他對知識的渴望促使他用功讀書。

37 **thirsty** [ˋθɝstɪ] (a.) 口渴的
I felt thirsty and hot after the exercise.
運動完我覺得又渴又熱。

7 **thirteen** [ˋθɝˋtin] (a.) 十三個的
There are thirteen students in the class.
這個班級有十三個學生。

7 **thirteenth** [ˋθɝˋtinθ] (a.) 第十三的
This is my thirteenth bike!
這是我第十三部腳踏車！

7 **thirtieth** [ˋθɝtɪɪθ] (a.) 第三十的
I can't see the thirtieth page.
我找不到第三十頁。

7 **thirty** [ˋθɝtɪ] (a.) 三十個的
You only have thirty minutes left for the test.
考試只剩下三十分鐘了。

28 **this** [ðɪs] (a.) 這個
I want to buy this jacket.
我想要買這件夾克。

37 **thorough** [ˋθɝo] (a.) 十足的，徹頭徹尾
After thorough consideration, I quit my job.
徹底考慮過後，我決定辭職了。

28 **those** [ðoz] (pron.) 那些
Are those your money on the desk?
桌上那些錢是你的嗎？

33 **though** [ðo] (conj.) 雖然
Sam is short, though he's not fat.
山姆矮矮的，但是他不胖。

35 **thought** [θɔt] (n.) 思考
At the thought of my dead grannie, I am all tears.
想起死去的奶奶，我淚流滿面。

37 **thoughtful** [ˋθɔtfəl] (a.) 細心的，注意的
She is always thoughtful to others.
她總是為他人著想。

7 **thousand** [ˋθaʊzənd] (n.) 千
Thousands of people were killed in the earthquake.
數千人在那起地震中喪命。

35 **thread** [θrɛd] (n.) 線，絲
The jobless young man didn't have a thread of hope.
這位失業青年沒有一絲希望。

35 **threat** [θrɛt] (n.) 威脅
The big dam is a threat to all the people downstream.
這座大水壩對所有下游居民構成威脅。

36 **threaten** [ˋθrɛtn̩] (v.) 威脅，恐嚇
The criminal threatened to kill all the hostages.
惡徒恐嚇要殺害全部人質。

7 **three** [θrɪ] (a.) 三個的
Aunt Maria has three daughters.
瑪麗亞姑姑有三個女兒。

3 **throat** [θrot] (n.) 喉嚨
Our teacher had a sore throat yesterday.
昨天我們的老師喉嚨痛。

32 **through** [θru] (prep.) 穿越
Grandmother is trying to put the thread into her needle.
奶奶試著把線穿過針。

32 **throughout** [θru`aʊt] (prep.) 遍及
The disease is spreading throughout the world wide.
這種疾病正在世界各地蔓延。

36 **throw** [θro] (v.) 丟
Don't throw your toys around.
不要把你的玩具亂丟。

3 **thumb** [θʌm] (n.) 拇指
He pressed the fingerprint of his thumb on the paper.
他在文件上蓋上拇指印。

25 **thunder** [`θʌndɚ] (n.) 雷
The thunder comes after lightening.
雷聲隨閃電而來。

8 **Thursday** [`θɝzde] (n.) 星期四
Halloween party will be held on Thursday.
萬聖節派對將於星期四舉行。

38 **thus** [ðʌs] (adv.) 因此
The train was late and thus our schedule was delayed.
火車誤點，我們的計畫因此延誤。

35 **ticket** [`tɪkɪt] (n.) 票
The concert ticket is so expensive.
演唱會的門票好貴喔。

36 **tickle** [`tɪkl̩] (v.) 逗…笑，呵癢
The grandpa tickled his baby grandson.
那個祖父給他的寶寶孫子呵癢。

25 **tide** [taɪd] (n.) 潮水，趨勢
The tide will start to rise in about an hour.
大概再過一小時就會漲潮。

36 **tidy** [ˋtaɪdɪ] (v.) 整潔的
Please tidy up this room.
請把房間整理乾淨。

36 **tie** [taɪ] (v.) 繫，綁
Little Macy is learning how to tie her shoelaces.
小玫希正在學習如何綁鞋帶。

27 **tiger** [ˋtaɪgɚ] (n.) 老虎
Tigers are vicious animals.
老虎是凶猛的動物。

37 **tight** [taɪt] (a.) 緊的，不鬆動的
The knot is so tight that I cannot untie it.
這個結好緊，我解不開。

36 **tighten** [ˋtaɪtn̩] (v.) 使變緊，使繃緊
The mechanic tightened a few screws on my bicycle.
技師幫我把腳踏車上的幾個螺絲鎖緊。

32 **till** [tɪl] (prep.) 直到
I was grounded till the end of this month.
我被禁足到這個月底。

35 **timber** [ˋtɪmbɚ] (n.) 木材，木料
There is less and less timber in the woods.
森林裡的木材越來越少了。

35 **time** [taɪm] (n.) 時間
Time is one thing that you can't buy.
時間是不能用金錢買到的。

37 **timid** [ˋtɪmɪd] (a.) 膽小的，易受驚嚇的

The timid pigeons are pecking grains on the ground.

膽小的鴿子在地上啄食穀粒。

19 **tiny** [ˋtaɪnɪ] (a.) 微小的

Fleas are tiny pests.

跳蚤是微小的害蟲。

35 **tip** [tɪp] (n.) 祕訣

I can give you a few tips for becoming a good learner.

我可以提供你一些成為好學習者的祕訣。

4 **tired** [taɪrd] (a.) 疲倦的

My sister was so tired when she got back from gym.

我姊姊從健身房回來時非常疲倦。

37 **tiresome** [ˋtaɪrsəm] (a.) 使人疲勞的，令人厭倦的

It's a tiresome task.

這是個討厭的工作。

35 **tissue** [ˋtɪʃu] (n.) 紙巾，面紙，衛生紙

The bathroom is out of tissues.

廁所裡沒有衛生紙了。

35 **title** [ˋtaɪtl̩] (n.) 標題

What's the title of the book you're reading.

你正在讀的這本書書名是什麼？

32 **to** [tu] (prep.) 到

I work from nine to five every day.

我每天都朝九點晚五。

10 **toast** [tost] (n.) 烤麵包片，吐司

I had a toast and some coffee for my breakfast.

我早餐吃了一片烤麵包。喝了一點咖啡。

35 **tobacco** [tə`bæko] (n.) 菸草製品
Teens should not use tobacco.
青少年不應該吸菸。

8 **today** [tə`de] (n.) 今天
Today is even colder than yesterday.
今天比昨天還要冷。

3 **toe** [to] (n.) 腳趾
I hurt my toe in a soccer game last week.
上星期我踢足球傷到大姆趾。

10 **tofu** [`tofu] (n.) 豆腐
Tofu is made from soybeans.
豆腐是用黃豆製成。

38 **together** [tə`gɛðɚ] (adv.) 一起，一共
My family usually have dinner together every Saturday.
我的家人經常在星期六共進晚餐。

15 **toilet** [`tɔɪlɪt] (n.) 馬桶，盥洗室
Mother cleans the toilet every day.
媽媽每天都清洗馬桶。

35 **tolerance** [`tɑlərəns] (n.) 忍耐，寬容
His behavior is beyond tolerance.
他的行為已超出容忍範圍。

36 **tolerate** [`tɑlə,ret] (v.) 容許，忍受
I can't tolerate his rude speech.
我無法忍受他無禮的言語。

10 **tomato** [tə`meto] (n.) 番茄
I like to have a lot of tomatoes in the pizza.
我喜歡在披薩裡加很多番茄。

17 **tomb** [tum] (n.) 墓，墓碑

Thieves sometimes uncover ancient tombs to steal jewelry.

竊賊有時會挖開古墓偷珠寶。

8 **tomorrow** [tə`mɔro] (n.) 明天

I don't have any big plans for tomorrow.

我明天沒有什麼特別的計劃。

19 **ton** [tʌn] (n.) 噸，公噸

Tons of garbage are dumped in this area.

好幾公噸的垃圾被倒到這個地區。

3 **tongue** [tʌŋ] (n.) 舌頭

I burned my tongue when drinking the hot coffee.

我喝咖啡時燙到舌頭。

8 **tonight** [tə`naɪt] (adv.) 今晚

Daddy is coming back from Hong Kong tonight.

爸爸今晚要從香港回來。

38 **too** [tu] (adv.) 太

It's too hot during summer days!

夏天太熱了！

35 **tool** [tul] (n.) 工具

Teachers must have a lot of tools to teaching with.

老師必須要有非常多的教學工具。

3 **tooth** [tuθ] (n.) 牙齒

We must brush our teeth every day.

我們必須每天刷牙。

4 **toothache** [`tuθ,ek] (n.) 牙痛

My little brother is having a terrible toothache.

我弟牙痛得很厲害。

15 **toothbrush** [ˋtuθ,brʌʃ] (n.) 牙刷
She'd like to buy an electronic toothbrush.
她想買一把電動牙刷。

17 **top** [tɑp] (n.) 頂部
Monica graduated at the top of her class.
莫妮卡以班上前幾名的成績畢業。

35 **topic** [ˋtɑpɪk] (n.) 主題
Today's discussion topic is movies and entertainment.
今天的討論主題是電影及演藝圈。

27 **tortoise** [ˋtɔrtəs] (n.) 陸龜，烏龜
Tortoises are not exactly the same as turtles.
陸龜和海龜不完全一樣。

36 **toss** [tɔs] (v.) 拋，擲幣
They tossed a coin to decide which side to take.
他們擲銅板決定要選哪一邊。

37 **total** [ˋtotḷ] (a.) 總共的
What is the total amount of the drinks?
飲料總共多少錢？

2 **touch** [tʌtʃ] (v.) 碰觸
Mother told me not to touch her jewelry.
媽媽叫我別碰她的珠寶。

37 **tough** [tʌf] (a.) 不屈不撓的，強硬的
He is tough and never gives up.
他非常堅強，凡事絕不放棄。

35 **tour** [tʊr] (n.) 遊覽
We had an hour to take a tour around London city.
我們在倫敦市區遊覽一個小時。

35 **tourism** [ˋturɪzəm] (n.) 旅遊業，觀光業
The war ruined the country's tourism.
戰爭毀了這國家的觀光業。

35 **tourist** [ˋturɪst] (n.) 旅遊者，觀光者
The tourists have been warned that the disease could break out.
觀光客已被警告疫情可能會爆發。

36 **tow** [to] (v.) 拖，拉
He parked his car in the disabled parking spot so it was soon towed away.
他把車停在殘障車位，所以很快就被拖吊了。

32 **toward** [təˋwɔrd] (prep.) 朝…方向
That stranger gradually walking towards me.
那陌生人慢慢朝我走來。

15 **towel** [ˋtauəl] (n.) 毛巾
My towel is wet; please give me another one.
我的毛巾濕了，請給我另一條。

35 **tower** [ˋtauɚ] (n.) 塔
The Eiffel tower in Paris is very famous.
巴黎的艾菲爾鐵塔非常有名。

17 **town** [taun] (n.) 鎮
We live in a small town.
我們住在一個小鎮裡。

14 **toy** [tɔɪ] (n.) 玩具
Can you ask John to pick up his toys?
你可以請約翰把玩撿起來嘛？

36 **trace** [tres] (v.) 追蹤
There is no trace of the robber who stole our TV.
那個偷電視的賊沒有留下珠絲馬跡。

35 **trace** [tres] (n.) 痕跡，遺跡
There is not a trace of deer.（用no trace of會不會好一點？）
那裡絲毫沒有鹿的蹤跡。

35 **track** [træk] (n.) 足跡
The rescuer tracked the foot prints to save the victims.
救難隊沿著腳印搜救受難者。

35 **trade** [tred] (n.) 貿易
My father does a lot of trade with many countries worldwide.
我爸爸與世界許多國家進行貿易。

24 **trader** [ˋtredɚ] (n.) 商人
I'd like to be a stock trader when I grow up.
我長大後要當股票交易員。

35 **tradition** [trəˋdɪʃən] (n.) 傳統
It is a tradition in my family to live with our parents.
與父母同住是我家的傳統。

37 **traditional** [trəˋdɪʃənl̩] (a.) 傳統的
We are a traditional Chinese family.
我們是一個傳統的中國家庭。

18 **traffic** [ˋtræfɪk] (n.) 交通
We must follow traffic rules.
我們必須遵守交通規則。

35 **tragedy** [ˋtrædʒədɪ] (n.) 悲劇，慘案
Romeo and Juliet is a tragedy.
《羅密歐與茱莉葉》是齣悲劇。

37 **tragic** [ˋtrædʒɪk] (a.) 悲劇性的，悲慘的
The tragic accident claimed five lives.
這起悲慘車禍奪走五條人命。

35 **trail** [trel] (n.) 痕跡，小徑
There is a trail leading to the seashore.
有一條小徑通到海岸。

18 **train station** [tren`steʃən] (n.) 火車站
I will meet you at the train station.
我會和你在火車站見面。

18 **train** [tren] (n.) 火車
She goes to work by train every day.
她每天搭火車去上班。

36 **transfer** [træns`fɝ] (v.) 使轉換，調動
He has been transferred to another school.
他已經轉到另外一個學校。

36 **transform** [træns`fɔrm] (v.) 使改變，使改觀
Julie transformed from a teenager to a beautiful woman in one year.
雪莉在一年之間從少女變成美麗的女人。

36 **translate** [træns`let] (v.) 翻譯，轉譯
Please translate the following passages.
請翻譯以下的文章。

35 **translation** [træns`leʃən] (n.) 譯文，譯本
The traslation is slightly different from the original.
這譯本和原著有點不一樣。

18 **transport** [træns`pɔrt] (v.) 運送，運輸
They need to transport the victim to the nearest hospital as soon as possible.
他們需要將受難者盡快運送至最近的醫院。

18 **transportation** [trænspɚ`teʃən] (n.) 運輸工具，交通車輛
The public transportation is quite convenient here.
這裡的大眾運輸相當方便。

(36) **trap** [træp] (v.) 被困住
I was trapped in the traffic jam.
我被困在車陣中。

(35) **trash** [træʃ] (n.) 廢物，垃圾
After the hurricane, trash was scattered everywhere.
颶風之後，到處都是垃圾

(14) **travel** [ˋtrævḷ] (v.) 旅行
I want to travel around Africa after leaving school.
我完成學業後想去非洲各地旅行。

(35) **traveler** [ˋtrævlɚ] (n.) 旅行者，旅客，遊客
Be a traveler, not a tourist.
當一位旅者，不要當觀光客。

(35) **tray** [tre] (n.) 盤子，托盤
Don’t put your tip on the waitress’ tray.
別將小費放在女服務生的托盤上。

(35) **treasure** [ˋtrɛʒɚ] (n.) 寶藏
There must be a lot of treasure on that ship.
那艘船上一定有很多寶藏。

(36) **treat** [trit] (n.)請客
The dinner is my treat.
晚餐我請客。

(36) **treat** [trit] (v.) 對待，款待
I’d like to treat you to dinner when you have time.
如果你有空的話，我想請你吃晚飯。

(35) **treatment** [ˋtritmənt] (n.) 治療
His cancer isn’t responding to the treatment.
他的癌症對這個療法沒有反應。

25 **tree** [tri] (n.) 樹木
Paper is made from trees.
紙張是樹木做的。

36 **tremble** [ˋtrɛmbl̩] (v.) 震顫，發抖
He was trembling with anger.
他氣得發抖。

37 **tremendous** [trɪˋmɛndəs] (a.) 極度的，驚人的
There will be a tremendous change after the election.
選舉過後會有很大的轉變。

35 **trend** [trɛnd] (n.) 趨勢，傾向，時尚
The fashion trend changes tremendously.
時尚趨勢的變化很大。

35 **trial** [ˋtraɪəl] (n.) 試用
You are on a trial period of three months.
你正在三個月的試用期內。

19 **triangle** [ˋtraɪ,æŋgl̩] (n.) 三角形
There are two triangles in the drawing.
書中有兩個三角形。

35 **tribe** [traɪb] (n.) 部落，種族
There are many different tribes of people on this small island.
小島上有許多不同種族的人。

35 **trick** [trɪk] (n.) 戲法，詭計
I know a few magic tricks.
我知道一些魔術戲法。

35 **trick** [trɪk] (v.) 欺騙
The salesperson tricked me into buying more than I needed.
這個推銷員騙我買一堆我不需要的東西。

37 **tricky** [ˋtrɪkɪ] (a.) 機警的，足智多謀的
Foxes are really tricky and not easily caught.
狐狸非常機警，不容易抓到。

14 **trip** [trip] (n.) 旅行
My parents took a trip to Japan.
我的父母親到日本去旅行。

36 **triumph** [ˋtraɪəmf] (v.) 獲得勝利
Our school team will triumph in the competition at the end.
我們的校隊最後一定會贏得比賽。

35 **troop** [trup] (n.) 軍隊，部隊
The general ordered his troops to retreat.
將軍命令他的軍隊撤退。

37 **tropical** [ˋtrɑpɪkl̩] (a.) 熱帶的，位於熱帶的
I love the tropical climate in Thailand.
我喜歡泰國的熱帶天氣。

35 **trouble** [ˋtəʌbl̩] (n.) 麻煩
Are you in some kind of trouble?.
你是不是惹了什麼麻煩？

12 **trousers** [ˋtraUzɚz] (n.) 長褲
He needs a new pair of trousers.
他需要一件新的長褲。

18 **truck** [trʌk] (n.) 卡車
Gina's father is a truck driver.
吉娜的父親是卡車司機。

37 **true** [tru] (a.) 真實的
This movie is based on a true story.
這部電影是由真實故事改編的。

14 **trumpet** [ˋtrʌmpɪt] (n.) 喇叭，小號
He's a good trumpet player.
他是很好的喇叭手。

35 **trunk** [trʌŋk] (n.) 樹幹
Jimmy's dad hit a huge tree trunk in his car.
吉米的爸爸開車撞上大樹幹。

36 **trust** [trʌst] (v.) 信任
Daddy wouldn't trust me with his car.
爸爸不放心把車交給我。

35 **truth** [truθ] (n.) 真實
We can only tell the truth in court.
在法庭上只能說實話。

2 **truthful** [ˋtrʊθfəl] (a.) 誠實的，講真話的，坦率的
They are truthful children.
他們是誠實的孩子。

36 **try** [traɪ] (v.) 嘗試
I tried hard to persuade him to join our soccer team.
我努力說服他加入我們的足球隊。

12 **T-shirt** [ˋti,ʃɜt] (n.) 短袖圓領杉
You look nice in a white T-shirt and jeans.
你穿白色圓領衫和牛仔褲很好看。

15 **tub** [tʌb] (n.) 浴缸
The little boy was jumping up and down in the tub.
這小男孩在浴缸裡蹦蹦跳跳。

8 **Tuesday** [ˋtjʊzde] (n.) 星期二
We'll have an English exam next Tuesday.
我們下星期二將會有英文考試。

36 **tug** [tʌg] (v.) 用力拉
Don't tug on my skirt, or you'll stretch it.
別拉我的裙子，

35 **tulip** [ˋtjʊləp] (n.) 鬱金香，鬱金香花
We went to some beautiful tulip gardens in Holland.
我們在荷蘭去了幾個美麗的鬱金香花園。

36 **tumble** [ˋtʌmbl̩] (v.) 跌倒，滾下
He tumbled down from the stairs.
他從樓梯上跌下來。

3 **tummy** [ˋtʌmɪ] (n.) 肚子
Grandpa has a huge tummy.
祖父有一個很大的肚子。

36 **tune** [tjun] (v.) 調整頻道
I always tune into this station to listen to the news.
我總是轉到這個電台收聽新聞。

18 **tunnel** [ˋtʌnəl] (n.) 隧道
This tunnel is 570 meters long.
這座隧道有五百七十公尺長。

27 **turkey** [ˋtɜkɪ] (n.) 火雞
I have a turkey sandwich for lunch every day.
我每天中午都吃火雞肉三明治。

18 **turn** [tɜn] (v.) 使轉向
Please turn left at the traffic lights and my house is on the right.
請在紅綠燈處左轉，我家在右邊。

27 **turtle** [ˋtɜtl̩] (n.) 海龜
Turtles have hard shells covering its bodies.
烏龜有硬殼包著身體。

24 **tutor** [ˋtjutɚ] (n.) 家庭教師，私人教師
He needs a tutor to help with his math.
他需要請一位家教補習數學。

15 **TV** [ˋti ˋvi] (n.) 電視（television的簡稱）
There is a huge TV outside by the department store.
百貨公司外面有一個巨大的電視螢幕。

7 **twelfth** [twɛlfθ] (a.) 第十二的
I live on the twelfth floor of this building.
我住在這棟大廈的十二樓。

7 **twelve** [twɛlv] (a.) 十二個
Mother has twelve brothers and sisters.
媽媽有十二個兄弟姐妹。

7 **twentieth** [ˋtwɛntɪɪθ] (a.) 第二十的
It's her twentieth birthday today.
今天是她二十歲生日。

7 **twenty** [ˋtwɛntɪ] (a.) 二十個
She wants twenty dolls.
她想要二十個洋娃娃。

7 **twice** [twaɪs] (adv.) 兩次
I go overseas twice a year.
我一年出國兩次。

35 **twig** [twɪg] (n.) 細枝，嫩枝
The ground was covered with twigs from the tree above.
地上原本都是樹上掉下來的小樹枝。

35 **twin** [twɪn] (n.) 孿生兒，雙胞胎
The twins have nothing in common.
這對雙胞胎沒有任何相似之處。

36 **twinkle** [ˋtwɪŋkl̩] (v.) 使閃爍，使閃耀
The stars twinkle in the night.
星星在夜裡閃爍。

36 **twist** [twɪst] (v.) 扭轉，扭彎，旋轉
The policeman twisted my arm and put handcuffs on me.
警察把我的手轉到背後戴上手銬。

7 **two** [tu] (a.) 二個
I have two cats and a dog.
我有兩隻貓和一隻狗。

35 **type** [taɪp] (n.) 種類
What types of clothes should I wear to your wedding?
我應該穿什麼種類的衣服去參加你的婚禮？

35 **typewriter** [ˋtaɪp,raɪtɚ] (n.) 打字機
The writer is used to writing with typewriters.
這位作家習慣用打字機寫作。

25 **typhoon** [taɪˋfun] (n.) 颱風
There is a huge typhoon around Japan at the moment.
目前日本附近有一個大颱風。

37 **typical** [ˋtɪpɪkl̩] (a.) 典型的，有代表性
He is a typical Japanese salesman.
他是一位典型的日本業務人員。

24 **typist** [ˋtaɪpɪst] (n.) 打字員，打字者
She works as a typist in the publishing company.
她在一家出版社擔任打字員。

U

2 **ugly** [`ʌglɪ] (a.) 醜的
That painting is ugly.
那張畫真醜。

12 **umbrella** [ʌm`brɛlə] (n.) 雨傘
She left her umbrella on the bus.
她把傘掉在公車上了。

6 **uncle** [`ʌŋkḷ] (n.) 伯父、姑父（等父執輩）
Uncle Bobby is my youngest uncle.
巴比叔叔是我最小的叔叔。

32 **under** [`ʌndɚ] (prep.) 在…下面
His dog is under the dinning table.
他的狗在餐桌下。

16 **underline** [,ʌndɚ`laɪn] (v.) 畫底線
I've underlined all the important notes in my textbook.
課本上的重點我都有經畫底線。

18 **underpass** [`ʌndɚ,pæs] (n.) 地下通道，下穿交叉道
The underpass was filled with water after the typhoon.
颱風過後地下道都是水。

16 **understand** [,ʌdɚ`stænd] (v.) 懂
Could you understand the teacher's explanation during class?
你聽得懂老師課堂上的講解嗎？

12 **underwear** [`ʌndɚ,wɛr] (n.) 內衣
I don't have any clear underwear to wear today.
我今天沒半條乾淨的內褲可以穿。

❷ **underweight** (a.) 體重不足的

If you are underweight, you won't be allowed to donate blood.

體重過輕的人不可以捐血。

❷ **unhappy** (a.) 不愉快的

He was unhappy to hear that you're moving away.

聽說你要搬走，他很難過。

⓬ **uniform** (n.) 制服

We all look the same in school uniforms.

我們穿學校制服，看起來都一樣。

㉟ **union** (n.) 工會，聯合會，協會

The teachers' union protested on the street for jobless teachers.

教師工會在街上為失業教師抗議。

㊲ **unique** (a.) 唯一的，獨一無二的

The unique and shining diamond attracts women's attention.

那顆獨一無二的閃亮鑽石吸引女人的目光。

㊱ **unite** (v.) 使聯合，使團結

People should unite together against the invaders.

人民應該團結一致對抗侵略者。

㉟ **unity** (n.) 團結，聯合，統一

The unity of the party won the election finally.

由於團結一致，該黨最後贏得了這場選舉。

㊲ **universal** (a.) 宇宙的，普遍的

Peace and freedom are universal values.

和平與自由是普世價值。

㉟ **universe** (n.) 宇宙，天地萬物

No scientist can figure out how vast the universe is.

沒有科學家可以算出宇宙有多遼闊。

16 **university** (n.) 大學，綜合性大學
After high school, Jean chose to attend a nearby university.
高中畢業後，珍選擇就讀附近的大學。

33 **unless** (conj.) 如果不，除非
I won't talk to him again, unless he apologizes.
我不會再和他說話了，除非他道歉。

33 **until** (conj.) 直到
I stayed up late until I finished studying.
我熬夜直到把書念完。

32 **up** (adv.) 向上的
I hike up that mountain to watch the sunrise almost every morning.
我幾乎每天早上都上山去看日出。

36 **upload** (v.) 上載
She uploaded her data into my computer.
她上傳一些資料到我的電腦。

37 **upon** (prep.) 在…上面
We climbed upon the roof.
我們爬到屋頂上面。

32 **upper** (a.) 上面的
The rooms in the upper floors of the hotel are more expensive because they have a better view.
這間飯店的高樓層房間比較貴，因為景觀比較好。

36 **upset** (v.) 使心煩意亂
The bad news upset me.
這個壞消息使我心煩意亂。

15 **upstairs** (adv.) 在樓上地
We have three bedrooms upstairs.
我們樓上有三個房間。

37 **urban** (a.) 城市的
I enjoy urban living but cannot afford it.
我喜歡城市生活，但負擔不起。

36 **urge** (v.) 催促
My mom urged me to go to bed immediately.
我媽媽催我立刻上床睡覺。

37 **urgent** (a.) 緊急的，急迫的
I have an urgent message for you.
我要給你一個緊急訊息。

29 **us** (pron.) 我們
The doctor gave us some medication.
醫生給我們一些治療藥物。

35 **usage** (n.) 使用，用法，處理
The usage of fresh herbs in our cooking is a family tradition.
做菜時使用新鮮香料是我們家的傳統。

36 **use** (v.) 使用
This old camera isn't used anymore.
這台老舊的相機已經不能用了。

37 **useful** (a.) 有用的
This toolbox will be useful to you.
這個工具箱會對你很有用處。

35 **user** (n.) 使用者
The number of Internet users is rapidly growing.
網路使用者的人數快速成長中。

37 **usual** (a.) 平常的
Ten o'clock is our usual bedtime.
十點是我們平常睡覺的時間。

38 **usually** (adv.) 通常地
I usually go to school at six in the morning.
我通常早上六點上學。

V

37 **vacant** (a.) 空著的，未被占用的
During the holidays, the city becomes vacant.
假日時，城市變得空蕩蕩的。

23 **vacation** (n.) 假期
Do you have any plans for your summer vacation?
你的暑假有任何計畫嗎？

35 **vain** (a.) 愛慕虛榮的
She is vain and arrogant.
她愛慕虛榮又自大。

23 **Valentine's Day** (n.) 情人節
Couples usually go out for dinner on Valentine's Day.
情侶在情人節時通常會出去吃晚餐。

26 **valley** (n.) 山谷
He chased the bear into a large valley.
他把那隻熊追進了一個大山谷。

37 **valuable** (a.) 值錢的，貴重的
My father bought me a valuable watch.
我的爸爸買了一支貴重的手錶給我。

35 **value** (n.) 價值
The value of the cars will drop at the end of this year.
車子的價格將於年底下跌。

⑱ **van** (n.) 廂形客貨兩用車
The school uses vans to transfer students.
學校用廂型車載運學生。

㊱ **vanish** (v.) 突然不見，消失
The magician vanished behind the curtain.
那個魔術師在布幕後面消失了。

㉟ **variety** (n.) 多樣化，變化
My girlfriend brought a variety of snacks home.
我的女朋友帶了很多種零食回家。

㊲ **various** (a.) 各式各樣的，形形色色的
People vote for various reasons.
人們因為各種不同因素投下選票。

㊱ **vary** (v.) 使不同，變更，修改
What we do on weekends varies, depending on our work schedules.
我們在週末做些什麼並不一定，端看工作時間表而定。

㊲ **vast** (a.) 廣闊的，浩瀚的
The vast desert stretches thousands of miles.
這片廣闊的沙漠綿延數千英里。

⑮ **VCR** (n.) 卡式錄放影機
Dad bought a new VCR for himself.
爸爸為自己買了一台新的卡式錄放影機。

⑩ **vegetable** (n.) 蔬菜
We grow vegetables in our backyard.
我們在自家後院種菜。

㉟ **vegetarian** (n.) 素食主義者
My mom is a vegetarian for religious reasons.
我的媽媽因為宗教因素成為素食主義者。

⑱ **vehicle** (n.) 運載工具，車輛
You're not allowed to park vehicles at the front door.
不准在前門停車。

㉔ **vendor** (n.) 小販
I've been working as a street vendor for weeks now.
我在街上當小販已經好幾個星期了。

㉟ **verb** (n.) 動詞
A verb usually comes after the subject.
動詞通常跟在主詞的後面。

㉟ **verse** (n.) 詩，韻文
He wrote a verse on Valentine's Day for his girlfriend.
他在情人節當天寫了一首詩給女朋友。

㊳ **very** (adv.) 非常地
Mother is a very nice woman.
媽媽是一位非常好的女人。

⑫ **vest** (n.) 背心，防護背心
The policeman survived because of his bulletproof vest.
這名警察因為穿防彈背心而保住一命。

㉔ **vice-president** (n.) 副總統
The vice-president didn't agree with the president.
副總統不同意總統的意見。

㉟ **victim** (n.) 犧牲者，遇難者
The victims were buried after the honorable ceremony.
罹難者在隆重的儀式後下葬。

㉟ **victory** (n.) 勝利
The basketball team had their first victory today.
籃球隊今天得到了第一場勝利。

15 **video** (n.) 錄影帶
He made a video of his wedding.
他為了他的婚禮拍了一支錄影帶。

35 **view** (n.) 觀點
He always mentions his point of view during meetings.
在會議上，他總是有自己的觀點。

17 **village** (n.) 村莊
My grandfather lives in a small village in the mountains.
我的爺爺住在山上的小村莊裡。

10 **vinegar** (n.) 醋
Vinegar and olive oil are good salad dressing.
醋和橄欖油是很好的沙拉醬汁。

36 **violate** (v.) 違犯，違背
Do not violate any traffic rule.
不要違背任何交通規則。

35 **violation** (n.) 違反行為
The man was fined $500 for traffic violations.
那人因為違反交通規則被罰五百元。

35 **violence** (n.) 暴力
The violence won't be allowed in the school.
學校內禁止暴力。

37 **violent** (a.) 激烈的，猛烈的
The airport is shut down because of the violent riot.
機場因激烈的暴動而關閉。

37 **violet** (a.) 紫羅蘭色的
She dressed in a violet blouse.
她穿了一件紫羅蘭色的上衣。

14 **violin** (n.) 小提琴

He has learned to play the violin since ten years ago.

他從十年前就已經開始學小提琴。

35 **virtue** (n.) 美德，優點

He has the virtue of patience.

他具有耐心的美德。

35 **virus** (n.) 病毒

Someone is spreading a virus on the Internet.

有人正在網路上散播一種病毒。

37 **visible** (a.) 可看見的

The light dot on the screen is still visible.

螢幕上的亮點還是沒消失。

35 **vision** (n.) 洞察力，眼光

The young man has great vision.

那年輕人很有遠見。

36 **visit** (v.) 參觀，拜訪

I will visit my grandmother this summer.

今年夏天我會去探望我的奶奶。

35 **visitor** (n.) 觀光客

We greeted the visitors with champagne and fruit.

我們用香檳和水果款待觀光客。

37 **visual** (a.) 視力的，視覺的

The teacher used visual aids including a projector and a computer to show the students examples.

老師用投影機和電腦等視覺輔助舉例給學生看。

37 **vital** (a.) 生命的，維持生命所必需的

Protein is a vital part of your diet and should be eaten daily.

蛋白質是飲食不可少的部分，每天都要吃到。

10 **vitamin** (n.) 維他命
Vegetables like broccoli and tomatoes are filled with vitamins.
花椰菜、番茄之類的蔬菜充滿維他命。

37 **vivid** (a.) 鮮豔的，鮮明的
I want the color of the wall to be vivid and eye-catching.
我希望牆壁的顏色鮮明搶眼。

16 **vocabulary** (n.) 字彙
My English homework is to memorize a list of vocabulary.
我的英文作業是背一張單字表。

35 **voice** (n.) 聲音
His voice sounds like a kid.
他的聲音聽起來像小孩子。

35 **volcano** (n.) 火山
While in Hawaii, we actually visited a volcano.
在夏威夷，我們真的去看了一座火山。

14 **volleyball** (n.) 排球
I was a member of the national volleyball team.
我曾經是排球國家代表隊的一員。

35 **volume** (n.) 音量
The volume of the speaker is too loud; please turn it down.
這個喇叭的音量太大了，請轉小聲一點。

36 **vote** (v.) 投票
I was too young to vote in the presidential election.
我年紀太小，無法在總統大選投票。

35 **voter** (n.) 投票人
The voters waited in line for two hours while they fixed the broken voting machines.
他們修理壞掉的投票機時，投票的人排隊等了兩小時。

W

㉟ wag (v.) 搖，擺動
The dog wags its tail when it's happy or excited.
狗快樂或興奮時，會搖尾巴。

㉟ wage(s) (n.) 薪水，報酬
The maid's wages are four hundred dollars a week.
這名侍女的薪水為每週四百美元。

⑱ wagon (n.) 運貨馬車
The horses dragged the wagon with goods.
這些馬匹拉著載有貨物的馬車。

❸ waist (n.) 腰部
She wore a fancy belt on her waist.
她在腰上繫了一條別緻的腰帶。

㊱ wait (v.) 等待
Please wait for me.
請等我一下。

㉔ waiter (n.) 男服務生
We asked the waiter for more water three times but he never brought any.
我們向服務生要了三次水，但他都沒拿來。

㉔ waitress (n.) 女服務生
The waitresses in the restaurant are very polite.
這間餐廳的女服務生都很有禮貌。

㊱ wake (v.) 醒來
Grandma wakes up early every morning.
奶奶每天都很早起床。

35 **waken** (v.) 醒來，睡醒
I was wakened by her screaming.
我被她的尖叫聲吵醒。

36 **walk** (v.) 走
She walks one kilometer to school every morning.
她每天早上走一公里的路去上學。

35 **walkman** (n.) 隨身聽
This is the smallest walkman I've ever seen!
這是我看過最小的隨身聽！

15 **wall** (n.) 牆壁
This wall is ten feet high and twelve feet long.
這面牆有十呎高，十二呎長。

12 **wallet** (n.) 皮夾
He pulled out his big fat wallet.
他拿出他那又大又鼓的皮夾。

36 **wander** (v.) 漫遊，閒逛
The little girl wandered in the streets.
這小女孩在街上亂逛。

36 **want** (v.) 想要
I want to go home now.
我現在想回家了。

35 **war** (n.) 戰爭
The Second World War went on for four years.
第二次世界大戰持續了四年。

25 **warm** (a.) 溫暖的，保暖的
This jacket looks warm.
這件夾克看起來很保暖。

A B C D E F G H I J K L M N O P Q R S T U V W X Y Z

35 **warmth** (n.) 親切，溫暖
We all stayed indoors to enjoy the warmth of the fire.
我們都待在室內享受爐火的溫暖。

36 **warn** (v.) 警告，告誡
My mother warned me it would be cold in Alaska, so I brought a very heavy coat.
我媽警告我阿拉斯加會很冷，所以我帶了一件超厚外套。

15 **wash** (v.) 洗滌
I have to wash the dishes every day.
我每天都得洗碗盤。

15 **washing machine** (n.) 洗衣機
Our new washing machine washes clothes faster and better than the old one.
我們的新洗衣機比舊的那台洗得快又好。

36 **waste** (v.) 浪費
She wastes so much money on food.
她浪費了好多錢在食物上。

8 **watch** (n.) 錶
I am not used to wearing a watch.
我不習慣戴手錶。

10 **water** (n.) 水
I drink at least six glasses of water a day, but I still don't think it's enough.
我一天至少喝六杯水，但我依然覺得不夠。

17 **waterfall** (n.) 瀑布
The waterfall we saw while hiking was at least twenty feet high!
我們登山健行時看到的瀑布至少有二十呎高！

10 **watermelon** (n.) 西瓜
The watermelon is sweet and watery.
這個西瓜甜又多汁。

36 **wave** (v.) 揮手
I waved at her.
我跟她揮手。

35 **wax** (n.) 蠟，蜂蠟
There is a thin layer of wax on his car.
他的車子表面有層薄薄的蠟。

35 **way** (n.) 方向，路徑
Can you show me the way to the airport?
你可以告訴我往機場的路嗎？

2 **weak** (a.) 衰弱的
I was tired and weak after the three-day journey.
三天行程之後，我又累又虛弱。

36 **weaken** (v.) 變弱，變衰弱
Adding water to the soup will weaken the spices.
在湯裡加水會減輕辣度。

35 **wealth** (n.) 財富，財產
Health is more important than wealth.
健康比財富重要。

37 **wealthy** (a.) 富有的
Most wealthy people pay someone to manage their money.
大多數有錢人付錢請人幫他們理財。

35 **weapon** (n.) 武器
A baseball bat is sometimes considered a weapon.
棒球棒有時被視為是一種武器。

12 **wear** (v.) 穿
I will wear a tuxedo to her wedding.
我會穿一件燕尾服參加她的婚禮。

㉕ weather (n.) 天氣
The weather in the mountains changes rapidly.
山上的天氣轉變很快。

㊱ weave (v.) 編織
The spider wove a web on a roof corner.
蜘蛛在屋頂的角落結了一個蜘蛛網。

㉟ wedding (n.) 婚禮
My best friend wasn't there on my wedding day.
我最好的朋友在我結婚當天沒來參加。

❽ Wednesday (n.) 星期三
Since Wednesday is in the middle of the week, it's a good time to have a staff meeting.
因為星期三是一週的中間，相當適合開員工會議。

㉟ weed (n.) 雜草，野草
The weeds grew very tall while we were on vacation.
我們去度假時，雜草長得好高。

❽ week (n.) 一星期，週
I usually have English classes twice a week.
我一星期通常有兩次英文課。

❽ weekday (n.) 平日，非週末
All students have to attend school on weekdays.
全部的學生平日都得上學。

❽ weekend (n.) 週末
My favorite thing to do on the weekend is go to the lake.
我週末最喜歡做的事，就是去湖邊。

❽ weekly (a.) 每週的
We have weekly exams on Fridays.
我們每星期五有週考。

36 **weep** (v.) 哭泣，流淚
Grandma wept over her sad life.
祖母為了她悲慘的人生而哭泣。

19 **weight** (n.) 重量，體重
What weight can this luggage carry?
這個行李箱可以負重多少？

36 **welcome** (v.) 歡迎
Welcome to the restaurant!
歡迎光臨本餐廳!

4 **well** (adv.) 很好地
My sister plays the piano very well.
我姊姊鋼琴彈得很好。

17 **west** (n.) 西方
The ship sails towards the west.
這艘船向西方航行。

17 **western** (a.) 西方的
Many people move to the western part of the US for the warm weather.
許多人為了溫暖的天氣搬到美國西岸。

25 **wet** (a.) 濕的
We've had wet weather for weeks!
這裡的天氣已經好幾個星期都濕答答的！

27 **whale** (n.) 鯨
The whale traveled from Alaska to Hawaii with its new baby.
鯨魚帶著牠的新生兒從阿拉斯加游到夏威夷。

30 **whatever** (pron.) 不管什麼
Whatever happens, you know I will be there for you.
不論發生什麼事，你都會有我支持。

⑩ **wheat** (n.) 小麥
This beer is made from wheat.
這啤酒是小麥製的。

⑱ **wheel** (n.) 車輪
My bicycle wheel was hit by a stone.
我的腳踏車輪被一顆石頭打中。

㉝ **whether** (conj.) 是否
I wasn't sure whether you want steak or fish.
我不確定你要吃牛排還是魚。

㉚ **which** (pron.) 哪一個，哪一些
Which do you prefer, eating in or eating out?
你比較喜歡哪一樣，在家裡吃還是出去外面吃？

㉚ **while** (conj.) 當…的時候
I read the article while you were on the phone.
你在講電話時，我已經看完這篇文章了。

㊱ **whip** (v.) 攪打
I whipped the eggs to make the cake.
我打蛋做蛋糕。

㊱ **whistle** (v.) 吹口哨，鳴笛，吹哨子
The police officer whistled at the jaywalker.
警察對橫越馬路的人吹哨子。

⑬ **white** (a.) 白色的
The man in the white suit is my father.
穿白色西裝的男人是我爸爸。

㊲ **whole** (a.) 全部的
I'm so hungry I could eat a whole cake!
我餓到可以吃下一整個蛋糕！

37 **wicked** (a.) 惡劣的，討厭的，有害的
She's such a wicked person, always trying to hurt other people's feelings.
她真是個討厭的人，老是想要傷害別人的感情。

19 **wide** (a.) 寬的
The table is a meter long and thirty cm wide.
這桌子長一公尺，寬三十公分。

19 **widen** (v.) 加寬
The street is too narrow; it needs to be widened.
這條街太窄了，需要拓寬。

19 **width** (n.) 寬度
The width of the table is perfect, but it's too short.
這張桌子的寬度完美，但是太矮了。

6 **wife** (n.) 妻子
His wife is a career woman.
他太太是職業婦女。

37 **wild** (a.) 野生的
I like to eat wild salmon rather than farmed salmon.
我喜歡吃野生鮭魚勝過養殖鮭魚。

31 **will** (aux.) 將
There will be times when you will want to be alone.
總會有些時候你會想獨處。

37 **willing** (a.) 願意的
He's willing to sacrifice his time for his children.
他願意為孩子犧牲自己的時間。

35 **willow** (n.) 柳，柳樹
The willows look gentle and elegant blowing in the wind.
風中的柳樹看起來柔和又幽雅。

36 **win** (v.) 贏
Did they win the game?
他們比賽贏了嗎？

25 **wind** (n.) 風
The wind is really strong in the desert.
沙漠的風真的很強。

15 **window** (n.) 窗戶
The boy next door broke the window.
隔壁的男孩打破這扇窗戶。

25 **windy** (a.) 刮風的，風大的
It's windy today.
今天的風很大。

10 **wine** (n.) 葡萄酒，酒
My roommate made some wine out of strawberries that tastes like heaven!
我的室友用草莓釀酒，嚐起來棒極了！

27 **wing** (n.) 翅膀
That bird can't fly because someone has clipped its wings.
那隻鳥不能飛，因為有人把牠的翅膀剪斷了。

36 **wink** (v.) 使眼色，眨眼
That man winked at me!
那個人在跟我眨眼耶！

14 **winner** (n.) 贏家
The winner will get all the prizes.
贏家將贏得所有獎品。

8 **winter** (n.) 冬天
It's usually cold in the winter in Canada.
加拿大的冬天經常很冷。

36 **wipe** (v.) 擦，揩乾
Please wipe the water off the table.
請擦乾桌上的水。

35 **wisdom** (n.) 智慧，才智
I admire my grandmother for her wisdom.
我很欣賞我祖母的智慧。

2 **wise** (a.) 有智慧的，聰明的
It's not very wise to spend more money than you make.
花得比賺得多是非常不智的行為。

36 **wish** (v.) 但願
I wish all my dreams would come true.
我希望我所有的夢想都能成真。

32 **with** (prep.) 和…一起
Jerry lives with roommates in an apartment.
傑瑞和幾位室友住在一間公寓裡。

36 **withdraw** (v.) 撤退，撤離
The troops were withdrawn from the front line.
部隊從前線被撤離。

32 **within** (prep.) 在…範圍裡
You have to finish this work within ten days.
你需要在十天內完成這項工作。

32 **without** (prep.) 沒有
I am not leaving without you.
沒有你我就不走。

35 **witness** (n.) 目擊者，見證人
The witness to the murder was killed.
這起謀殺案的目擊者被殺身亡。

35 **wok** (n.) 鐵鍋，炒菜鍋
A wok is a useful item for a stir-fry.
中華炒鍋這種用具,拿來炒菜很好用。

27 **wolf** (n.) 狼
The wolf ran to catch the rabbit.
那匹狼跑去追兔子。

1 **woman** (n.) 女人
My mother is a wonderful woman.
我媽媽是個很棒的女人。

36 **wonder** (v.) 想知道，感到疑惑
Students always wonder about their future.
學生對未來總是感到好奇。

37 **wonderful** (a.) 極好的
It's a wonderful morning!
真是一個美妙的早晨!

35 **wood** (n.) 木材
Please gather some wood to build a fire.
請找些木材生火。

37 **wooden** (a.) 木製的
This is a wooden house.
這是一間木屋。

26 **woods** (n.) 樹林，森林
Let's take a walk in the woods after dinner!
晚餐後一起到樹林裡散步吧!

35 **word** (n.) 單字，生字
This essay is about 3000 words long.
這篇文章長度大約是三千字。

24 **work** (v.) 工作
Dad works hard every day.
爸爸每天都認真工作。

16 **workbook** (n.) 作業簿
The exercises in the workbook are harder than the examples they show in the textbook.
作業本上的練習題比課本上的範例難。

24 **worker** (n.) 工人，工作人員
There are only two workers in this supermarket.
這家超級市場只有兩名員工。

20 **world** (n.) 世界
The world is a big place and I'd like to explore all of it!
世界遼闊，我想要探索每一處！

36 **worry** (v.) 擔心
Don't worry about me.
別擔心我。

37 **worth** (a.) 有…價值的，值得的
That chair is worth one hundred dollars.
那一張椅子價值一百美元。

31 **would** (aux.) 委婉請求（will過去式）
Would you bring some bread home?
你可否帶一些麵包回家？

4 **wound** (n.) 傷口
Keep your wound away from water.
不要讓你的傷口碰到水。

36 **wrap** (v.) 包，裹
Could you wrap up my book?
可以把我的書包起來嗎？

35 **wreck** (n.) 船難事故

The rescuers tried their best to save the victims from the wreck.

救難人員盡力搶救船難的受難者。

35 **wrinkle** (n.) 皺，皺紋

The face of the old lady is scattered with wrinkles.

這位老太太的臉上滿是皺紋。

3 **wrist** (n.) 腕，腕關

She wore a diamond bracelet around her wrist.

她在手腕上戴了一只鑽石手環。

16 **write** (v.) 書寫

She doesn't know how to write a formal letter.

她並不知道如何書寫正式信件。

24 **writer** (n.) 作家

It takes a lot of skill and patience to be a good writer.

成為好作家需要許多技巧和耐性。

37 **wrong** (a.) 錯的

She gave me the wrong telephone number.

她給了我錯誤的電話號碼。

Y

15 **yard** (n.) 院子

Megan's mother grows vegetables in the yard.

梅根的媽媽在院子裡種菜。

19 **yard** (n.) 碼

Three feet is equal to one yard.

三呎等於一碼。

36 **yawn** (v.) 打呵欠

The sleepy boy yawned in a loud voice in class.

這個想睡覺的男孩上課時大聲地打了個哈欠。

8 **year** (n.) 年

I've stayed in Taiwan for three years.

我已經在台灣住三年了。

8 **yearly** (a.) 每年的

I visit my parents yearly, usually at Christmas time.

我每年都去探望我的父母，一般是在耶誕節。

36 **yell** (v.) 叫喊，吼叫

Stop yelling and calm down, please.

請停止叫喊，冷靜下來。

13 **yellow** (n.) 黃色

Yellow is a bright and cheery color.

黃色是明亮活潑的顏色。

8 **yesterday** (adv.) 昨天

We had an English exam yesterday.

我們昨天有一場英文考試。

38 **yet** (adv.) 還沒

Dad is not home yet.

爸爸還沒回來。

10 **yolk** (n.) 蛋黃

I like to eat the yolk in moon cakes.

我喜歡吃月餅裡的蛋黃。

2 **young** (a.) 年輕的

His aunt looks so young.

他的姑姑看起來好年輕。

❶ **youngster** (n.) 小孩
Youngsters need special care.
小孩需要特別費心照顧。

㉙ **yourself** (pron.) 你自己
You can do that question by yourself.
你可以自己完成那個題目。

❶ **youth** (n.) 青春，青少年時期
Jimmy spent his youth in the States.
吉米青少年時期在美國度過。

❿ **yummy** (a.) 美味的
The apple pie is very yummy.
這個蘋果派非常美味。

Z

㉗ **zebra** (n.) 斑馬
I really like the black and white stripes of the zebra.
我真喜歡斑馬身上的黑白條紋。

❼ **zero** (n.) 零
Jimmy got zero on the math test.
吉米數學考了零分。

㉟ **zipper** (n.) 拉鍊
My zipper got stuck in the middle.
我的拉鍊卡在中間了。

㉟ **zone** (n.) 地區，地帶
This is a non-smoking zone so you'll have to put out that cigarette.
這是禁菸區，你必須把菸熄掉。

⑰ **zoo** (n.) 動物園

Many schools take a field trip to the Zoo.

許多學校會去動物園校外教學。

1 People 人

adult	成年人
audience	觀眾，聽眾
baby	嬰兒
boy	男孩
child	小孩
couple	夫妻，一對情侶
customer	顧客
examiner	主考官
expert	專家
fellow	(口)夥伴，傢伙
female	女性的，雌的
fool	傻瓜
foreigner	外國人
genius	天才
gentleman	紳士
giant	巨人
girl	女孩
guardian	監護人
guest	客人
guy	傢伙(指男性)，各位
hero	英雄
host	主人
infant	嬰兒
kid	小孩
king	國王
lady	小姐
lover	情人
male	雄性，男性
man	男人
mass	大眾，民眾
master	主人，雇主
neighbor	鄰居
neighborhood	鄰近地區
pal	朋友，同伴
partner	夥伴
patient	病患
people	人
person	人
prince	王子
prisoner	囚犯
queen	皇后，女王
stranger	陌生人
teenager	青少年(尤其是十三至十九歲)
woman	女人
youngster	小孩
youth	青春，青少年時期

2 Personal Characteristics 人格特質

angry	生氣的	diligent	勤勉的
beautiful	漂亮的	dishonest	不誠實的
blind	眼盲的	dumb	啞的
blush	臉紅	energetic	有活力的
boast	自誇，吹噓	envy	嫉妒，羨慕
bored	無聊的	evil	邪惡的
boring	乏味的	evil	邪惡，罪惡
brave	勇敢的	excited	興奮的
busy	忙碌的	exciting	令人激動的
careful	小心的	faithful	忠實，忠誠
careless	粗心的	famous	出名的，有名的
characteristic	特徵，特色	fat	胖
charm	魅力，撫媚	fear	害怕
childish	幼稚的	foolish	愚笨的
childlike	天真的，像小孩子的	frank	坦白的，直率的
chubby	圓胖的，嬰兒肥的	friendly	友善的
clever	聰明的	funny	好笑的
clumsy	笨手笨腳的	generosity	慷慨
confident	自信的	generous	大方的
considerate	體貼的	gentle	溫和的
contain	包含	gifted	有天賦的
crazy	瘋狂的	good	好的
cruel	殘忍的	grateful	感激的
curiosity	好奇	greedy	貪心的
curious	好奇的	grief	悲痛
cute	可愛的	guilty	有罪的
deaf	聾的	handsome	英俊的，好看的
delighted	高興的	happy	高興的

2 Personal Characteristics 人格特質

hard-working	努力的，勤勉的	polite	禮貌的
honest	誠實的	poor	貧窮的
honesty	誠實	pretty	漂亮的
honorable	可敬的，正直的	proud	自豪的，驕傲的
humble	謙遜的	reasonable	講道理的
humor	幽默	rich	富有的
humorous	幽默的，詼諧的	rude	粗魯的，無禮的
impolite	無禮的	sad	悲傷
independent	獨立	scared	驚恐的
innocent	清白的，單純的	selfish	自私的
intelligent	有才智的	sensible	意識到的，察覺到的
interested	感興趣的	short	短的，矮的
jealous	嫉妒	shy	害羞的
kind	親切的	silly	傻的
lazy	懶惰的	sincere	真心的
liberal	開明的，自由主義的	skinny	皮包骨的
		slender	苗條的
lonely	孤獨的	slim	苗條的
lovely	可愛的	smart	聰明伶俐的
mad	生氣的，瘋的	sneaky	鬼鬼祟祟的
naughty	頑皮的	stingy	小氣的，吝嗇的
nervous	緊張	stubborn	倔強的，頑固的
nice	美好的	stupid	蠢笨的
nice-looking	漂亮的，好看的	successful	成功的
old	老的	talkative	多話的
over-weight	過重的	tall	高的
patient	有耐心的	tame	溫順的，馴服的
personality	個性	tender	溫柔的，體貼的

2 Personal Characteristics 人格特質

thin	薄的，細瘦的	underweight	體重不足的
touch	碰觸	unhappy	不愉快的
truthful	誠實的，講真話的，坦率的	weak	衰弱的
		wise	有智慧的，聰明的
ugly	醜的	young	年輕的

3 Parts of body 人體部位

abdomen	腹部	foot	腳（複數形為feet）
ankle	足踝	forehead	額頭，前額
appearance	外觀	hair	毛髮
arm	手臂	hand	手
back	背部	head	頭
beard	鬍子	heart	心
belly	肚子	hip	髖部，臀部
body	身體	jaw	下巴
bone	骨頭	joint	關節
breast	乳房	kidney	腎臟
brow	眉毛，眉頭	knee	膝蓋
cheek	臉頰	knuckle	（供食用的）蹄、肘，關節
chest	胸膛		
chin	下巴	leg	腿
ear	耳朵	limb	肢，臂，腳
elbow	肘部	lip	嘴唇
eye	眼睛	liver	肝臟
face	臉	lung	肺部，肺
finger	手指	mouth	嘴
fist	拳打，拳	muscle	肌肉

3 Parts of body 人體部位

nail	指甲	throat	喉嚨
neck	頸部	thumb	拇指
nerve	神經，焦慮	toe	腳趾
nose	鼻子	tongue	舌頭
shoulder	肩膀	tooth	牙齒
skin	皮膚	tummy	肚子
soul	心靈，靈魂	waist	腰部
stomach	胃	wrist	腕，腕關

4 Health 健康

ache	痛	healthy	健康的，有益健康的
AIDS	愛滋病	ill	生病的
cancer	癌症	itch	癢
comfortable	舒服的	life	生命
cough	咳嗽	medicine	藥
cure	治療	pain	疼痛
death	死亡	painful	痛的
disease	疾病	sick	生病的
dizzy	頭暈的	sore throat	喉嚨痛
drug	藥物，毒品	stomachache	胃痛
examine	檢查	strong	強壯的
fever	發燒	tired	疲倦的
flu	（口）流行性感冒	toothache	牙痛
headache	頭痛	vitamin	維他命
health	健康	well	很好地
healthful	有益健康的	wound	傷口

5 Forms of address 表達方式

ma'am	(口)女士	Mrs.	太太(Mistress的簡稱)
method	方法	Ms.	女士
Miss	小姐	name	名字
Mr.	先生(mister的簡稱)	sir	先生

6 Family 家庭

aunt	伯母,姑母(等女性長輩)	husband	丈夫
born	出生的	live	活,住
brother	哥哥,弟弟	marriage	婚姻
cousin	堂、表親(兄弟姊妹)	married	已婚的
dad	爸爸(亦稱daddy)	marry	娶,嫁
daughter	女兒	mother	母親(口語稱mommy或mom)
divorce	離婚	nephew	姪兒,外甥
elder	年紀大的	niece	姪女,外甥女
elderly	年老的,上了年紀的	parent	父親,母親
family	家庭	relative	親戚
father	父親	sister	姐妹
granddaughter	(外)孫女	son	兒子
grandfather	(外)祖父(暱稱grandpa)	stepchild	配偶前夫/妻所生的孩子,繼子女
grandmother	(外)祖母(暱稱grandma)	stepfather	繼父
grandson	(外)孫子	stepmother	繼母
		uncle	伯父、姑父(等父執輩)
		wife	妻子

7 Numbers 數字

all	所有的	million	一百萬
billion	十億	more	更多的
both	兩者，雙方	much	很多
double	雙的	nine	九（個的）
eight	八個	nineteen	十九個（的）
eighteen	十八	nineteenth	第十九的
eighteenth	第十八的	ninety	九十
eighth	第八的	ninth	第九的
eighty	八十	number	電話號碼，數字
eleven	十一個	one	一個的
eleventh	第十一的	only	唯一的
few	很少的	our	我們的
fifteen	十五個	second	第二的
fifteenth	第十五的	seven	七
fifth	第五的	seventeen	十七
fifty	五十	seventeenth	第十七的
first	第一的	seventh	第七的
five	五個	seventy	七十
forty	四十	several	幾個
four	四	six	六個
fourteen	十四	sixteen	十六個
fourteenth	第十四	sixteenth	第十六的
fourth	第四的	sixth	第六的
half	一半	sixty	六十
hundred	一百	some	一些
last	最後的	ten	十
less	較少的	tenth	第十的
many	很多的	third	第三的

7 Numbers 數字

thirteen	十三個的	twelfth	第十二的
thirteenth	第十三的	twelve	十二個
thirtieth	第三十的	twentieth	第二十的
thirty	三十個的	twenty	二十個
thousand	千	twice	兩次
three	三個的	two	二個

8 Time 時間

afternoon	下午	evening	晚間
ago	在…以前	fall	秋天
alarm	鬧鐘	February	二月
already	已經	forever	永遠，老是
April	四月	Friday	星期五
August	八月	future	未來
autumn	秋天	hour	小時
calendar	日曆	idle	虛度光陰
century	世紀	January	一月
clock	鐘	July	七月
current	當前的	June	六月
daily	日常的	late	遲的，晚的
dawn	黎明	lately	最近
day	天，白天	later	稍晚的
deadline	最後期限	latest	最新的，最近的
decade	十年	lifetime	一生，終生
December	十二月	March	三月
early	早	May	五月
eve	前夕	midnight	午夜

8 Time 時間

minute	分	second	一秒鐘
moment	短暫時刻	soon	很快地
Monday	星期一	spring	春季
month	月	September	九月
monthly	每月的	stop watch	碼錶
morning	早晨	summer	夏天
next	緊接的，居後的	Sunday	星期天
night	夜	Thursday	星期四
noon	中午	today	今天
November	十一月	tomorrow	明天
now	現在	tonight	今晚
o'clock	點鐘	Tuesday	星期二
once	一次	watch	錶
October	十月	Wednesday	星期三
p.m.	下午（post meridiem的縮寫）	week	一星期，週
		weekday	平日，非週末
past	過去	weekend	週末
perhaps	或許	weekly	每週的
quarter	四分之一，一刻鐘	winter	冬天
recent	最近的	year	年
recently	近來	yearly	每年的
Saturday	星期六	yesterday	昨天
season	季節		

9 Money 金錢

bill	帳單，紙鈔	cash	現金
buy	買	cent	分

9 Money 金錢

change	零錢	fund	資金，基金
charge	收費，索價	generation	世代
cheap	便宜的	income	收入
coin	硬幣	lend	把…借給
cost	花費	loan	貸款
credit card	信用卡	money	錢
discount	折扣	pay	付費
dollar	元（美金）	penny	一分錢
earn	賺取	price	價格
economic	經濟的	spend	花費
expense	費用，開支	sum	金額，一筆
expensive	昂貴的	tax	稅，稅金
fee	費用		

10 Food & drink 飲食

alcohol	酒類，含酒精飲料	breakfast	早餐
apple	蘋果	brunch	早午餐
bacon	培根，燻豬肉	bun	小圓麵包
bake	烘烤	burger	漢堡
banana	香蕉	butter	奶油
bean	豆子	cabbage	高麗菜
beef	牛肉	cake	蛋糕
beer	啤酒	candy	糖果
berry	漿果	carrot	紅蘿蔔
bitter	苦的	cereal	穀類食品
boil	煮沸	cheese	乳酪
bread	麵包	cherry	櫻桃

10 Food & drink 飲食

chocolate	巧克力
cocktail	雞尾酒
coconut	椰子
coffee	咖啡
Coke	可口可樂
cookie	餅乾
corn	玉米
cream	鮮奶油乳脂
dairy	乳製品，牛奶的
delicious	美味的
dessert	點心
diet	節食
dine	進餐，用餐
dinner	晚餐
doughnut	甜甜圈
drink	飲料
dumpling	餃子
eat	吃
egg	蛋
fast food	速食
flour	麵粉
food	食物
French fries	薯條
fruit	水果
full	滿的
garlic	大蒜
ginger	薑
grain	穀物，穀類
grape	葡萄
guava	番石榴
gum	口香糖(chewing gum的簡稱)
ham	火腿
hamburger	漢堡
honey	蜂蜜
hot dog	熱狗
hunger	飢餓
hungry	飢餓的
ice cream	冰淇淋
ice	冰
instant noodles	泡麵
jam	果醬
juice	果汁
ketchup	番茄醬
lemon	檸檬
lettuce	萵苣
liquid	液體
lobster	龍蝦
lollipop	棒棒糖
lunch	午餐
mango	芒果
meal	一餐
meat	肉
melon	瓜
menu	菜單
milk shake	奶昔

10 Food & drink 飲食

milk	牛奶	seafood	海鮮
mushroom	蘑菇	shrimp	蝦
noodle	麵	snack	點心
nut	堅果	soda	蘇打，汽水
oil	油	soft drink	不含酒精的飲料
onion	洋蔥	soup	湯
orange	柳橙	sour	酸的
pancake	煎薄餅	soy sauce	醬油
papaya	木瓜	spaghetti	義大利麵
pea	豌豆	steak	牛排
peach	桃子	strawberry	草莓
pear	梨	sugar	糖
pepper	胡椒	supper	晚餐
pickle	酸黃瓜	sweet	甜的
pie	派，餡餅	tangerine	橘子
pineapple	鳳梨	tea	茶，茶葉
pizza	比薩	toast	烤麵包片，吐司
plum	梅子	tofu	豆腐
popcorn	爆米花	tomato	番茄
pork	豬肉	vegetable	蔬菜
potato	馬鈴薯	vinegar	醋
pumpkin	南瓜	water	水
raisin	葡萄乾	watermelon	西瓜
rice	米飯	wheat	小麥
salad	沙拉	wine	葡萄酒，酒
salt	鹽	yolk	蛋黃
sandwich	三明治		

11 Tableware 餐具

biscuit	餅乾	knife	刀
bowl	碗	plate	碟子，盤子
chopsticks	筷子	saucer	淺碟
cup	杯子	spoon	湯匙
dish	盤子	straw	吸管
fork	叉子		

12 Clothing & accessories 衣服配件

backpack	背包	gown	（女用）長禮服，睡袍
bag	袋子	handkerchief	手帕
belt	皮帶	hat	帽子
blouse	短上衣女士用)，短衫	heel	高跟鞋
bracelet	手鐲	helmet	安全帽
button	扣（鈕釦）	jacket	夾克
cap	鴨舌帽	jeans	牛仔褲
cape	披肩	jewel	寶石飾物，首飾
clothes	衣服	jewelry	珠寶，首飾
coat	大衣	linen	亞麻布，亞麻紗
comb	梳子	lipstick	口紅
contact lens	隱形眼鏡	mask	面具
cotton	棉花	necklace	項鍊
diamond	鑽石	necktie	領帶
dress	洋裝	overcoat	外套，大衣
earnings	收入	pajamas	睡衣
glove	手套	pants	褲子，長褲
gold	金子		

12 Clothing & accessories 衣服配件

pocket	口袋	socks	襪子
purse	錢包	stockings	長襪
raincoat	雨衣	suit	套裝，西裝
ring	戒指	sweater	毛衣
scarf	圍巾	swimsuit	（女）泳裝
shirt	襯衫	trousers	長褲
shoes	鞋子	T-shirt	短袖圓領衫
shorts	短褲	umbrella	雨傘
silver	銀	underwear	內衣
skirt	裙子	uniform	制服
sleeve	袖子	vest	背心，防護背心
slippers	拖鞋	wallet	皮夾
sneakers	運動鞋	wear	穿

13 Colors 顏色

black	黑色的	orange	橘色的
blue	藍色的	pale	蒼白
brown	棕色的	pink	粉紅色的
color	顏色	purple	紫色的
colorful	鮮豔的	red	紅色
golden	金色的	white	白色的
gray	灰色的	yellow	黃色
green	綠色的		

14 Sports, interests & hobbies 運動、興趣及嗜好

badminton	羽毛球	fan	迷
band	樂團，一群	film	影片
barbecue	烤肉	fishing	釣魚
baseball	棒球	flute	長笛
basketball	籃球	football	美式足球
bowling	保齡球	Frisbee	飛盤
camping	露營	gamble	賭掉，賭博
card	卡片	game	遊戲
cartoon	卡通動畫，漫畫	golf	高爾夫球
CD	雷射唱片(compact disc的縮寫)	guitar	吉他
		harmonica	口琴
chess	西洋棋	hiking	健行，遠足
collect	收集	hobby	嗜好
collection	收集，收藏	instrument	樂器
comic book	漫畫書	interest	興趣
computer game	電腦遊戲	Internet	網際網路
cooking	烹飪	jazz	爵士樂
dancing	舞蹈	jogging	慢跑
disco	迪斯可舞廳(原為discotheque)	kite	風箏
		mountain climbing	登山
dive	跳水，潛水	movie	電影
dodge ball	躲避球	music	音樂
doll	洋娃娃	novel	小説
drama	戲劇	piano	鋼琴
draw	畫圖	picnic	野餐
drawing	畫圖，圖畫	play	玩，打球，玩樂器
drum	鼓，鼓聲	pottery	陶藝
exercise	運動	puzzle	拼圖

14 Sports, interests & hobbies 運動、興趣及嗜好

race	種族，賽跑	swimming	游泳
rollerblades	直排輪鞋	table tennis	桌球
roller-skate	四輪溜冰	team	隊
skate	溜冰	tennis	網球
ski	滑雪，滑雪板	tent	帳篷
skiing	滑雪	toy	玩具
soccer	足球	travel	旅行
song	歌	trip	旅行
sport	運動	trumpet	喇叭，小號
sportsman	運動家	violin	小提琴
sportsmanship	運動家精神	volleyball	排球
stamp	郵票	winner	贏家
surf	滑水，上網搜索資料		

15 Houses & apartments 房屋住宅

address	地址	bench	長凳，長椅
air conditioner	空調	blanket	毯子
apartment	公寓	bookcase	書架
armchair	扶手椅	brick	磚塊
balcony	陽台	bucket	桶子
basement	地下室	build	建，蓋
bath	洗澡	building	建築物
bathroom	浴室	cabin	小屋
bed	床	cabinet	櫃子
bedroom	臥室	camera	照相機

15 Houses & apartments 房屋住宅

candle	蠟燭	gate	大門
carpet	地毯	hall	大廳
cassette	卡帶	hammer	鐵鎚
ceiling	天花板	hanger	衣架
chair	椅子	heater	暖氣
clean	乾淨的	home	家
closet	衣櫥	house	房子
container	容器	housework	家事
couch	長沙發，躺椅	iron	熨斗
cupboard	食櫥，碗櫃	iron	熨燙
curtain	窗簾	kettle	水壺
decorate	裝飾	key	鑰匙
desk	書桌	kitchen	廚房
dining room	飯廳	lamp	燈
door	門	light	燈
downstairs	在樓下	living room	客廳
drawer	抽屜	mat	地墊，墊子
dresser	化妝台	microwave	微波爐，微波
drier	吹風機	mirror	鏡子
fan	扇子，電扇	needle	針
faucet	龍頭	nest	巢
fence	籬笆	oven	烤箱
fix	修理，安排	palace	皇宮
flashlight	手電筒	pan	平底鍋
floor	地板	pillow	枕頭
freezer	冰箱，冷藏庫	pot	鍋，罐，壺
furniture	家具	radio	收音機，無線電設備
garden	花園		

15 Houses & apartments 房屋住宅

refrigerator	冰箱	toilet	馬桶，盥洗室
road	道路	toothbrush	牙刷
roof	屋頂	towel	毛巾
room	房間	tub	浴缸
shelf	（書櫥等的）架子	TV	電視（television的簡稱）
sink	水槽	upstairs	在樓上地
soap	肥皂	VCR	卡式錄放影機（video cassette recorder的縮寫）
sofa	沙發	video	錄影帶
stool	凳子，腳凳	wall	牆壁
stove	爐子	wash	洗滌
street	街道	washing machine	洗衣機
study	學習	window	窗戶
tape recorder	錄音機	yard	院子
tape	膠帶		
teapot	茶壺		
telephone	電話		
television	電視機		

16 School 學校

academic	學術的，學業的	book	書
adjective	形容詞	campus	校園，校區
alphabet	字母	chalk	粉筆
art	藝術，美術	chapter	章，回
behave	守規矩	cheerleader	啦啦隊員
biology	生物學	chemistry	化學
blackboard	黑板	class leader	班長

16 School 學校

class	班級
classmate	同班同學
classroom	教室
college	大學
computer	電腦
course	課程
crayon	蠟筆
diary	日記
dictionary	字典
educate	教育，培養
elementary school	小學
envelope	信封
eraser	橡皮擦，板擦
exam	考試
examinee	應試者
example	範例
exercise	練習，習題
explain	解釋
fail	失敗，不及格
final	最終的
friend	朋友
geography	地理學
glasses	眼鏡
grade	成績
grammar	文法
gym	體育館，健身房（gymnasium的簡稱）
history	歷史
homework	功課，家庭作業
ink	墨水
junior high school	國中
kindergarten	幼稚園
knowledge	知識
language	語言
law	法律
learn	學習
lecture	授課
lesson	課
letter	字母
library	圖書館
literature	文學，文學作品
magazine	雜誌
major	主修
map	地圖
marker	麥克筆
math	數學（mathematics的簡稱）
mathematical	數學的
note	筆記
notebook	筆記型電腦
painting	畫作
paper	紙
PE	體育課（physical education的縮寫）

16 School 學校

pen	筆，鋼筆	senior high school	高中
pencil	鉛筆	sheet	（紙等的）一張，床單
pencil box	鉛筆盒	slide	滑梯
pencil case	鉛筆盒	social science	社會科學
physics	物理學	sophomore	二年級
picture	圖畫，照片	speak	說話
playground	(學校的)運動場，操場	spell	拼字
poem	詩	spelling	拼寫
politics	政治（學）	story	故事
practice	練習	student	學生
pronounce	發…音	subject	主題，科目
pronunciation	發音	talk	講話
question	疑問	teach	教
quiz	小考	teacher	老師
read	閱讀	term	學期
record	紀錄	test	測驗，考試
record	記錄	text	課文，文字
repeat	重複	textbook	教科書
review	複習	underline	畫底線
ruler	統治者，尺	understand	懂
say	說	university	大學，綜合性大學
science	科學		
score	分數	vocabulary	字彙
seesaw	蹺蹺板	workbook	作業簿
semester	學期	write	書寫

17 Places & locations 地點及位置

backward	向後地	ground	地面
bakery	麵包店	hallway	玄關，走廊
bank	銀行	headquarters	總部，總公司
bookstore	書店	heaven	天堂
buffet	自助餐	hell	地獄
cafeteria	自助餐廳	here	這裡
central	中間的	homeland	祖國，故國
church	教堂	hometown	故鄉，家鄉
city	都市	hospital	醫院
convenience store	便利商店	hotel	旅館
country	國家	indoor	室內的，戶內的
department store	百貨公司	indoors	在室內，在屋裡
downtown	市區，市中心	inn	(公路邊或鄉間的)旅館
drugstore	藥局	international	國際的
east	東方	jail	監獄，拘留所
eastern	東方的，東部的	left	左邊
factory	工廠	lighthouse	燈塔
farm	農場	lobby	大廳
fast food restaurant	速食店	local	當地的，本地的
field	田野	mall	購物中心
fire station	消防局	market	市場
flower shop	花店	men's room	男廁
forward	向前地	middle	中間的
front	前面，正面	motel	汽車旅館
gallery	畫廊	museum	博物館
grave	墓穴	north	北方
greenhouse	溫室，暖房	northern	北方的
grocery	食品雜貨，雜貨店	office	辦公室

17 Places & locations 地點及位置

paradise	天堂	southern	南方的
parking lot	停車場	stadium	體育場
party	舞會，社交聚會	stationery store	文具店
passage	走廊	studio	攝影棚，影音製作公司
pavement	人行道		
place	地方	suburb	郊區
police station	警察局	supermarket	超級市場
pool	池子	temple	寺廟
position	位置	territory	領土，版圖，領地
post office	郵局	there	在那裡
prison	監獄	tomb	墓，墓碑
pub	酒吧	top	頂部
region	地區	town	鎮
regional	地區的	village	村莊
restaurant	餐廳	waterfall	瀑布
restroom	化妝室	west	西方
south	南方	western	西方的

18 Transportation 運輸

aircraft	飛行器	avenue	大道
airline	航班	bicycle	腳踏車
airplane	飛機	bike	腳踏車
airport	機場	block	街區
ambulance	救護車	boat	船
arrival	到來	bridge	橋
arrive	到達	bus stop	公車站
automobile	汽車（簡稱auto）	bus	巴士

18 Transportation 運輸

canoe	獨木舟	railroad	鐵道
car	車	railway	鐵路
cross	越過	ride	騎
drive	開（車、船等）	sail	航行
escalator	電扶梯	scooter	機車
fare	票價	ship	船
fast	快速地	sidewalk	人行道
ferry	渡輪	slow	緩慢的
flat tire	爆胎	subway	地下鐵
flight	班機	tank	坦克車
fly	飛	taxi	計程車
freeway	高速公路	traffic	交通
gasoline	汽油	train station	火車站
harbor	港灣，海港	train	火車
helicopter	直昇機	transport	運送，運輸
highway	公路	transportation	運輸工具，交通車輛
jeep	吉普車	truck	卡車
jet	噴射機	tunnel	隧道
lifeboat	救生艇，救生船	turn	使轉向
motor	汽車的	underpass	地下通道，下穿交叉道
motorcycle	摩托車	van	廂形客貨兩用車
MRT	大眾捷運系統	vehicle	運載工具，車輛
overpass	天橋	wagon	運貨馬車
passenger	乘客	wheel	車輪
path	路徑		
platform	月台		

19 Sizes & measurements 度量衡

account	理由，根據，說明	little	小的
big	大的	loaf	一條
bottle	瓶子	long	長的
centimeter	公分	low	低矮的
deep	深的	majority	多數，過半數
distance	距離	maximum	最大量
distant	遠的	measure	測量
dot	點	medium	適中的
dozen	一打	meter	公尺，米
extra	額外的	mile	英里
fair	公平的	minus	減去
far	遙遠的	narrow	狹窄的
foot	英尺（複數形為feet）	near	近的
		nearly	幾乎
gallon	加侖	often	常常
gigantic	巨大的	pack	包
glass	玻璃	page	頁
gram	公克	pail	桶
height	高度	pair	一對
high	高的	piece	一片，一小塊
inch	英寸	pint	品脱
kilogram	公斤（縮寫為kg）	plus	加上
kilometer	公里（縮寫為km）	point	點，分數
large	大的	portion	份量，部分
least	最少地	pound	英鎊
length	長度	rectangle	矩形，長方形
light	輕的	round	圓形的
liter	公升	scale	刻度

19 Sizes & measurements 度量衡

shape	形狀	triangle	三角形
size	尺寸	weight	重量，體重
small	小的	wide	寬的
square	正方形	widen	加寬
straight	筆直的	width	寬度
tiny	微小的	yard	碼
ton	噸，公噸		

20 Countries and areas 國家區域

America	美國	foreign	外國的
area	地區	France	法國
Asia	亞洲	Germany	德國，德語
Australia	澳洲	Japan	日本
Britain	英國，大不列顛	kingdom	王國
Canada	加拿大	Korea	韓國
China	中國	nation	民族，國家
England	英國，英格蘭	national	全國的
Europe	歐洲	Russia	俄羅斯
European	歐洲的	world	世界

21 Languages & nationality 語言及國籍

accent	口音	Asian	亞洲人
American	美國的，美式的	Australian	澳洲人
American	美國人	British	英國人

21 Languages & nationality 語言及國籍

Canadian	加拿大人	German	德國人
Chinese	中文	Japanese	日本人
Chinese	中國人	Korean	韓國(人、語)的
citizen	公民	Korean	韓國(人、語)
English	英文	Mandarin	華語
Englishman	英國人	Russian	俄國人(的)
French	法國人	Taiwanese	台灣人

22 Cities 城市

mayor	市長，鎮長

23 Holidays & festivals 節慶假日

anniversary	週年紀念日	holiday	假日，節日
celebrate	慶祝	Moon Festival	中秋節
Christmas	耶誕節	New Year	新年
cultural	文化的	New Year's Eve	除夕
culture	文化	Thanksgiving	感恩節
custom	習俗	vacation	假期
Easter	復活節	Valentine's Day	情人節
festival	節日		
Halloween	萬聖節前夕		

24 Occupations 職業

actor	男演員	designer	設計師
actress	女演員	detective	偵探
adviser	顧問(也拼做advisor)	diplomat	外交官
		director	導演
agency	經銷商,代理,仲介	doctor	醫生(縮寫為Dr.)
agent	代理商,仲介人	doctor	醫師
artist	藝術家	driver	司機
assistant	助理的	editor	編輯
baby sitter	保母	employ	雇用
banker	銀行業者,銀行家	engineer	工程師
barber	理髮師	farmer	農夫
beggar	乞丐	fisherman	漁夫
boss	老闆	founder	創立者,奠基者
business	生意	governor	州長
businessman	商人	guard	警衛
career	職業的	guide	嚮導,導遊
career	職業,事業	hairdresser	美髮師
carpenter	木匠	hire	雇用
chairman	主席,董事長	housekeeper	(女)管家
chief	等級最高的,主要的	housewife	家庭主婦
		hunter	獵人
clerk	店員	inspector	檢查員,視察員
coach	教練	job	工作
company	公司	journalist	新聞記者
cook	廚師	judge	法官
cowboy	牛仔	lawyer	律師
dealer	業者,商人	librarian	圖書館館長,圖書館員
dentist	牙醫		

24 Occupations 職業

lifeguard	救生員	president	總統
magician	魔術師	priest	教士，神父
maid	侍女，女僕	princess	公主
mailman	郵差	principal	校長
manager	經理，負責人	profession	職業
mechanic	技工	professional	職業的
merchant	商人	professor	教授
miner	礦工	psychologist	心理學家
model	模型，模特兒	publisher	出版者，出版社
musician	音樂家	reporter	記者
nanny	保母	sailor	水手，船員
navy	海軍的	salesman	推銷員
novelist	小說家	scholar	學者
nun	尼姑，修女	scientist	科學家
nurse	護士	secretary	祕書
official	官員	servant	佣人
operator	接線生	shepherd	牧羊人
organization	組織	shopkeeper	店主
owner	擁有者	singer	歌唱家、歌手
painter	畫家	soldier	士兵
photographer	攝影師	tailor	裁縫師
pilot	飛行員	trader	商人
player	選手	tutor	家庭教師，私人教師
plumber	水管工		
poet	詩人	typist	打字員，打字者
police officer	警員，警官	vendor	小販
policeman	警察	vice-president	副總統
politician	從政者	waiter	男服務生

24 Occupations 職業

waitress	女服務生	worker	工人,工作人員
work	工作	writer	作家

25 Weather & nature 自然氣候

air	空氣	humid	潮溼的
brook	小溪,小河	jungle	叢林
bush	灌木,灌木叢	landslide	土石流
canyon	峽谷	leaf	葉子
clear	清楚的,晴朗的	lightning	閃電
climate	氣候	meadow	草地,牧草地
cloud	雲	mist	薄霧
cloudy	陰天的	moon	月亮
cold	寒冷的	natural	自然的
cool	涼爽的	nature	自然
damp	潮溼的	oak	橡樹
degree	度數	pine	松樹
dry	把…弄乾	rain	雨
earth	地球	rainbow	彩虹
earthquake	地震	rainy	下雨的
flower	花	ray	光線,射線
fog	霧	rock	岩石
foggy	多霧的	sand	沙
fossil	化石	shower	淋浴,陣雨
freezing	寒冷的	sky	天空
grass	草	snow	雪
hay	牧草,乾草	snowman	雪人
hot	熱	snowy	下雪的

25 Weather & nature 自然氣候

solar	太陽能的，日光	thunder	雷
star	星星	tide	潮水，趨勢
stone	石頭	tree	樹木
storm	暴風雨	typhoon	颱風
stormy	風強雨大的	warm	溫暖的，保暖的
sun	太陽	weather	天氣
sunny	陽光充足的	wet	濕的
table	桌子	wind	風
temperature	溫度，氣溫	windy	刮風的，風大的

26 Geographical terms 地理條件

bay	海灣	mountain	山
beach	海灘	ocean	海洋
coast	海岸	plain	平原，原野
continent	大陸，陸地，洲	pole	極地區域
desert	沙漠	pond	池塘
environment	環境	river	河流
forest	森林	sea	海洋
hill	丘陵，小丘	stream	溪流
island	島嶼	valley	山谷
lake	湖	woods	樹林，森林
land	陸地		

27 Animals & insects 動物及昆蟲

animal	動物	bark	吠叫
ant	螞蟻	bat	蝙蝠

27 Animals & insects 動物及昆蟲

bear	熊	frog	青蛙
bee	蜜蜂	fur	毛皮，軟毛
bird	鳥	goat	山羊
buffalo	水牛	goose	鵝
bug	小蟲	grasshopper	蚱蜢，蝗蟲
bull	公牛	hawk	鷹
butterfly	蝴蝶	hen	母雞
cat	貓	hippo	河馬
caterpillar	毛毛蟲	horse	馬
cattle	牛	insect	昆蟲
chicken	雞	ivory	象牙
cockroach	蟑螂	kangaroo	袋鼠
cow	母牛	kitten	小貓
crab	螃蟹	koala	無尾熊
cricket	蟋蟀	lamb	羔羊
deer	鹿	lion	獅子
dinosaur	恐龍	monkey	猴子
dog	狗	monster	怪物
dolphin	海豚	mosquito	蚊子
donkey	驢	mouse	老鼠
dragon	龍	ox	牛，複數為oxen
duck	鴨子	panda	貓熊
eagle	鷹	parrot	鸚鵡
elephant	大象	paw	爪子
feather	羽毛	pet	寵物
fish	魚	pig	豬
flea	跳蚤	pigeon	鴿子
fox	狐狸	pony	小馬

27 Animals & insects 動物及昆蟲

puppy	小狗	tail	尾巴
rabbit	兔子	tiger	老虎
rat	鼠	tortoise	陸龜，烏龜
shark	鯊魚	turkey	火雞
snail	蝸牛	turtle	海龜
snake	蛇	whale	鯨
sparrow	麻雀	wing	翅膀
spider	蜘蛛	wolf	狼
swallow	燕子		

28 Articles & determiners 冠詞及限定詞

athlete	運動員	this	這個
every	每一個	those	那些
out	出外		

29 Pronouns & reflexives 代名詞與反身動詞（反身代詞）

anybody	任何人	most	最…
anyone	任何一個人	myself	我自己
anything	任何事物	nobody	沒有人
each	每一個	none	沒有任何人(物)
everybody	每人	nothing	沒什麼
everyone	每一個人	oneself	自身
everything	每一件事	other	其他的
herself	她自己	ours	我們的(東西)
himself	他自己	ourselves	我們自己
mine	我的東西	part	部分

29 Pronouns & reflexives 代名詞與反身動詞（反身代詞）

somebody	某人	themselves	他/她/它們自己
someone	某人	us	我們
something	某事	yourself	你自己

30 Wh-words 疑問詞

how	如何	which	哪一個，哪一些
whatever	不管什麼	while	當…的時候

31 Be & auxiliaries Be動詞及助動詞

are	是	shall	應當，將
may	可能	should	應該
might	（may的過去式）可能	will	將
must	必須	would	委婉請求（will過去式）
ought to	應當		

32 Prepositions 介系詞

about	大約	before	在…之前
after	在…之後	behind	在…之後
against	倚靠	below	在…之下，低於
along	沿著	beside	在…旁邊
among	在…之中	between	在…之間
around	附近，到處	beyond	在…另一邊
at	在	by	在…旁

32 Prepositions 介系詞

despite	儘管	outside	在…外
down	向下	over	在…上面
during	在…的期間	since	自從
except	除…之外	than	比
for	為了	through	穿越
from	從	throughout	遍及
in	在…裡面	till	直到
inside	在…裡面	to	到
into	進入到…中	toward	朝…方向
next to	隔壁，旁邊	under	在…下面
of	（屬於）…的	up	向上的
off	離開	upper	上面的
on	在…上	with	和…一起
onto	向…之上	within	在…範圍裡
opposite	對面	without	沒有
out of	phr.) 自…離開		

33 Conjunctions 連接詞

although	儘管	however	不過
and	和	if	如果
as	當…，以…的身	or	或，否則
份		therefore	因此
as	同樣地	though	雖然
because	因為	unless	如果不，除非
besides	除了…之外	until	直到
but	但是	whether	是

34 interjections 感嘆詞

good-bye	再見	hello	哈囉

35 Other nouns 其他名詞

ability	能力	ancestor	祖先
accident	事故	angel	天使
action	行動	anger	憤怒
activity	活動	angle	角度
addition	附加	announcement	宣布
admiration	欽佩	anywhere	任何地方
admission	許可	aquarium	水族館，水族箱
advance	發展		
advantage	優點	arithmetic	算術技巧，計算
adventure	冒險		
advertisement	廣告	army	軍隊
advice	忠告	article	物品，文章
affair	事件	ash	灰燼
age	年齡	attention	注意力
agriculture	農業	attitude	態度
aid	幫助	author	作者
aid	幫助	average	平均數
aim	目標	bacteria	（複數）細菌。單數為 bacterium
album	相簿		
alley	小巷		
allowance	零用錢	bait	餌
Mambassador	大使	balance	平衡
ambition	抱負	balloon	氣球
amount	數量	bandage	綳帶

bar	酒吧	bottom	底部
barn	穀倉	box	盒子
barrel	木桶	brain	頭腦
base	底部，基座	brake	煞車
basic	基礎，基本	branch	樹枝
basis	準則，基礎	brass	銅
basket	籃子	bravery	勇敢
battery	電池	breath	呼吸，氣息
beam	光線	breeze	微風
beast	野獸	bride	新娘
beauty	美女	bridegroom	新郎（也稱作 groom）
beginner	新手		
beginning	開始	broom	掃把
belief	信仰	bubble	泡沫
bell	鈴	bud	花蕾
benefit	利潤	budget	預算
Bible	聖經	bulb	電燈泡
biography	傳記	bullet	子彈
birthday	生日	bulletin	公告
bit	一點	bunch	束，串
blade	刀片	bundle	捆，束
blame	罪過	burden	負擔，重任
blank	空白處	burglar	強盜
blood	血	button	鈕釦，按鈕
board	木板，布告欄	buzz	嗡嗡聲
bomb	炸彈	cable	有線電視
boot	靴子	cage	籠子
border	邊境	campaign	活動

35 Other nouns 其他名詞

can	罐頭，桶子	circle	圓圈
candidate	候選人	circus	馬戲團
cane	拐杖，籐條	client	客戶
capital	首都	climax	頂點，高潮
captain	隊長	clinic	診所
case	案例	clip	迴紋針
castle	城堡	club	俱樂部，社團
catalogue	目錄（也拼做 catalog）	clue	線索，跡象
		code	密碼
cause	原因	collar	衣領
cellphone	手機，行動電話	colony	殖民地
center	中心	column	專欄
chain	鏈，鎖鏈	combination	組合
challenge	挑戰	comma	逗號
champion	優勝者，冠軍	committee	委員會
chance	機會	comparison	比照，比喻，對照
channel	管道，頻道	complaint	抗議，怨言
character	角色	complex	複合物，集合住宅
charity	慈善		
chart	圖表	composition	作文
chemical	化學物品	concert	音樂會，演唱會
childhood	童年時期	conclusion	推論，結論
chill	寒顫	condition	情況，症狀
chimney	煙囪	conflict	衝突
choice	選擇	Confucius	孔子
chore	雜事	congratulation	恭喜
cigar	雪茄	connection	關聯，關係
cigarette	香菸	consideration	考慮

35 Other nouns 其他名詞

contact	接觸	dash	破折號
contract	契約書，合同	data	資料
control	控制	debate	辯論
convenience	便利	debt	借款
conversation	對話	decision	決定
corner	角落	deck	甲板，一副(紙牌)
countryside	鄉村	deed	行動，契約
county	郡，縣	definition	定義，解譯
courage	勇氣	delivery	投遞，傳送
court	法庭	democracy	民主，民主主義
coward	懦夫，膽怯者	description	描寫，敘述，形容
cradle	搖籃	desire	慾望
creator	創造者，創作者	determination	決心
creature	生物	devil	惡魔
credit	榮譽，信譽，	dialogue	對話
crew	人員，一群	difference	差別，差異
crime	罪	difficulty	困難
criminal	罪犯	dime	一角硬幣
crisis	危機	direction	方向
crowd	一群人	dirt	灰塵，泥
crown	王位，王冠	disappointment	失望
crutch	拐杖	disaster	災難
curve	彎曲、彎道	discovery	發現
cycle	週期，循環	discussion	討論
dam	水壩	disk	磁碟
damage	傷害	dispute	爭論
danger	危險	ditch	溝
darling	心愛的，寵兒	division	部門

35 Other nouns 其他名詞

dock	碼頭，港區	error	錯誤
document	文件	event	事件
dose	一劑，一服	evidence	證據
drain	下水道，排水溝	excellence	傑出，卓越
dream	夢	excuse	藉口
dust	灰塵，塵土	exhibition	展覽會，展覽
duty	責任	existence	存在
edge	邊緣	exit	出口
edition	版，版本	expectation	期望，期待
education	教育	experience	經驗
effect	影響	experiment	實驗
effort	努力	explanation	解釋
election	選舉	expression	表達，表示
electricity	電力	extreme	極端
element	成份	fable	寓言，虛構
e-mail	電子郵件	fact	事實
emergency	緊急狀況	factor	因素，原因
emotion	情感	failure	失敗，失敗者
emperor	皇帝	faint	昏倒，暈倒
emphasis	強調	faith	信任，信念
employee	員工，受雇者	fake	仿冒品
employer	雇主	fame	名氣
enemy	敵人	fantasy	空想，夢想
energy	精力	fashion	流行樣式，時尚
engine	引擎	fate	命運
enthusiasm	熱心	fault	錯誤
entrance	入口	favor	恩惠
entry	進入，入口	feast	大餐，大吃大喝

35 Other nouns 其他名詞

feature	特徵，特色	fuel	燃料
feeling	感覺，情感	fun	有趣的
fiction	小說	fun	樂趣
figure	外型	function	功能
fire	火	funeral	喪葬，葬儀
firecracker	爆竹，鞭炮	gang	一幫，一群
fireplace	壁爐	gap	間隔，空隙
firework	煙火，煙火大會	garage	車庫
flag	旗幟	garbage	垃圾
flame	發火焰，燃燒	gas	汽油
flavor	味道，風味	gesture	姿勢，手勢
flesh	肉，肌肉	ghost	鬼
flock	(飛禽、牲畜等的)群	gift	禮物
folk	(口)家屬，親屬	glance	一瞥，掃視
follower	追隨者，部下	glory	光榮，榮譽
force	力量	glue	黏膠
formula	慣例，配方	goal	目標
fortune	財產，財富	god	神明，上帝
foundation	地基，基礎	goodness	(感嘆語)天啊
fountain	噴水池，噴泉	government	政府
fragrance	香味，香氣	group	群
frame	框架，框子	growth	成長
freedom	自由	guidance	輔導，諮詢
frequency	頻繁，屢次	gun	槍
freshman	一年級生，新生	habit	習慣
friendship	友誼	haircut	理髮
frost	冰凍，霜	handful	一把，少量
frustration	挫折，失敗	handwriting	筆跡

35 Other nouns 其他名詞

hardship	艱難，困苦
harmony	和諧，協調
hatred	憎恨，增惡
headline	頭條，大標題
	headphones)
	頭戴式耳機
heap	堆積，積聚
heat	熱
hesitation	躊躇，猶豫
historian	歷史學家
hive	蜂窩
hole	洞
honeymoon	蜜月旅行
honor	榮譽，名譽
hook	掛鉤
horizon	地平線
horn	角，觸角
horror	恐怖，震驚
human	人類
hut	小屋
idea	想法
identity	身分，本身
ignorance	愚昧，無知
image	形象，肖像
imagination	想像力，創造力
impact	衝擊，影響
importance	重要性
industry	工業，產業
inferior	次級的，較劣質的
influence	影響
information	資料
ingredient	成份，原料
injury	損壞，傷害
instance	實例
instinct	本能
instruction	用法說明，操作指南
interview	面試，採訪
introduction	介紹，正式引見
inventor	發明家，發明者
invitation	邀請（函）
item	項目，品項
jar	罐，瓶
jelly	果凍
joke	玩笑
journal	日記，日誌
journey	旅程，行程
joy	喜悅
junk	廢棄的，垃圾
justice	正義，公平
keyboard	鍵盤
kit	工具箱
knight	騎士，武士
knob	球形把手
knot	結
label	貼紙，標籤
lace	鞋帶，帶子

35 Other nouns 其他名詞

ladder	梯子
landmark	地標
landscape	風景
laughter	笑，笑聲
laundry	洗衣店，洗衣
lawn	草坪，草地
leader	領導者
leadership	領導
leather	皮革製品
legend	傳奇
leisure	閒暇，空暇時間
lens	透鏡，鏡片
level	程度，標準
liar	說謊的人
liberty	自由，自由權
license	執照
lid	蓋子
line	線
link	連結
locker	置物櫃
Lord	上帝
loss	損失
loudspeaker	擴聲器，喇叭
luggage	行李
lullaby	催眠曲，搖籃曲
machine	機器
magnet	磁鐵，磁石
mail	郵件
mankind	人類（亦稱 humankind）
manner	方法，態度
manners	禮貌，規矩
manual	手冊
marble	彈珠
mark	記號
material	原料
matter	事件
meaning	意思，意義
means	手段，方法
medal	獎章，紀念章
media	傳播媒體（medium的複數）
meeting	會議
member	成員
membership	會員身分，全體會員
memory	記憶，回憶
mention	提到，說起
mercy	慈悲
mess	混亂，凌亂的狀態
message	訊息
metal	金屬
microphone	擴音器，麥克風（簡稱mike）
microscope	顯微鏡
might	力量，威力

35 Other nouns 其他名詞

military	軍方，軍隊
mill	磨坊
millionaire	百萬富翁
minority	少數的
miracle	奇蹟
misery	痛苦，不幸的
missile	飛彈，導彈
mission	任務
mistake	錯誤
mixture	混合
mob	犯罪集團
moisture	溼氣，水分
monk	修道士，僧侶
mood	心情
mop	拖把
motion	移動
motor	馬達，引擎
movement	動作
mud	泥巴
MV	音樂錄影帶 Music Video的縮寫)
nap	午睡，打盹兒
napkin	餐巾(紙)
necessity	必需品
network	網路系統，廣播網
news	新聞
newspaper	報紙
nickname	別名，小名
noise	噪音
object	物體
occasion	場合，時機
operation	操作
opinion	觀點
opportunity	機會
order	命令
origin	起源
orphan	孤兒
outline	外型，輪廓
ownership	所有權
pack	打包，包裝
package	包裹
parade	閱兵，慶祝遊行
parcel	包裹
passion	熱情
passport	護照
password	密碼
patience	耐心
pattern	圖案
peace	平靜，和平
peak	高峰的
pearl	珍珠
performance	演出
period	時期
permission	准可
pest	討厭的人

35 Other nouns 其他名詞

photo	照片	prayer	祈禱文
photograph	照片	preparation	準備
pile	堆	present	禮物
pill	藥丸	pressure	壓力
pin	別針	principle	原則，原理
pipe	管子	printer	印表機
pit	凹處	prize	獎品
pity	憐憫	problem	問題
plan	計劃	process	過程，步驟
planet	行星，星球	product	產品
plant	植物，種植	production	製作
pleasure	愉快	profit	利潤，利益
plenty	豐富 ，充足	program	節目
plug	插頭	progress	前進，進步
poison	毒藥，毒物	project	企畫，方案
policy	政策	promotion	提升
poll	民意調查	proof	證據
pollution	污染	property	資產
population	人口	proposal	建議，提案
porcelain	瓷器	protection	保護
portrait	肖像	protest	抗議
postage	郵資	proverb	諺語，俗語
postcard	明信片	psychology	心理學
poster	海報	publication	出版
poverty	貧窮	publicity	名聲
powder	粉末	purpose	目的
power	權力	pursuit	追求，尋求
praise	讚美	quality	品質

35 Other nouns 其他名詞

quarrel	爭吵	robbery	搶劫案
quilt	被子	robe	睡袍
radar	雷達	robot	機器人
rag	抹布，碎布	rocket	火箭
rage	狂怒，肆虐	role	角色
range	範圍	root	根，地下莖
rank	等級，身份	rope	繩子
rate	比率	rose	玫瑰
razor	剃刀，刮鬍刀	routine	例行公事
reaction	反應	row	排，列
reason	理由	rubber	橡膠
receipt	收據	rug	小地毯，毛皮地毯
receiver	收件人	rule	規則
recorder	錄音器	rumor	謠言
relief	緩和，寬心	sack	袋，(俚)床
religion	宗教	safety	安全
remote	遙控器	sake	利益
report	報告	salary	薪水
representative	代表人，典型	sale	販售
request	請求	sample	樣本
resource	資源	sausage	香腸
response	回答，答覆	saving	節儉，節省
responsibility	責任	scarecrow	稻草人
result	結果	scene	地點，背景，現場
ribbon	蝴蝶結	scenery	風景
riddle	謎語	schedule	清單，目錄
risk	風險	scholarship	獎學金
robber	搶劫者，強盜	scoop	一勺

scout	搜索	similarity	類似
screen	螢幕，銀幕	sin	罪孽
screw	螺絲釘	sincerity	真誠
seat	座位	sip	一小口
secret	祕密	situation	處境
section	段落	skill	技術
security	安全，保全措施	skyscraper	摩天樓
seed	種子	slave	奴隸
sense	理智，道理	slice	切片，片
sentence	句子	slope	坡，斜面
service	服務	smile	微笑
set	一套	society	社會
sex	性別	software	軟體
shade	蔭暗	solution	解決方式
shadow	影子，陰暗的地方	source	來源
shallow	淺的	souvenir	紀念品
shame	羞恥	space	空間，空地
shampoo	洗髮精	spade	鏟子
sheep	羊，綿羊	spark	火花，火星
shock	震驚	speaker	擴音器，喇叭
shore	岸	spear	矛，魚叉
shot	投，射	speech	演講
shovel	鏟子	speed	速度
show	表演	spice	香料
side	邊	spin	旋轉
sight	視覺	spirit	精神，志氣
signal	信號，暗號	spite	怨恨，惡意
silence	寂靜	spot	斑點

35 Other nouns 其他名詞

spy	間諜	survivor	倖存者，生還者，殘存物
staff	職員，（全體）工作人員	suspect	嫌疑犯，可疑分子
stage	舞台	suspicion	懷疑，疑心
stairs	樓梯	swan	天鵝
standard	標準	sweat	汗，汗水
state	狀態	swing	鞦韆
statue	雕像	sword	劍，刀
steam	蒸氣	symbol	符號
stem	（工具）柄，把手	sympathy	同情，同理心
step	腳步，步驟	symphony	交響樂團，交響曲
stereo	立體聲效果	system	系統
stick	棒，棍	tablet	藥片
strategy	策略，計謀，對策	tag	牌子，標籤
strength	力量，力氣	talent	天才
stress	壓力	target	目標
structure	結構，構造	task	任務，工作
style	風格，作風	tear	眼淚
submarine	潛艇	technician	技術人員，技師
substance	物質	technique	技巧，技術
success	成功	technology	科技，技術
suicide	自殺，自殺行為	telegram	向…發電報，用電報發送
summary	摘要，總結	telescope	望遠鏡
summit	頂峰，絕頂	temper	情緒，性情
sunshine	陽光	tension	神經緊繃，緊張狀況
surface	表面	terror	恐怖，驚駭
surroundings	環境，周圍的事物	theme	主題，主題思想
survival	倖存，殘存		

35 Other nouns 其他名詞

theory	理論，學理	trash	廢物，垃圾
thief	小偷	traveler	旅行者，旅客，遊客
thing	事，物	tray	盤子，托盤
thirst	渴望	treasure	寶藏
thought	思考	treatment	治療
Thread	線，絲	trend	趨勢，傾向，時尚
threat	威脅	trial	試用
ticket	票	tribe	部落，種族
timber	木材，木料	trick	戲法，詭計
time	時間	trick	欺騙
tip	祕訣	troop	軍隊，部隊
tissue	紙巾，面紙，衛生紙	trouble	麻煩
title	標題	trunk	樹幹
tobacco	菸草製品	truth	真實
tolerance	忍耐，寬容	tulip	鬱金香，鬱金香花
tool	工具	twig	細枝，嫩枝
topic	主題	twin	孿生兒，雙胞胎
tour	遊覽	type	種類
tourism	旅遊業，觀光業	typewriter	打字機
tourist	旅遊者，觀光者	union	工會，聯合會，協會
tower	塔	unity	團結，聯合，統
trace	痕跡，遺跡	universe	宇宙，天地萬物
track	足跡	usage	使用，用法，處理
trade	貿易	user	使用者
tradition	傳統	vain	愛慕虛榮的
tragedy	悲劇，慘案	value	價值
trail	痕跡，小徑	variety	多樣化，變化
translation	譯文，譯本	vegetarian	素食主義者

35 Other nouns 其他名詞

verb	動詞	walkman	隨身聽
verse	詩，韻文	war	戰爭
victim	犧牲者，遇難者	warmth	親切，溫暖
victory	勝利	wax	蠟，蜂蠟
view	觀點	way	方向，路徑
violation	違反行為	wealth	財富，財產
violence	暴力	weapon	武器
virtue	美德，優點	wedding	婚禮
virus	病毒	weed	雜草，野草
vision	洞察力，眼光	willow	柳，柳樹
visitor	觀光客	wisdom	智慧，才智
voice	聲音	witness	目擊者，見證人
volcano	火山	wok	鐵鍋，炒菜鍋
volume	音量	wood	木材
voter	投票人	word	單字，生字
wag	搖，擺動	wreck	船難事故
wages	薪水，報酬	wrinkle	皺，皺紋
waken	醒來，睡醒		

36 Other verbs 其他動詞

absorb	吸收	adapt	使適應
accept	接受	add	添加
accompany	陪伴	admire	欣賞
accomplish	完成	admit	承認
achieve	達成	adopt	收養，採納
act	表現	advertise	廣告

36 Other verbs 其他動詞

advise	勸告	award	頒獎
affect	影響	bang	猛撞
afford	買得起	bathe	洗澡
agree	贊成	beat	打
allow	允許	become	變成
amaze	使驚奇	begin	開始
amazement	驚愕	believe	相信
announce	宣布	belong	屬於
answer	回答	bite	咬
apologize	道歉	blame	責怪
appeal	有吸引力	bleed	流血
appear	出現	blend	混合
apply	申請	bless	祝福
appreciate	欣賞，感激	blink	眨眼
approach	接近	blow	吹
approve	贊同	bore	厭煩
argue	爭論	borrow	借入
arrange	安排	bother	煩擾
arrest	逮捕	bow	鞠躬
ask	問	break	打破
assist	幫助	breathe	呼吸
assume	假設	breed	飼養
attack	攻擊，襲擊	bring	攜帶
attempt	企圖，嘗試	broadcast	廣播，播報
attend	出席	brush	刷
attract	吸引	bump	碰，撞
avoid	避免	burn	燃燒
awaken	意識到，弄醒	burst	破裂

36 Other verbs 其他動詞

bury	埋，使…沈浸	clap	鼓掌
buzz	嗡嗡叫	classify	分類
calculate	計算	click	卡嗒聲，喀嚓聲
call	呼叫，打電話	climb	攀登
calm	冷靜	close	關
cancel	取消	collapse	坍塌（情緒）崩潰
capture	捕獲	combine	使結合，使聯合
care	在意，關懷	come	來，到
care	關心	comfort	安慰，慰問
carry	攜帶	command	命令，指揮
carve	雕刻	comment	評論
cast	投，丟	commercial	廣告
catch	接住，趕上	communicate	傳達，傳遞，溝通
change	改變	compare	比較
chase	追逐	compete	競爭，比賽，對抗
chat	聊天，閒談	complain	抱怨
cheat	欺騙	complete	完成
check	檢查	concern	關心
cheer	歡呼	concentrate	專心
cherish	珍惜	conclude	斷定，決定
chew	咬，嚼	comfirm	確認
chill	凍結，凝結	confuse	使困惑
chip	形成缺口、瑕疵	connect	連接，連結
choke	使窒息，窒息	consider	考慮
choose	選擇	continue	繼續
chop	砍，劈，剁	control	控制
circulate	循環	convince	說服
claim	要求	copy	抄襲，複製

36 Other verbs 其他動詞

correct	修正
count	計算
cover	遮蓋
crash	碰擊
crawl	爬行，蠕動
create	創造
creep	躡手躡腳，爬行
criticize	批評
cry	哭
cut	剪，切割
dare	敢，膽敢，竟敢
date	約會
deafen	使聾，使聽不見
deal	處理
decide	決定
decrease	減少
deepen	使變深，使加深
defeat	擊敗
defend	防守
define	解釋，給…下定義
delay	延期
deliver	傳遞
demand	要求
deny	否認
depend	依賴
deposit	儲存，存放
depress	使沮喪
describe	描寫
deserve	應得
design	設計
destroy	毀壞，破壞
detail	詳述，詳細說明
detect	察覺
determine	決定，使下定決心
develop	發展
dial	撥號，打(電話)
die	死亡
dig	挖
digest	消化
dip	浸，泡
direct	導演，執導
disappear	消失
discourage	勸阻
discover	發現
discuss	討論
disguise	偽裝
dislike	不喜歡，討厭
divide	分配
dissmiss	解散，下課
disturb	打擾
dodge	閃開，躲開
doubt	懷疑
doze	打瞌睡
drip	留下，滴下
drop	使掉下

36 Other verbs 其他動詞

drown	淹死，淹沒	expect	預期
dump	傾倒，拋棄	explode	爆炸，爆發
dye	染色	explore	探險
eager	熱心，渴望	export	出口
ease	舒緩	express	表達
echo	產生回音	fade	枯萎，褪去
edit	編輯，剪接	fall	掉下
elect	選舉	fasten	紮牢，繫緊
eliminate	消除，消滅	fax	傳真
embarrass	尷尬	feed	餵食
emerge	浮現	feel	感覺
emphasize	強調	fetch	拿來，去拿…給
employment	聘雇	fight	打架
enable	使能夠	file	把…歸檔
encourage	鼓勵	fill	充滿
end	結束	finance	供資金給…，為…籌措資金
enforce	實施執行		
engage	從事	find	發現
engagement	婚約，承諾	finish	完成
enjoy	喜愛	fit	適合
enter	進入	flatter	使感到滿意，諂媚
entertain	使歡樂		
erase	擦掉，抹去	flee	消失，逃走
escape	逃出，脫逃	float	飄，漂泊
establish	建立	flow	流動
excite	刺激	flunk	（口）不及格
exist	存在	flush	沖洗
expand	擴大	focus	聚焦，集中

36 Other verbs 其他動詞

fold	折疊，對折	graduate	畢業
follow	跟隨	grasp	抓牢，握緊
forbid	阻止，妨礙	greet	問候
forecast	預測，預報	grin	露齒而笑
forget	忘記	grow	生長
forgive	原諒	guess	猜測
form	形成，組成	handle	處理
found	設立	hang	把…掛起
freeze	凍僵，凍結	happen	發生
frighten	使害怕	harm	損害，危害
frown	皺眉額，對…表示不滿	harvest	收穫
		haste	急忙，迅速
frustrate	挫敗，阻撓	hatch	孵化
fry	煎，炸，炒	hate	討厭
fulfill	達到，滿足	heal	治癒，使恢復健康
fulfillment	實現，成就（感）	hear	聽見
gain	增加	help	幫助
gather	聚集	hesitate	躊躇，猶豫
gaze	注視	hide	藏
get	獲得，得到	hike	健行
giggle	咯咯地笑	hint	暗示，示意
give	給	hit	打，擊中
glide	滑行，划水前行	hold	握住
glimpse	一瞥	hop	單腳跳，躍過
glow	發光，灼熱	hope	希望
go	去	horrify	使恐懼，使驚懼
gossip	閒話，聊天	hug	擁抱
grab	攫取，抓取	hunt	打獵

36 Other verbs 其他動詞

hurry	趕緊	invite	邀請
hurt	使受傷	involve	使牽涉
hush	安靜下來，沈默	isolate	隔離
ignore	忽略	join	參與
illustrate	用圖說明	judge	判斷，評斷
imagine	想像	jump	跳
imitate	模仿	keep	保存
immigrate	遷入	kick	踢
import	進口，輸入	kill	殺死
impress	給極深的印象，使感動	kiss	親吻
improve	改善	kneel	跪，跪下
include	包含	knit	編織
increase	增加	knock	敲打
indicate	指示	know	知道
infect	感染	lack	缺少
inform	通知，告知	laugh	笑
injure	傷害，損害	launch	發射
insist	堅持	lay	放，鋪設
inspect	檢查，審查	lead	帶領
inspire	鼓舞	leak	漏洞，裂縫
insult	侮辱	leap	跳，跳躍
intend	打算	leave	離開
interpret	解釋	lengthen	使加長，使延長
interrupt	打斷	let	允許，讓
introduce	介紹，引薦	lick	舔
invade	入侵	lie	躺，位於
invent	發明	lift	舉起
investigate	調查，研究	like	喜歡

36 Other verbs 其他動詞

limit	限制	nod	點頭
list	把…編列成表，列出	notice	注意
listen	聽從	obey	服從
litter	丟垃圾	observe	觀察
load	裝，裝載	occur	發生
lock	鎖	offer	提供
look	看	omit	遺漏，刪除
loosen	鬆開，鬆弛	open	打開
lose	失敗	operate	運作
loser	輸家	order	點菜
love	愛	organize	組織
maintain	保持，維持	owe	欠，應該給…
make	使得，做	paint	油漆，上顏色
manage	設法做到，得以完成	panic	恐慌
march	行進，行軍	pardon	原諒
match	相配，適合	park	停車
mean	意指	participate	參與
meet	遇見，會面	pass	傳遞
melt	融化，熔化	paste	黏貼
memorize	記住，背熟	pause	暫停
mend	改善，改良	peel	削
merry	歡樂的，愉快的	peep	偷窺
mind	在意	perform	表演
miss	錯失	permit	允許
mix	使混合	persuade	説服
move	移動	pick	揀選
murder	(v., n.) 謀殺	please	請
need	需要	pollute	污染

36 Other verbs 其他動詞

pop	突然出現	puzzle	使困惑
postpone	延期	quake	震動，顫抖
pour	倒，灌入	quote	引用
pray	祈禱	raise	舉起
prefer	更喜歡	reach	抵達
prepare	準備	react	做出反應
present	呈現，提交	realize	明白
press	按	reason	理論
pretend	假裝	receive	收到
prevent	預防	recognize	識別
print	印	recover	恢復
proceed	繼續進行	recycle	回收
produce	生產，製造	reduce	縮短
promise	承諾	refuse	拒絕，不肯
promote	晉升	regard	認為
propose	提議	regret	後悔，遺憾
protect	保護	reject	拒絕
prove	證實	relate	有關，涉及
provide	提供	relax	輕鬆
publish	出版，發行	release	釋放
pull	拉	rely	依靠，信賴
pump	打水，汲水	remain	剩下
punch	用拳猛擊	remember	記得
punish	懲罰	remind	提醒
purchase	購買	remove	移走
pursue	進行，從事	renew	更新
push	推	rent	租
put	放	repair	修理

36 Other verbs 其他動詞

replace	取代	save	拯救，儲蓄
reply	回答	scatter	灑，散布
represent	代表	scream	尖叫
request	請求	scrub	用力擦洗，揉
require	需要	seal	密閉，蓋章
reserve	儲備，保存	search	搜尋
resist	抗拒	see	看見
respect	尊敬	seek	搜索
respond	回答，回應	seem	好像
rest	休息	seize	抓住
restrict	限制	select	選擇
return	歸還	sell	賣
reveal	展現	send	發送，寄
revise	修訂	separate	分開
rid	使擺脫	serve	服務
rise	上升	sew	縫，縫製
risk	冒險	shake	搖動
roar	大聲喊叫	share	分享
roast	烤，烘烤	shave	刮
rob	搶劫	shine	照耀，閃耀
roll	滾動，轉動	shoot	發射
rot	腐爛，腐敗	shorten	縮短，減少
rub	摩擦	shout	大叫
ruin	毀壞	show	告知，指出
run	跑	shrink	收縮，縮短
rush	倉促行動	shut	關上
rust	鏽	sigh	嘆息，嘆氣
satisfy	使滿意	sign	符號，標誌

36 Other verbs 其他動詞

sing	唱歌	start	開始
sit	坐	starve	餓死
skip	略過，漏掉	stay	停留
sleep	睡覺	steal	偷，竊取
slip	失足	sting	刺，螫，叮
smell	聞到	stir	攪動
smoke	抽菸	stitch	縫，繡
snap	拉斷	stop	中斷，阻止
sneeze	打噴嚏	strengthen	加強
sob	啜泣	strike	打擊
solve	解決	strip	剝，剝去，剝光
sorrow	悲傷	strive	努力，奮鬥
sort	分類	struggle	奮鬥，爭扎
sound	聽起來	stuff	把…裝滿，把…塞進
spare	騰出	succeed	成功
spill	溢出，流出	suck	吸，吮，啜
spit	吐	suffer	受苦，患病
splash	濺，濕	suggest	建議
split	劈開，切開	summarize	作總結，作概括
spoil	寵愛，溺愛	supply	提供
sprain	扭傷	support	支持
spray	噴液，噴灑	suppose	猜想，以為
spread	散播	surprise	驚訝，驚喜
sprinkle	點綴	surrender	投降，自首
squeeze	擠，壓，榨	surround	圍，圍繞
stab	刺，刺入	survey	考察，審視
stand	站立	survive	生存
stare	盯，凝視		

36 Other verbs 其他動詞

swallow	嚥下，吞	tremble	震顫，發抖
swear	發誓，宣誓	triumph	獲得勝利
sweep	掃	trust	信任
swell	腫起，腫脹	try	嘗試
tack	釘（圖釘）	tug	用力拉
take	拿，取	tumble	跌倒，滾下
tap	輕拍，輕叩	tune	調整頻道
taste	嚐	twinkle	使閃爍，使閃耀
tease	戲弄，逗弄	twist	扭轉，扭彎，旋轉
tell	說	unite	使聯合，使團結
tend	走向，趨向	upload	上載
terrify	使害怕，使恐怖	upset	使心煩意亂
thank	感謝	urge	催促
think	想，認為	use	使用
throw	丟	vanish	突然不見，消失
tickle	逗…笑，呵癢	vary	使不同，變更，修改
tidy	整潔的	violate	違犯，違背
tie	繫，綁	visit	參觀，拜訪
tighten	使變緊，使繃緊	vote	投票
tolerate	容許，忍受	wait	等待
toss	拋，擲幣	wake	醒來
tow	拖，拉	walk	走
transfer	使轉換，調動	wander	漫遊，閒逛
transform	使改變，使改觀	want	想要
translate	翻譯，轉譯	warn	警告，告誡
trap	被困住	waste	浪費
treat	請客	wave	揮手
treat	對待，款待	weaken	變弱，變衰弱

36 Other verbs 其他動詞

weave	編織	worry	擔心
weep	哭泣，流淚	wrap	包，裹
welcome	歡迎	yawn	打呵欠
whip	攪打	yell	叫喊，吼叫
whistle	吹口哨，鳴笛，吹哨子	devote	將…奉獻給，致力於
win	贏	dismiss	解散，下課
wink	使眼色，眨眼	disturb	打擾
wipe	擦，揩乾	grind	磨碎
wish	但願	switch	切換，打開／關掉
withdraw	撤退，撤離	threaten	威脅，恐嚇
wonder	想知道，感到疑惑		

37 Other adjectives 其他形容詞

able	能夠	alike	相似的
absent	缺席的	alive	活著的
absolute	根本的	ancient	古老的
abstract	抽象的	another	另一
acceptable	可接受的	any	任一
accurate	正確的	apparent	明顯的
acid	酸	asleep	睡著的
active	活躍的	attractive	吸引人的
actual	真實的，實際的	automatic	自動的
additional	附加的	available	有空的
advanced	高級的，進階的	awake	醒的
afraid	害怕的	aware	察覺的
aggressive	積極進取的，侵略性的	awful	可怕的
		bad	壞的
agreeable	宜人的	bare	沒有…的

37 Other adjectives 其他形容詞

basic	基礎的，基本的
best	最好的
better	較好的
blank	空白的
bold	大膽的
brief	簡略的
bright	明亮的
brilliant	傑出的，聰明的
broad	廣泛的
brutal	殘忍的
capable	有能力的
casual	不拘禮節的，隨意的
certain	確定的
changeable	易變的，不定的
cheerful	愉快，歡欣的
chilly	冷颼颼的
civil	公民的
classic	經典的，古典的
classical	古典的
common	常見的，普遍的
conscious	有知覺的，神智清醒的
considerable	相當大的
constant	固定的，不變的
convenient	方便的
correct	正確的
creative	創造的，創造性的
crispy	脆的，酥的，鬆脆的
crowded	擁擠的
crunchy	酥脆的
dangerous	危險的
dark	黑暗的
dead	死的
dear	親愛的
democratic	民主政治的，民主黨的
depressed	沮喪的
desirable	值得嚮往的
different	不同的
difficult	困難的
dim	微暗，暗淡
dirty	骯髒的
distinct	明顯的
domestic	家庭的，家事的
doubtful	疑惑，懷疑
dramatic	戲劇性的
drowsy	昏昏欲睡的，睏倦的
drunk	喝醉的
due	由於，因為
easy	簡單的
educational	教育的
effective	有效的
efficient	有能力，能勝任的
either	兩者之一
electric	電的
electrical	電力學的，電的

37 Other adjectives 其他形容詞

electronic	電子的
elegant	優雅的
else	其他
empty	空的
enjoyable	有趣的，有樂趣的
enormous	巨大的
enough	足夠的
entire	全部的
equal	相同的
essential	必要的，不可或缺的
exact	精確的
excellent	傑出的
exchange	交換
expressive	表現的，表達的
fairy	幻想中的
false	不正確的
familiar	熟悉的
fancy	別緻的，花俏的
fantastic	（好到）難以置信的，棒的
farewell	再會，別了
farther	更遠的，更往前
fashionable	流行的，時髦的
fatal	致命的
favorite	最愛的
fierce	兇猛的，殘酷的
financial	財政的，金融的
firm	堅固的
flat	平坦的
flexible	可彎曲的，有彈性的
fluent	流利，流暢
following	接著的，下面的
fond	喜歡的，愛好的
formal	正式的
former	前者
fortunate	幸運的，僥倖的
fragrant	香的，芳香的
free	自由的，空閒的
fequent	時常發生的
fresh	新鮮的
furious	狂怒的，猛烈的
further	另外的，進一步的
general	一般的
glad	高興的
global	全世界的，總體的
gradual	逐漸的，逐步的
grand	雄偉的
great	非常好的
handy	就手的，方便的
hard	困難的
harmful	有害的
harsh	嚴厲的，惡劣的
hasty	匆忙的，急忙的
heavy	沉重的
helpful	有幫助的
historic	歷史上著名的
historical	歷史的，史學的
hollow	空的，中空

37 Other adjectives 其他形容詞

holy	神聖的，獻身於宗教的
homesick	想家的
hopeful	抱有希望的，充滿希望的
horrible	可怕的
hourly	每小時的
huge	龐大的
icy	結冰的，覆蓋著冰的
ideal	理想的，完美的
identical	相同的
immediate	立即的，即刻的
important	重要的
impossible	不可能的
impressive	予人深刻印象的，感人的
individual	個人的
industrial	工業的，產業的
inner	內部的，裡面的
instant	立即的
interesting	令人感興趣的
internal	內在的，固有的
joyful	高興的，充滿喜悅的
latter	後面的
legal	合法的
likely	可能的
lively	生動的，栩栩如生的
loose	鬆開的，鬆散的
loud	吵鬧的
lousy	差勁的
lucky	幸運的
magic	魔法的，魔術的
magical	魔術的，魔法的
main	主要的
major	主要的
manageable	可控制的
marvelous	令人驚訝的
mature	成熟的，穩重的
meaningful	意味深長的，有意義的
medical	醫學的，醫術
mental	內心的，在腦中進行的
mighty	強大的，強而有力的
minor	次要的
missing	失蹤的
mobile	可移動的
modern	現代化的，時髦的
moist	溼的，含淚的
moral	道德的，精神上的
musical	音樂的
mystery	神祕，謎
native	祖國的，本國的
necessary	必須的
negative	否定的，負面的
new	新的
noble	貴族的，高貴的
noisy	吵雜的

37 Other adjectives 其他形容詞

normal	正常的	probable	很有可能的
obvious	明顯的	productive	具有生產力的
odd	古怪，奇特	profitable	有利潤的
optimistic	樂觀的	prominent	突出的，顯眼的
oral	口頭的	promising	大有可為的
ordinary	平常的	proper	適合的
original	原始	protective	防護，保護
outdoor	戶外的	public	公眾的，公共的
outer	在外的，外面的	pure	純粹的
overseas	國外的	queer	古怪，奇怪
own	自己的	quick	快速的
particular	特定的，獨特的	quiet	安靜的
peaceful	和平的，寧靜的	racial	人種的
perfect	完美的	rapid	迅速的
personal	私人的	rare	半生的
plastic	塑膠的，整形的	raw	生的，未煮過
pleasant	令人愉快的	ready	準備好的
pleased	愉悦的	real	真實的
poetic	詩意的	regular	正常的，固定的
poisonous	有毒的	reliable	可靠的
political	政治的	religious	虔誠的
popular	受歡迎的	responsible	負責的
positive	肯定的，正面的	right	正確的
possible	可能的	ripe	成熟的，適合食用
powerful	有力量的	romantic	浪漫的
practical	實際的	rotten	腐爛
precious	寶貴的	rough	粗糙
previous	先前的	royal	皇室的
private	私人的	rusty	荒廢的

37 Other adjectives 其他形容詞

safe	安全的	sorry	感到難過的
same	相同的	special	特別的
satisfactory	令人滿意的	specific	特定的
scarce	缺乏	spicy	辛辣的
scary	恐怖的	spiritual	精神上，心靈上
scientific	科學的	splendid	輝煌的
secondary	第二的	stable	可信賴的，穩重的
sensitive	敏感的，易受傷的	stale	不新鮮的，厭倦的
serious	嚴重的	steady	平穩的，堅定的
sexual	性的，兩性的	steep	陡峭的，驟升/降的
sexy	性感，迷人的	sticky	黏
shady	成蔭	stiff	僵硬的
sharp	銳利的	strange	奇怪的
sharp	銳利的	such	如此
shiny	發光的，閃亮的	sudden	突然的
significant	有意義的	sufficient	足夠的，充分的
silent	沈默的	suitable	適當的，合適的
similar	相似的	super	超級的
simple	簡易的	superior	較高的，上級的
single	單一的	sure	確定的
skillful	技巧的	surprised	驚訝的
sleepy	想睡的	suspicious	猜疑的，疑心的
slippery	滑的	swift	即時的，迅速的
smooth	平滑的	technical	專門的，技術性的
social	社會的	temporary	臨時的，暫時的
soft	柔軟的	terrible	可怕的，糟糕的
solid	堅固	terrific	很棒的
sore	疼痛	thankful	感謝的，感激的
sorrowful	悲傷的，傷心的	thick	厚的

37 Other adjectives 其他形容詞

thirsty	口渴的
thorough	十足的，徹頭徹尾
thoughtful	細心的，注意的
tight	緊的，不鬆動的
timid	膽小的，易受驚嚇的
tiresome	使人疲勞的，令人厭倦的
total	總共的
tough	不屈不撓的，強硬的
traditional	傳統的
tragic	悲劇性的，悲慘的
tremendous	極度的，驚人的
tricky	機警的，足智多謀的
tropical	熱帶的，位於熱帶的
true	真實的
typical	典型的，有代表性
unique	唯一的，獨一無二的
universal	宇宙的，普遍的
upon	在…上面
urban	城市的
urgent	緊急的，急迫的
useful	有用的
usual	平常的
vacant	空著的，未被占用的
valuable	值錢的，貴重的
various	各式各樣的，形形色色的
various	各式各樣的，形形色色的
vast	廣闊的，浩瀚的
violent	激烈的，猛烈的
violet	紫羅蘭色的
visible	可看見的
visual	視力的，視覺的
vital	生命的，維持生命所必需的
vivid	鮮豔的，鮮明的
wealthy	富有的
whole	全部的
wicked	惡劣的，討厭的，有害的
wild	野生的
willing	願意的
wonderful	極好的
wooden	木製的
worth	有…價值的，值得的
wrong	錯的

38 Other Adverbs 其他副詞

aboard	上船，登機
above	在上面
abroad	國外地
across	越過
actually	實際上，竟然
afterward	之後（也拼做 afterwards）
again	再一次

38 Other Adverbs 其他副詞

ahead	在前面	maybe	也許
almost	幾乎	meanwhile	同時
alone	獨自地	neither	兩者皆不
aloud	大聲地	never	從不
also	也	nor	(既不)…也不
altogether	全然，一起	outdoors	在戶外
always	總是	quite	相當地
anyway	無論如何	rather	寧願
anywhere	在任何地方	really	真的
apart	分離	seldom	不常
around	圍繞	Shortly	立刻，不久
aside	在一旁	simply	簡單地，只要
away	離開	so	非常
barely	幾乎不	someday	有朝一日
beneath	在…之下	somehow	不知怎麼了
besides	此外	sometime	在某一時候
certainly	確實地	sometimes	有時候
especially	特別	somewhat	有點，稍微
even	甚至	somewhere	在某處
ever	在任何時候	still	仍然
everywhere	每一個地方	suddenly	突然地
finally	最後	then	然後，接下來
forth	向前，向前方	thus	因此
furthermore	而且，此外	together	一起，一共
hardly	幾乎不…	too	太
indeed	真正地，確實	usually	通常地
instead	反而，卻	very	非常地
just	只是	yet	還沒

國家圖書館出版品預行編目資料

豬頭也要會的3500初/中級英撿必考單字
朱立安 -- 初版. --臺北市
:日月文化, 2006[民95]
480面：11 × 17 公分. -- （易說館：9）
ISBN 9789867057624
1.詞彙
805.12　　　95020209

易説館 09

豬頭也要會的3500字初/中級英檢必考單字

作　者：朱立安
總編輯：陳思容
責任編輯：趙育芳
文字編輯：漆聯榮．鄭彥谷．洪世民．張逸枕
英文錄音：Robert Williem Fher．Kronis Kent Krahn
美術設計：Rabbits (www.rabbits.tw)

發行人：張水江
總經理：蕭豔秋
行銷總監：蔡美倫
法律顧問：孫隆賢
財務顧問：蕭聰傑

出　版：日月文化出版股份有限公司
發　行：日月文化出版股份有限公司
地　址：台北市信義路三段151號9樓
電　話：(02) 2708-5509
傳　真：(02) 2708-6157
E-mail：service@heliopolis.com.tw
郵撥帳號：19716071 日月文化出版股份有限公司

總經銷：大和書報圖股份有限公司
電　話：(02) 2298-3838
傳　真：(02) 2298-1498
印　刷：禹利電子分色有限公司
二版二刷：2008年12月
定　價：320元
ISBN：9789867057624

日月文化集團 HELIOPOLIS CULTURE GROUP

親愛的讀者您好：

感謝您購買易說館的書籍。
為提供完整服務與快速資訊，請詳細填寫下列資料，傳真至(02)2708-6157，或免貼郵票寄回，我們將不定期提供您新書資訊，及最新優惠訊息。

易說館 讀者服務卡

感謝您購買《豬頭也要會的3500 初/中級 英檢必考單字》敬請填寫以下問題：

*1. 讀友姓名：＿＿＿＿＿＿＿＿＿＿＿＿＿＿＿＿

*2. 身分證字號：＿＿＿＿＿＿＿＿＿＿＿＿＿＿＿＿

*3. 聯絡地址：＿＿＿＿＿＿＿＿＿＿＿＿＿＿＿＿

*4. 電子郵件信箱：＿＿＿＿＿＿＿＿＿＿＿＿＿＿＿＿

(以上欄位請務必填寫，身分證字號為您的讀友編號，僅供內部使用，日月文化保證絕不做其他用途，請放心！)

5. 購自何處：＿＿＿＿＿ 縣/市 ＿＿＿＿＿ 書店 ＿＿＿＿＿

6. 您的性別：□男 □女 生日：＿＿年＿＿月＿＿日

7. 您的職業：□製造 □金融 □軍公教 □服務 □資訊 □傳播 □學生 □自由業 □其他

8. 您從哪裡得知本書消息？ □書店 □網路 □報紙 □雜誌 □廣播 □電視 □他人推薦 □其他

9. 您通常以何種方式購書？ □書店 □網路 □傳真訂購 □郵購劃撥 □其他

10. 您希望我們為您出版哪類書籍？ □文學 □科普 □財經 □行銷 □管理 □心理 □健康 □傳記 □小說 □休閒 □旅遊 □童書 □家庭 □其他

11. 您對本書的評價：＿＿＿＿＿＿＿＿＿＿＿＿＿＿＿＿

(請填寫代號 1.非常滿意 2.滿意 3.普通 4.不滿意 5.非常不滿意)

書名＿＿＿ 內容＿＿＿ 封面設計＿＿＿ 版面編排＿＿＿ 文／譯筆＿＿＿

12. 請給我們建議：

＿＿＿＿＿＿＿＿＿＿＿＿＿＿＿＿＿＿＿＿＿＿＿＿

＿＿＿＿＿＿＿＿＿＿＿＿＿＿＿＿＿＿＿＿＿＿＿＿

日月文化集團
HELIOPOLIS
CULTURE GROUP

讀者服務部　收

10658 台北市信義路三段 151 號 9 樓

對折黏貼後，即可直接郵寄

日月文化集團之友長期獨享郵撥購書 75 折優惠 (單筆購書金額 500 元以下請另附掛號郵資 60 元)，請於劃撥單上註明身分證字號 (即會員編號)，以便確認。

成為日月文化集團之友的 2 個方法：

- 完整填寫書後的讀友回函卡，傳真或郵寄 (免付郵資) 給我們。
- 直接劃撥購書，於劃撥單通訊欄註明姓名、地址、電子郵件信箱、身分證字號以便建檔。

劃撥帳號：19716071　　戶名：日月文化出版股份有限公司
讀者服務電話：(02)2708-5509　讀者服務傳真：(02)2708-6157
客服信箱：service@heliopolis.com.tw

大好書屋　寶鼎出版　唐莊文化　山岳文化　易說館